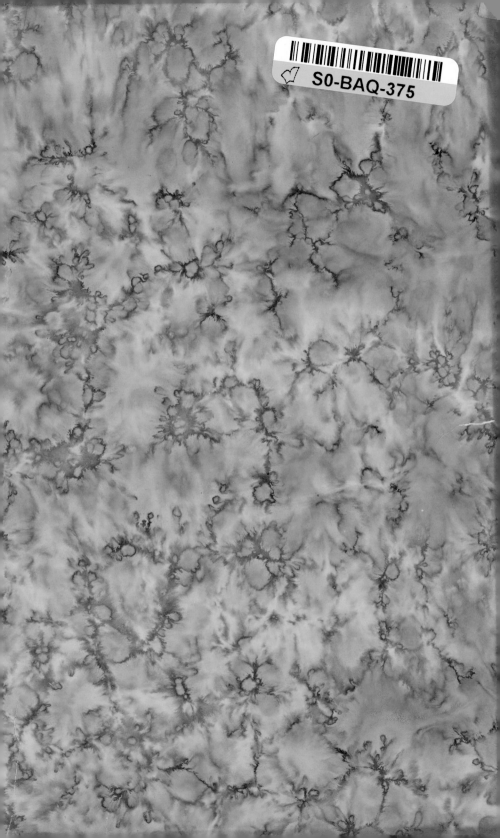

Special Edition

PRESENTED TO

The Library Ohio Northern in honor of my friend, former President Albert Edwin Smith

WITH THE COMPLIMENTS OF THE AUTHOR

Frederick Eland Seete

CHRISTIANITY IN SCIENCE

By
FREDERICK D. LEETE

THE ABINGDON PRESS
NEW YORK   CINCINNATI

TO HER

WHOSE COMPANIONSHIP HAS MADE LONG YEARS
DELIGHTFUL AND HEAVY BURDENS LIGHT,
AND TO THOSE WHOM GOD HAS
GIVEN US

ACKNOWLEDGMENTS

I

I wish to express special obligation for some of their own writings furnished me with consent to print the same, or for suggestive correspondence to the following eminent scholars and authors:

Frank D. Adams, McGill University, Research Council of Canada.

Andrew J. Bigney, Evansville College.

William Lowe Bryan, University of Indiana.

John Wright Buckham, Pacific School of Religion.

Edwin Grant Conklin, Princeton University.

John Merle Coulter, Boyce Thompson Institute.

Heber Doust Curtis, Allegheny Observatory, University of Pittsburgh.

Arthur Lee Foley, University of Indiana.

Edwin Brant Frost, Yerkes Observatory, University of Chicago.

William M. Goldsmith, Southwestern College.

The late Charles W. Hargitt, Syracuse University.

Herman Harrell Horne, New York University.

Vernon Lyman Kellogg, National Research Council.

Cassius Jackson Keyser, Columbia University.

Joseph Edward Kirkwood, University of Montana.

Sir Oliver Joseph Lodge, University of Birmingham.

Thomas Martin Lowry, Cambridge University.

The Right Reverend William T. Manning, Bishop of New York.

William McDougall, Harvard University.

Dayton Clarence Miller, Case School of Applied Science, Cleveland.

Robert Andrews Millikan, California Institute of Technology.

Louis Trenchard More, Graduate School, University of Cincinnati.

The Reverend Bishop John L. Nuelsen, Zurich.

Henry Fairfield Osborn, American Museum of Natural History, New York.

Ismar J. Peritz, Syracuse University.

Michael Idvorsky Pupin, Columbia University.

7

William North Rice, Wesleyan University.
William Emerson Ritter, University of California.
Henry Norris Russell, Princeton University.
James Y. Simpson, New College, Edinburgh.
Edwin Emery Slosson, Science Service, Washington,
D. C.
William Benjamin Smith, Tulane University.
Francis Lorette Strickland, Boston University.
J. Arthur Thomson, University of Aberdeen.
James Joseph Walsh, Fordham University.
Herbert B. Workman, Westminster Training College,
London.
Friedrich Wunderlich, University of Leipsic.

II

For the use of lines from their poems gratitude is
expressed to:
Major Harry Webb Farrington.
Edwin Markham.
Colonel Sir Ronald Ross.

III

Grateful recognition should also be made of aid received in correcting proof and in confirming items of fact
from the Rev. Clarence E. Flynn, D.D., and also from
the late Rev. Harry Andrews King, D.D., and the Rev.
William G. Seaman, D.D., former college presidents.
Miss Hazel Funk, my secretary, and the members of my
household have given valuable service in typewriting and
indexing.

IV

The following publishers and owners of copyrights are
given thanks for permission to print in this volume citations from works named and credited to the authors
quoted:

Abingdon Press, New York:
   Jesus as a Philosopher, Herman Harrell Horne; *Methodist Review; The Return to Faith,* William North Rice;
Psychology of Religious Experience, Francis L. Strickland.

D. Appleton and Company, New York:
   Life and Letters of Charles Darwin, Francis Darwin;
Darwiniana, Asa Gray; *Lay Sermons,* Thomas H. Hux-
ley; *History of European Morals,* and *History of Ration-*

alism in Europe, W. E. H. Lecky; *Evolution*, Joseph LeConte; *Contributions of Science to Religion*, Shailer Mathews; *Fragments of Science*, Vols. I and II, and *New Fragments of Science*, John Tyndall; *Pioneers of Science*, W. J. Youmans; *The Sun*, C. A. Young.

Richard G. Badger, The Gorham Press, Boston:
The Higher Usefulness of Science, William E. Ritter.

A. and C. Black, Ltd., London, England:
Confessions of a Man of Science; or Monism as the Link between Religion and Science, Ernst Haeckel.

Ernest Benn, Ltd., London, England:
The Life of Sir William Crookes, E. E. Fournier d'Albe.

Cassell and Company, Ltd., London, England:
Charles Lyell and Modern Geology, Thomas G. Bonney; *James Clerk Maxwell and Modern Physics*, R. T. Glazebrook.

Dodd, Mead and Company, New York:
Science Remaking the World, Caldwell and Slosson; *The Life of Jean Henri Fabre*, Abbe Fabre.

George H. Doran Company, New York:
Passages reprinted from: *A Living Universe*, by L. P. Jacks, copyright 1924; *Evolution and Creation*, by Sir Oliver Lodge, copyright 1926; *The Holy Bible: a New Translation*, by James Moffatt, copyright 1926; *The Humanizing of Knowledge*, by James Harvey Robinson, copyright 1924.

E. P. Dutton and Company, New York:
Passages from the following books have been quoted by permission: copyright by E. P. Dutton and Company: *Lectures on Preaching*, by Phillips Brooks; *Daedalus*, by J. B. S. Haldane (To-day and To-morrow Series); *Manhood of Humanity*, Alfred Korzybski; *Major Ronald Ross: Memoirs, with a Full Account of the Great Malaria Problem and Its Solution*, London, John Murray; *Icarus*, by Bertrand Russell (To-day and To-morrow Series).

Haldeman-Julius Company, Girard, Kansas:
Evolution or Christianity, William M. Goldsmith.

Harcourt Brace and Company, New York:
Sermons of a Chemist, Edwin E. Slosson.

Harper and Brothers, New York:
Sketches of Creation, Alexander Winchell.

Hodder and Stoughton, Ltd., London:
The Spiritual Interpretation of Nature, and *Man and the Attainment of Immortality,* James Y. Simpson. George H. Doran Company also consent.

Henry Holt and Company, New York:
Leading American Men of Science, David Starr Jordan; *The Kingdom of Man,* Edwin Ray Lankester; *The Limitations of Science,* Louis Trenchard More; *Emergent Evolution,* C. Lloyd Morgan; *Introduction to Science,* J. Arthur Thomson.

Houghton, Mifflin and Company, Boston:
Contributions to the Natural History of the United States, Louis Agassiz; *What Men Live By,* Richard C. Cabot; *Essays,* Ralph Waldo Emerson; *Through Nature to God,* and *Excursions of an Evolutionist,* John Fiske; *Science and Immortality,* William Osler; "Butterflies," poem, Alice Freeman Palmer; *Autobiography,* Nathaniel Southgate Shaler.

H. K. Lewis and Company, Ltd., London:
Endocrine Therapeutics, Thomas Bodley Scott.

J. B. Lippincott Company, Philadelphia:
I Believe in God and in Evolution, and *Everlasting Life,* William W. Keen.

Longmans, Green and Company, New York and London:
New Light on Immortality, Edmund E. Fournier d'Albe. *Outspoken Essays,* William Ralph Inge; *Life and Letters of Michael Faraday,* Henry Bence Jones; *Thoughts on Religion,* George John Romanes.

Macmillan and Company, Ltd., London:
The Life of James Clerk Maxwell, Campbell and Garnett; *On Light,* Sir George G. Stokes.

The Macmillan Company, New York:
Charles Lyell and Modern Geology, Thomas G. Bonney; *Except Ye Be Born Again,* Philip Cabot; *Where Evolution and Religion Meet,* J. M. and M. C. Coulter; *Modern Astrophysics,* Herbert Dingle; *Space, Time and Gravitation,* A. S. Eddington; *Body and Mind,* William McDougall; Lines of poetry, William Wordsworth.

Magazines and Reviews:
American Magazine, "Science Is Leading Us Closer to God," M. I. Pupin, q. v.; *Catholic World,* "Appreciation of Faraday," James J. Walsh; *Edinburgh Review,* Henry Rogers on Pascal; *Encyclopædia Britannica,* London and

New York, 13th edition, Clerke on Humboldt; *Hibbert Journal*, L. P. Jacks, editor, Quotations from J. S. Haldane and Sir Oliver Lodge; *Homiletic Review*, Funk and Wagnalls, "Science and Religion," J. A. Thomson; International Feature Service, New York, Garrett P. Serviss on Materialism; *Medical Review of Reviews*, New York, Doctor Fagan, "Mandombi and Sleeping Sickness"; *Methodist Magazine*—Epworth Press, London, Interview with T. M. Lowry; The Nineteenth Century and After, and Leonard Scott Co., London, Huxley, Knowles, Kelvin; Open Court Publishing Company, article by W. E. Ritter; *Science Press*, New York, quotations from Ira Remsen, William McDougall and W. E. Ritter; *Yale Review*, "Science and the Soul," Vernon L. Kellogg.

Fleming H. Revell and Company, New York:
Religion of the Mature Mind, George A. Coe; *The Fact of Conversion*, George Jackson.

Science Press, New York:
Science and Hypothesis, Jules Henri Poincaré.

Charles Scribner's Sons, New York:
Nature and the Supernatural, Horace Bushnell; *Every-Day Topics*, Josiah Gilbert Holland; *Evolution and Religion* and *Impressions of Great Naturalists*, Henry Fairfield Osborn; *From Immigrant to Inventor* and *The New Reformation*, Michael Idvorsky Pupin.

Smithsonian Institution:
Smithsonian Reports.

University Presses:
Cambridge University, England, Cambridge Readings in the Literature of Science; *Stories of Scientific Discovery*, D. B. Hammond; The University of Chicago, *Christianity in Education*, Ernest DeWitt Burton; Columbia University, *The Human Worth of Rigorous Thinking*, Cassius J. Keyser; Fordham University, *Makers of Modern Medicine*, James J. Walsh; Harvard University, *The Order of Nature*, Lawrence J. Henderson; The University of Indiana, *The Mortal Immortal*, William Lowe Bryan; Princeton University, *The Dogma of Evolution*, Louis T. More; *Evolution and Christian Faith*, Henry H. Lane; Yale University, *Science and Religion*, Cassius Jackson Keyser; *Christianity and Modern Thought*, essay by Richard S. Lull; *Fate and Freedom*, Henry Norris Russell; *Christian Belief in God*, D. S. Robinson's tr. Georg Wobbermin.

CONTENTS

Ὁ Λόγος Τοῦ Βίου

Ἡ ἐπιθυμία τῆς σαρκὸς καὶ ἡ ἐπιθυμία τῶν ὀφθαλμῶν καὶ
ἡ ἀλαζονία τοῦ βίου, οὐκ ἔστιν ἐκ τοῦ πατρός, ἀλλὰ
ἐκ τοῦ κόσμου ἐστίν· καὶ ὁ κόσμος παράγεται
καὶ ἡ ἐπιθυμία αὐτοῦ, ὁ δὲ ποιῶν τὸ
θέλημα τοῦ θεοῦ μένει εἰς
τὸν αἰῶνα.

PREFACE

THIS book outlines the service rendered by scientists to the general cause for which in its own field Christianity also is toiling, namely, the discovery and impartation of the truth which creates liberty, ministry to the content and satisfaction of human life, and the elevation of man and his preparation for the highest destiny through the development and use of accessible forms of power. There is a definite parallelism and interaction between the two greatest realms of adventure and discovery, Christianity and science. This correspondence has been traced as far as possible from the point of view of students of nature who have expressed themselves by word and deed. The effort has also been to disclose in their diversity the unquestionable tribute and aid of scientific achievements and personalities to the reality and influence of the Christian religion.

It may be that some will desire to consider carefully for themselves and to place in the hands of others a discussion of the relationship between science and Christianity as copartners in divine work, rather than as pathological disputants. If any one has been told that he must choose between Christian confidence and scientific intelligence, herein may be found evidence that, when one has thoroughly informed himself, he will find that such a dilemma is artificial and unnecessary. The aim has not been to confirm or oppose any dogma of religion or of science, but to emphasize the consistency of truth and the indubitable fact that Christian faith and character inhere conformably in personalities devoted to natural researches and precision. It is indicated by what is presented on this theme that both science and Christianity are of divine origin and development,

17

and that their labors and discoveries are complementary as well as co-operative.

The items set forth in this volume with respect to the ideas, acts, and affiliations of eminent men are as truly scientific data as are facts about atoms, electrons, cells, bacteria, flora, mammalia, seasons, planets, or cosmic laws. The Christianity of scientists, widely and typically witnessed, must be interpreted and explained. A portion of the memorabilia connected with the subject is given here, leaving it to the reader to add thereto as he may be able to compare particular views expressed and to draw his own inferences from such details.

It is insisted that science and Christianity do not need to be reconciled. A "reconciled" Christianity would have as little beauty, fragrance, or life as an artificial flower, while a "reconciled" science would be a mere falsehood. Compromises are neither scientific nor religious. Truth is wholly, not partially true. Religion has no right to require a Montalembert to say, "I bow my intellect to my faith." It does have the right to ask and to help him to bring his intelligence up to the level of divine truth, and aid suitable to this end should be more completely and sympathetically offered. Similarly, science very properly demands respect for truth determined, and should so far as possible make its principles clear to the laity.

The true agreement between science and religion is in experience. The incommensurables of the world of sense and of the realm of religious conceptions and life should not be robbed of distinctive qualities by coercion or by osmotic processes. Each exists *ipso jure,* and with mutual values. When research and reflection have gone far enough it begins to be apprehended, as one of the clearest thinkers of the early church, Clement of Alexandria, boldly asserted, that there is an ultimate unity of all knowledge. Clement declared that "geometry, music, poetry, medicine, law, philosophy, come from God, and lead back to him." Measurably, this principle has been realized by profound minds. In the meantime, as the effort to attain wisdom progresses, Christianity and science are one in the lives and activities of many who are devoted to truth in all its forms and to service in its various relations, human and divine.

In view of the evidence at hand, only a small part of which can be presented in one writing, no one will deny that many good Christians have been scientists and many scientists firm believers in religion. This is a record of history. But more is to be said, for it can also be shown that the progress of science has not only been coincident with that of Christianity but is to a large extent the outgrowth of the environment which Christianity creates. With reference to observations made in this book concerning the logic of scientific topography in relation to religion, I have received the following comment:

"Science and fine arts flourished in countries where Christianity flourished. There is a quickening spirit in Christianity which no other religion has ever exhibited. If we read the lives of the great men in science and in the fine arts, we will convince ourselves that their successful efforts were in a great measure due to the stimulating influence of the Christian religion. Neither science nor the fine arts alone can produce that fullness of life as we understand it today."[1]

Much of the material in this book, because of the limitations of scientific biography, has been difficult to secure. In order that the reader might be enabled to make his own interpretations, the *ipsissima verba* of eminent and representative scientists have been presented to a greater extent than would have been the case had the author wished merely to express his own judgments. Items have, of course, been included, as

---

[1] Letter from Doctor M. I. Pupin.

reflecting various views of truth, with the implications of which, at least in part, I am not able to agree. They are included for purposes of comparison as well as for historic reasons. Let it also be noted that approval of one or more expressions of an author quoted herein is not to be taken as a general indorsement of his life and views. Those who have attempted to study the personal traits and conduct of students of nature will not need to be told that intimate facts of this kind are sometimes especially difficult to obtain.

The acts of the apostles of science and the relationship and service to religion of scientific workers deserve high praise. During the five centuries of the history of modern science no greater figures have appeared than those enrolled beneath the banners of Christianity. Religion has trained, inspired, and crowned the greatest observers and discoverers. Despite all efforts thus far made by coworkers in behalf of the world's good, however, civilization has not yet satisfied the highest hopes of humanity. If the motivation furnished by Christian teachings and by the Spirit of Christ is not greatly strengthened, there will be further and still more serious outbreakings of greed, crime, lust, hatred and war. The Church of God is therefore looking to all leaders of men, and particularly to those who are acquainted with physical and mental science, to bring to its undertakings, with increasing loyalty and determination, the might of their wisdom and influence, and to help create new heavens and a new earth wherein shall dwell righteousness. The moral state of the world justifies the demand for an ethical revival which naturalistic ideophrenias can never effect. When science and religion join hand in hand in a resolute effort to lift humanity into the realm of idealism, and to give it power to dwell and act in that environment in the manner proposed by Jesus Christ, the outcome

cannot fail to honor their efforts.   Nor should the
question of priority or of leadership be raised.   A
host of Christian men would welcome a new day of
spiritual progress brought on by scientific teaching,
labor, and prophecy. That such an event might occur,
and that it could only occur without attempt on the
part of scientists to reduce religion to obedience to
physical laws, methods and conduct seems evident.

FREDERICK D. LEETE.

FOREWORD

THE author's justification for presenting the collection of facts and judgments contained in this volume is not based upon the few scientific courses which he pursued in undergraduate and in postgraduate days, and which were mainly in geology and zoology. The inception of the volume is to be attributed to an early admiration of scientific researches and of the chief personalities who have conducted them. It is also due to a conviction, the result of forty years of reading of scientific history and biography, that in essence and in its deepest significance science is spiritual and even Christian.

The date of my birth was during the time when the chief works of Charles Darwin were being published. When I began to take note of contemporary thought a lively discussion of new scientific doctrines and of their bearing with reference to religion was proceeding vigorously. Of course I was interested, and it has been a life-long pleasure to continue the habit then formed of keeping in touch with the men, the methods, and the achievements of science. Much inspiration has come to me from these sources.

This is a book, not of science, but of Christianity in science, as the writer thinks he observes and appreciates this incarnation. It has been no part of my purpose to defend or to deny particular theological or scientific doctrines, however important. The outlook of the book is higher and more synthetic. No one who is informed can deny the Christian element in scientific biography. This is characteristically and abundantly evidenced when one takes pains to investigate the lives of men who are not given to parading their most sacred convictions. The

23

writer has been thoughtfully advised and counseled as to scientific achievements and principles mentioned herein. If errors nevertheless appear, as may be expected in a mass of data covering long periods of time and relating to abstruse subjects, I claim these as my own, and also acknowledge full responsibility for the general tenor and for the individual items of this treatise.

THE AUTHOR.

CHAPTER I

THE SPIRIT AND SERVICE OF SCIENCE

A BEAUTIFUL bronze tablet, erected by the faculty of a medical college in honor of an eminent surgeon, at the end and as the climax of tributes paid to his ability and usefulness, bears the words, "Servant of God through service to mankind." Such an encomium as this may be justly paid to many a notable character in the history of science.

The physicist and inventor Michael Idvorsky Pupin once remarked, "Service is the watchword of both science and Christianity." When the friend with whom he was conversing exclaimed, "And the purpose of life," the reply was, "All there is to it." To emphasize the importance of service is by no means to discount other values. Nor will any intelligent person misunderstand the sweeping statement, true within proper limits, that service is the whole purpose and plan of life. Other interests exist, but service is closely related to all of them.

Is it not a fact that Christianity presents a gospel of labor as well as a gospel of faith? "My Father worketh hitherto and I work" is one of the recorded utterances of the founder of the Christian plan of life. This saying has found new meaning and value in our generation. Jesus "went about doing good." He gave his disciples tasks to perform, not simply ideals. His whole system of thought and behavior was related to useful activities. He was a servant and a creator of servants.

The service of science is closely allied in principle and practice with the Christian effort and aim.[1] It

[1] See the strong statement to this effect in *Evolution in Science and Religion*, R. A. Millikan, p. 83.

25

will be shown in this volume that many of the foremost scientists have exhibited the best qualities of Christian knowledge and experience. Very properly they have put the strength of their life-work into the duties of their special calling. Many of them seem to have had the conviction that in so doing they were rendering both human and divine service, and these toilers in closet, laboratory and field might well have adopted as their own the scriptural saying, "I will show thee my faith by my works."

Since service is a rule and expression of science, as it is of religion, it should be of general interest to review more carefully than most people have done the records of scientific achievements. This is the more important because the minds of many seem to be confused as to what science is all about anyhow. Few comprehensive, brief accounts of its results get before the public. Many have a notion that a number of the more recent and well-known inventions constitute the chief outcome of scientific research. Others read popular and none too accurate statements of certain theories which are set forth as being scientific, and, regarding these as products of unsupported imagination and conjecture, are inclined to form unfavorable judgments of science in general. It is true that a better understanding than that of former times exists concerning the labors and results attained by observation, experimentation, and verification of physical phenomena. Nevertheless, complaint is justly made by patient investigators that what they are doing is none too well comprehended and appreciated.

A recent outburst of discussion of evolution seems to have led many to identify this one theory with the whole of science, and their state of mind is sometimes like that of the maid described in an incident preserved by Lord Rayleigh. During an earlier period of similar agitation this woman was late when required for some task. She explained that she had

become absorbed by a dispute among the servants
below stairs as to whether or not we are all descended
from Darwin! However much we may be interested
in the kitchen question of descent, it is not the only
issue to be considered. Let us see what scientific
investigation and discovery have done in God's world
for us and for him. When the results of the exploration of nature have been considered, the question will
be raised, What in all this is inimical to the facts and
interests of Christianity? Our answer, based upon
history and upon excellent scientific testimony, is that
neither in itself nor in the lives and beliefs of its chief
representatives is science anti-Christian.

Before passing in review the acts of the apostles of
science, it may be said that the deeper and truer faith
of the world probably awaits, among other needed
adjustments which will ultimately bring on a great
spiritual awakening, a broader synthesis of all forms
of knowledge, and a deeper sympathy for human conditions and needs. There are indications which make
it appear that the peculiar interest which many scientific leaders are showing with reference to religion
may lead to important new developments in this
direction.

The history of science begins with the dawn of
human observation and reason. Assyria and Baby-
lonia, Phœnicia and Egypt must be mentioned.
Greece is still more important, though it is too much
to believe, with Sir Henry Sumner Maine, that in its
origin everything in our world which moves is Greek,
natural forces alone excepted. While it is undoubtedly true that before all other peoples the
Greeks esteemed knowledge for its own sake, and possessed a passion for meanings and adjustments of
relations, they owed much to Chaldean theorems, to
Phœnician numbers and calculation, and to Egyptian
geometry.

The earliest golden age of science, that of Greece,

began with the fifth century B. C. Its achievements succeeded the work of Thales, 640-548, who determined the length of the year and the inequality of days and nights at various seasons, and of Anaximander, who introduced the sundial and made a world map, as did Eratosthenes, much later. These are the "fathers" of geography. Pythagoras disclosed the spherical shape of the earth, and the fact that it moves. He invented important geometrical theorems, and is said to have originated stringed musical instruments. Xenophanes explained fossils as remains of life. Many other great names appeared during the fifth and the succeeding century. Parmenides of Elis also recognized the sphericity of the earth, and attributed the glory of the moon to reflected light. Anaxagoras correctly explained eclipses, though he had been anticipated somewhat by the Egyptians and by Thales. Democritus of Abdera developed Leucippus' theory of atoms, which may have had a Hindu origin, and explained the Milky Way as composed of vast numbers of stars. "With no data of experience," says Louis T. More, "he conceived and stated a theory of the world which is still the foundation of modern science."[2] Hippocrates was first to look upon disease as a natural and not a supernatural process, and is known as the "father" of medicine. His saying, as later put into Latin, *"vis medicatrix naturae"*—the healing power of nature—is to this day one of the great lights of medical wisdom. Meton introduced the "Metonic period" or cycle of nineteen years by which the calendar is adjusted with the course of the sun and moon. The "Golden Number" used to find Easter is calculated in reference to the Metonic period. Hippias of Elis invented the curve known as the quadratrix, and thus furnished the solution of important geometrical problems. Plato added mental and moral to natural

---

[2] *Dogma of Evolution*, p. 41, Princeton University Press.

philosophy, and thus removed himself from the technical designation of scientist. However, he rendered distinguished service to mathematics by his own problems and solutions and by his discovery of the analytical method, as well as by the interest in the subject which he created. The introduction of "mathematical form in the determination of individual things" gave to science a new and lasting impetus. Plato's great pupil, Aristotle, wrote eight books on physics—four on the heavens and four on meteorology—and ten books on animals: the first attempts to systematize all accessible knowledge of nature. He is often called the "Father of Zo-ology." He announced the inductive method, but himself used deduction as his scientific instrument. Theophrastus, called "Father of Botany," described more than five hundred species of plants, producing the most important ancient treatises on the subject. Heraclides of Pontus taught in the fourth century B. C. that the earth turns on its own axis from west to east in twenty-four hours.

Passing to Alexandria, after the conqueror's subjugation of Greece in 330 B. C., Grecian science produced Euclid, the founder of mathematical logic, who taught that light travels in "rays"; and Archimedes, geometer and engineer, who laid down the principles of mechanics. The latter invented a screw for raising water and discovered the principle of the lever, which so excited him that he called for a ποῦ στῶ that he might move the earth.[3] Anatomy was given serious study. Herophilus ascribed the pulse to contractions of the heart and named the duodenum. Erasistratus described the two divisions of the brain, cerebrum and cerebellum, and is said to have recognized and named the valves of the heart. Galen, 130 B. C., became the most notable medical man of the ancient Roman civilization. During the decline of the Alexandrian period

---

[3]Pappus of Alexandria, *Geometer, book viii, on Mechanics,* p. 1060.

came Ptolemy and the Ptolemaic system, and after
that the so-called, but often misrepresented, Dark
Ages.

That a relationship between science and religion
existed even in pre-Christian times is a well-known
fact of history. "Where Paul found faith exemplified in the altar to the unknown God," says Charles
W. Hargitt, zo-ologist, in the *Methodist Review,* November-December, 1924,[4] "science found such patrons
as Democritus and Aristotle; and in Lucretius' 'De
Rerum Natura' we have a poem of evolution compar-
able in some degree with that of 'In Memoriam.' But
science went into Rip Van Winkle slumber." Alchemy
and astrology were the outstanding foibles from the
twelfth to the sixteenth centuries. However, the long
ages from Julius Cæsar and his calendar, and from
the architectural, medical, and mathematical achievements of Rome up to the fifteenth century are not
unmarked by smaller lights. Arabs, Hindus, and
Spanish Moors did valuable work in astronomy and
mathematics. The organ was brought to excellence
in the ninth century. Musical notation and harmony
were created in the tenth to the twelfth centuries, the
chief names being Hucbald, d'Arezzo, and Franco.
Windmills came from the East during the crusades or
were invented in the eleventh and twelfth centuries.
In the thirteenth century came the dawn which fore-
tokened the Renaissance of the fourteenth century.
Paper came from the East. The *Almagest* of Ptolemy, astronomical and geometrical, was translated
in 1231 by order of Frederick II of Germany. Coal
was discovered in 1264. Alphonso X of Castile composed the Alphonsene astronomical tables in 1253.
Marco Polo is often said to have produced the first
mariner's compass in 1260, but the account is declared
to be mythical. The compass came from the East at

---

[4] "Problems of Science and Faith," p. 840.

about this time, the Chinese having known its use for many centuries. Albertus Magnus, 1193-1280, studied natural history and mineralogy and explained thermal springs. Roger Bacon is the great name of the period. He insisted on an experimental basis for natural science, and attributed the tides to lunar rays. In 1252 he invented convex magnifying glasses, and the first magic lantern in 1260. His *Opus Majus* epitomized ancient and current knowledge, and gave later encouragement to Columbus to think that the western ocean was not too broad for passage. About 1300, Alessandra da Spina of Pisa, or Salvinus Armatus, a Florentine, invented spectacles for the eyes, though some authorities think they were anticipated by Bacon.

In general, the whole period of modern science, from the middle of the fifteenth century to the present, might be termed the Age of Discovery. The invention of printing from movable type, the discovery of the Western world, and the Reformation opened up an era of advances in almost every direction. In the sixteenth and seventeenth centuries occur the names of Copernicus, Tycho Brahe, Kepler, Galileo, Newton, stars of the first magnitude in the history of human attainment and progress. Copernicus replaced the long-standing geocentric theory of Ptolemy with the heliocentric theory of our physical system. Tycho was a maker of instruments and a great observer of astronomical bodies. On his data later results were based. Kepler improved the telescope, described the correct use of the parts of the eye, and deduced the celebrated laws of planetary orbits. Galileo determined the regularity of pendulum vibrations, described the acceleration of falling bodies, discovered sunspots, the revolution of the sun on its axis in twenty-eight days, the satellites of Jupiter, the rings of Saturn, the phases of Venus, and many new stars. He invented the thermometer and rendered much service to physics and dynamics. Sir Isaac Newton is, of course, best known for his theory of gravitation. His monumental work, *Principia,* contained the famous laws of motion which form the starting point of modern dynamics. He rendered mighty service to mathematics. His discovery of fluxional or infinitesimal calculus was perfected by Leibnitz. His achievements in optics were so important as to mark one of the chief epochs in scientific history. He has often been called the greatest intellect and most notable figure in the annals of science.

During the time made resplendent by the genius of the extraordinary leaders just mentioned, many other important events may be cited. Among these were the invention of logarithms by Napier and Bürgi, of the telescope in Holland by Lippershey, if indeed he rather than Galileo deserves this credit, the description of the valves of the veins by Fabricius, the discovery of the law of refraction of light by Willebrord Snellius (Snell), about 1621, and the discovery of the circulation of the blood by Harvey.[5] Torricelli, amanuensis of Galileo, invented the barometer, later improved by Hooke. Van Helmont revealed scientifically the existence of invisible, impalpable substances, and first named them gases. Malpighi applied the microscope to botany, and detected cellular tissue and the process of seed growth. He discovered capillaries, air cells, and the parts of the skin. Huygens applied the pendulum to the measurement of time, devised the achromatic eyepiece, and took some of the first steps in establishing the undulatory theory of light. Leeuwenhoek, 1683, sometimes called the "Father of Scientific Microscopy," studied *infusoria,*

---

[5]James J. Walsh, in *What Civilization Owes to Italy,* recognizes the observations of Canani of Ferrara in 1547, repeated to Vesalius, better understood by Fabricius, clarified by the work of Steno and Malpighi, and brought to scientific public demonstration by Harvey. *Vide,* pp. 251 and 252.

and discovered the Rotifers and other animalcules. He first observed the mischievous nature of the work of *aphides* on plant life. He gave the earliest accurate description of the red corpuscles of the blood and extended Malpighi's investigations of capillary circulation. Boerhaave founded organic chemistry. Ray and Willoughby made great advances in natural history, Ray being both an expert botanist and zoologist. Halley made the first magnetic map, discovered the elliptical orbits of some comets, and successfully predicted their reappearance. Réaumur in 1731 invented the thermometer scale which bears his name, discovered the tinning of iron, and made valuable additions to natural history. Mention should certainly be made of the fact that to this period belong the names of two most distinguished philosophers, Bacon and Descartes. The former gained consideration for scientific methods, especially that of investigation by induction. His *Novum Organum* may be justly regarded as the starting-point of modern science. It develops the doctrine that science depends on observation, and that scientific theory must conform to the data of experience. René Descartes similarly aroused intellectual activity, and was proficient in anatomy, optics, physiology and other studies. He originated inquiry into the mechanism of living bodies.

The eighteenth century has been described as the time of the scientific renaissance. A new interest in science, aroused by the great discoveries of the preceding two hundred years, the barest outline of which has just been given, began to be felt somewhat generally, although the day of high regard for science as a branch of learning had not yet come. Several of the names previously given come over into the early part of this century. James Bradley, who as a youth was called by Newton "the best astronomer in Europe," about 1727 explained the cause of the phenomenon known as the "aberration of light," furnishing the first demonstration of the earth's motion around the sun. In 1747 he announced the discovery of the "nutation of the earth's axis," or the inconstancy of its inclination to the ecliptic. Chemistry now attained higher distinction by the labors of Priestley, Lavoisier, Cavendish, and others. Cavendish separated and studied hydrogen and determined the composition of water; Rutherford, nitrogen; Priestley, nitric oxide; and, most important, Priestley and Scheele independently discovered oxygen, so named by Lavoisier, who also analyzed and named carbonic acid and established the principle of the conservation of matter.

Among achievements in other branches of discovery should be noted the work of Chladni, "Father of Modern Acoustics," and of Black and Rumford in the study of heat. Count Rumford exploded the caloric theory, and described heat as the result of molecular motion. Joule and Davy experimentally verified Rumford's conclusions. Davy did important work in both chemistry and physics, discovering potassium, sodium, barium, calcium, and magnesium. Watt made practical the steam engine. Hawksbee, DuFay, Franklin, Galvani, and Volta, by their investigations of electricity, laid foundations for undreamed wonders. To Buffon and Linnæus are due the beginnings of modern natural history and classification. The steam engine and other machinery, spinning "jenny," "waterframe," "mule," "power loom" caused the industrial revolution of the last quarter of the century. Whitney invented the cotton "gin." Jenner created preventive medicine, and introduced vaccination. Outstanding features of the century were Hutton's theory of the earth, Lagrange's *Analytical Mechanics,* and the nebular hypothesis of Kant and Laplace. The blind Euler determined longitude at sea, and Harrison made a ship's chronometer. In 1781 Herschel discovered the planet Uranus. He catalogued more than eight hundred double stars and over two thousand nebulæ.

After such a list of notable achievements, it might be thought that little opportunity for progress was left for the nineteenth and twentieth centuries. That the present is justly termed an age of science is nevertheless indicated by exceedingly substantial facts. The age of discovery has still gone forward, and inventions have multiplied with amazing variety. New sciences have been born. All themes have been subjected to scientific treatment. The jealousies and injustices of past history, from which a number of the boldest, the most useful, and the most unselfish men of science suffered, have been succeeded by a period, not free from misunderstandings certainly, and not without opposition to theories formed or even to truth revealed, but of the most widespread understanding and approval of the aims and service of science itself which the world has ever known. Despite all that had been attempted and accomplished during the long experience of human life upon the earth, and in the very face of the records of great deeds and famous names which the earlier centuries present, so marvelous have been the recent developments in the scientific world that it has been declared by responsible historians that the beginning of the nineteenth century found science, as such, without existence, either as a branch of learning or as a special discipline. That is to say, while mathematics had been cultivated and was recognized by the schools, and while some teachers and courses in natural philosophy were found, science, properly so called, yet awaited the specialization, the separate foundations, the elaborate curricula, the independent associations, academies and funds which are so characteristic of our era.

It is hard to realize that within the memory of people yet living, education, even in the highest institutions, was almost wholly "classical." Cajori in *A History of Physics* recounts the slow development of scientific buildings and equipment. In 1871, Trowbridge of Harvard was compelled to borrow needed apparatus. There were then but four physics laboratories in the United States, the oldest of which was that of the Massachusetts Institute of Technology. The public schools were without adequate books or equipment for the teaching of either applied or speculative science. It should not be surprising in view of these conditions, that many who essayed to teach or to publish scientific facts were but poorly prepared for the undertaking.

An oft-recounted illustration of imperfect acquaintance with nature, even on the part of learned men, in the early part of the nineteenth century, is connected with the preparation for the sixth edition of the dictionary issued by the French Academy in 1835. It is said that the forty immortals were at work in their assembly-room when Cuvier entered. "Glad to see you, M. Cuvier," said one of the company. "We have just finished a definition which we think quite satisfactory, but on which we should like to have your opinion. We have been defining the word 'crab,' and explain it thus: 'Crab, a small red fish, which walks backward.'" "Perfect, gentlemen," said Cuvier; "only, if you will give me leave, I will make one small observation in natural history. The crab is not a fish, it is not red, and it does not walk backwards. With these exceptions, your definition is excellent." At a time even later than this incident, Alexander Wilson records a visit to the professor of natural history at one of the most noted American colleges. He says that he soon found that this man scarcely knew a sparrow from a woodpecker.

The teaching profession, whatever its past limitations may have been, has now to contend with no such ill treatment as that of comparatively recent history.

In his first school, in 1841, Pasteur rejoiced in the munificent salary of somewhat less than sixty dollars per year. Fabre, in 1843, taught in a cellar, oozing with damp, lighted by a narrow barred window, with school properties consisting of a plank bench fastened around the room, one seatless chair, a blackboard and chalk. Popular education was not a matter of concern in England until 1818, and the first annual educational grant by the government was in 1833. In America log school buildings were common in many regions for fifty years after the Revolution. District schools, even when better constructed, were roughly furnished, often had no maps or pictures, and blackboards were uncommon until 1820. In Massachusetts, until 1789, only reading and writing were required in elementary schools. In that year arithmetic, English, orthography, and "decent behavior" were required by law. In colonial days geography was considered a diversion. Its study was not conducted in elementary schools until after the Revolution, and it was first made an entrance condition at Harvard in 1815. Until after the opening of the nineteenth century the most notable function of American colleges was the education of clergymen. The studies were classical, with a little mathematics and no electives. Scientific themes were introduced into the curriculum slowly, and often against opposition, while scientific courses were a late arrival. Schools of applied science, Lawrence, Sheffield, and others, appeared about the middle of the century. Many men now living recall college days when all branches of natural science were taught by a single professor. In the light of present experience his apparatus was simply pitiable, and the college laboratories but a few years since were cheap toyshops. In England, Cambridge as well as Oxford was long wedded to the old classical traditions. In France, noted scientific leaders—Pasteur, Bernard, Sainte-Claire Deville—did not have and could not get laboratories in which they could have a reasonable number of associates and pupils. Germany made the first sound beginnings of modern scientific training. The Liebig laboratory attracted foreigners by 1825. German scientific education was so unique that even at the beginning of the twentieth century things scientific were viewed in America through German ideas.

How vast are the changes which have recently taken place! Data might be easily assembled with respect to present scientific curricula, numbers and personnel of teachers and investigators, and as to resources in appropriations, endowments and new and improved physical properties. The sum of such items taken into comparison with former statistics would be so amazing as of themselves to justify the statement that however admirable and important have been the researches of scientific genius at other times, no previous period can establish a right equal to that of our epoch to be called an age of scientific recognition and opportunity. Even to-day, however, the charge is occasionally made that science is neglected or that the discoveries and conclusions of the scientific world are unheeded, ignored and resisted. When the latter is the case, is it not sometimes evident that the conduct of the public is caused either by unwillingness to accept unproven hypotheses, and even bald assertions, on the basis of authority, or by the natural hesitation of careful thinkers to move to new positions until they have had sufficient time in which to examine them and to determine their firmness? Scientists themselves should—and most of them do—approve both of these attitudes.

In passing, it should be noted that the improved position occupied by science and by its representatives has been attained well-nigh wholly in countries which are most influenced by Christianity. Inasmuch as especial care was taken of the training of clergymen in the earlier years of American history, it is interesting to recall the fact that it was in large part due to this influence that educational attention was drawn to scientific subjects. As we shall see, not a few of the early students and teachers of natural courses were Christian ministers, often of such eminence as Edward Hitchcock, geologist, Amherst president, and author of *The Religion of Geology*. This accentuates the fact, mentioned elsewhere in this volume, that the topography of scientific progress considered in relation to the highest types of religion is both interesting and instructive to lovers of truth, and would repay most thoughtful study.

The coming into vogue of scientific method, which has attended the changes which have been noted, has made natural its application to all departments of knowledge and experience. History, literature, art, philosophy, religion have felt the irresistible impact, not only of a new spirit of inquiry, but also of its modes of action. With whatever new key is found every door of experience and thought is being tried. Every modern principle is tested in each realm of knowledge and life. Nothing but ignorance and error need be afraid of this attack, except as to the peril of stupidity or vandalism on the part of some of those who approach treasure-houses of assured values. Not everything lends itself to the same kind of scientific approach. Even the sciences themselves must be protected against each other by careful study of varieties and applications of methods. Truth has no universal solvent, except that of good will. Religious teaching and literature, however divine in their origin and content, have their human side, and cannot separate themselves successfully from all other forms of information and wisdom. They must recognize that every science is founded on eternal principles, whose verity cannot be out of harmony with the basis of any science. Theology and biblical interpretation must, it is true, have their own methods, but these will relate themselves, so far as this is reasonable, with modes of inquiry used elsewhere. It is gradually becoming evident that scientific approach has made necessary and delightful a restudy of religious ideas and systems; it has produced new areas of investigation and has uncovered veins of wealth which it is confidently believed will enrich the religious thinking and experience of coming generations. Many are those also to whom the constant discoveries of science in its own realm have brought God nearer, and have elevated man into possession of sufficient spiritual stature to make him again appear as a being worthy of the highest place in the universe, and of divine relationships.

We will now consider in some detail the recent acts of the leaders of science. If scientific history began with astronomy and mathematics, the end, as we have seen and will continue to observe, was not there. Both in extension and in intension, the labors and influence of students of natural phenomena are probing all regions. The first day of the nineteenth century was distinguished by the discovery of a new world. At that time there was not an astronomical observatory in the southern hemisphere, nor was there one in the United States; but the Italian astronomer, Piazzi, January 1, 1801, observed and christened Ceres, the first known minor planet, or planetoid. Since that time several hundred of these bodies have been named, and other hundreds described. It is interesting to record the fact that Piazzi's triumph was preceded by anticipations of this event, caused by the application of Bode's law, based on Titius, concerning the relations of planetary distances. In accordance with this principle, it was believed that the wide hiatus between Mars and Jupiter should be found occupied by some planet, and preparations were making for a concerted search when Piazzi made out an apparent star of about the eighth magnitude, later seen to have moved, and thus shown to be vastly nearer the earth than any so-called fixed star. Olbers, Harding, Hencke, and then many, found other asteroids, as they are often called. The bulk of all these minor planets is believed to be but a fraction of that of the earth, but the puzzles and discussions which they excited drew widespread attention to astronomy, mathematics, and all physical studies.

In the same year, the first of the new century, Thomas Young discovered the interference of light and went forward with his researches concerning the undulatory theory and physiological optics. Fresnel soon independently discovered interference and more fully determined its application. The result was the knowledge of the analysis and polarization of light and the calculation of its velocity, concerning the more exact determination of which Albert A. Michelson has conducted new researches.

During the succeeding period such names are found as Oersted, of Copenhagen, who in 1819 recognized the magnetic force produced by the motion of electricity, finding that a magnetic needle was deflected by a current in a wire passing under or over it. This first experiment in electric magnetism was at once followed by Ampère, whom the French call the Newton of electricity, who discovered the effect of current on current, and made possible the galvanometer, the electro-magnet and various later appliances. He called his science electro-dynamics. In 1825, Arago received the Copley medal for making known the development of magnetic forces by the rotation of a copper disk above a magnet. Ohm's Law, a fundamental principle, presented as underlying all electrical theory and measurements, was stated in 1826. The Paris Congress of Physicists, in 1881, gave the name "ohm" to the unit of electrical resistance. The practical unit of electric current strength is called an "ampere," and was carefully defined by the London Conference of 1908. The term "farad,"[6] used as the practical unit of electric capacity, like the terms just mentioned, preserves the name of a discoverer who is one of the stars of first magnitude in the history of experimentalism. He has even been called "the greatest experimental philosopher the world has ever seen." Michael Faraday, 1791–1867, opened the realm of magneto-electricity. His first important discovery, in 1821, was the revolution of a magnetic needle about a current of electricity. He reversed the experiments of Ampère and others who had generated magnetism electrically, and showed that on certain conditions magnets are able to produce electric currents. This achievement has been called "the most important single discovery ever made by a physicist." Besides the induction of electrical currents, he identified electricity produced by various means, and established the laws of definite electrolytic action. It was Faraday also who determined the effect of magnetism on polarized light, and elucidated diamagnetism. To him are due the terms "anode" and "cathode." He accomplished much valuable work in chemistry.

Joseph Henry, 1797-1878, is one of the most notable names in the annals of American science. He was the first to use for the magnetic coil insulated or silk-wrapped wire, and "spool" winding for the limbs of magnets. To him is due the first magnetizing of iron at a distance, anticipating by many years the work of Hertz on electric waves. In 1832 he discovered the induction of a current on itself, self-induction, and was one of the early experimenters whose work aided in the development of the telegraph. His investigations of illuminants and of acoustics resulted in important additions to knowledge.

Great value is attached to the work of Maxwell and

-----

[6]Most frequently used in "microfarad."

Hertz in the field of electro-magnetism. When the former, late in the fifties, stated his belief that electricity and magnetism are but manifestations of stress and motion in ether, the notion was almost as unpopular as was his theory in 1863 that ethereal undulations producing light differ from those of electro-magnetism only in wave-lengths. Helmholtz formulated, at about this time, an electro-magnetic theory of light; and it was the experiments of his pupil, Heinrich Hertz, who, between 1885 and 1889, made investigations on the basis of a prize problem of the Berlin Academy of Sciences, which supplied the demonstration (1887) that ordinary light consists of electrical vibrations in an all-pervading ether. The term "Hertzian waves" commemorates his accomplishment. In lists of inventions appear many results of the principles determined by the profound investigators who have just been mentioned.

To turn backward for a new series of discoveries, it may be noted that Gay-Lussac found cyanogen in 1815. Benzine, the "key-ring compound," was made by Faraday in 1825. About 1831 chloroform was independently recognized by Guthrie in America, Soubeiran in France, and Liebig in Germany. It was probably first used as a general anæsthetic by Simpson, of Edinburgh, in 1848. In 1834 Runge found carbolic acid; in 1836 Edmund Davy, acetylene gas. In 1844 Wells used laughing-gas in extracting a tooth, and at about the same time ether was used independently by Morton and Long, as a surgical anæsthetic. It was the former who made public announcement and demonstration of his method in the Boston Hospital, October 16, 1846. Of numerous instances of related, successive scientific discoveries, cocaine is typical: it was isolated by Niemann, 1860: its anæsthetic properties were realized by von Anrep in 1880: it was used as a local anæsthetic by Koller in 1884. One of the most humane gifts of all time was Lord

Lister's method of antiseptic surgery, made known
in 1867. When one thinks of the unnumbered cases
lost by operators during all preceding times by lack
of antisepsis, and when he attempts to visualize the
horrors of gangrene in army hospitals during wars
and in all other places of surgical care during peace,
the benefits conferred upon the race by this single
achievement only begin to be realized.

Among other events which should be listed as discoveries rather than inventions bare mention can be
made of Lord Kelvin's studies in thermo-dynamics,
and his doctrine of the dissipation of energy, formulated in 1852, in which year Sir G. G. Stokes
received the Rumford medal for his inquiries into the
refrangibility of light; Mendeléeff's Periodic Law of
the Elements announced in his *Elements of Chemistry,* 1868; of the theory of electrolytic dissociation,
Svante Arrhenius, 1874; of "cathode rays," Sir William Crookes, 1879; "X-rays," Röntgen, 1895; and
of radio-activity, Becquerel, 1896. The work of the
Curies in the discovery of radium occurred at this
time. By 1898 Sir James Dewar, completing Faraday's labor, had liquified oxygen, nitrogen, and air in
quantity and secured a considerable amount of liquid
hydrogen which he soon solidified, as he did oxygen
also. The great and beneficial effect of the new
knowledge and practice which have come from these
events is a matter of general information. In 1876
Robert Koch published the history of anthrax. In
1880 Koch and Eberth became benefactors of humanity by isolating the bacillus of typhoid. Sternberg, in
the same year, found the pneumonia bacillus. In
1882 Koch isolated the bacillus of tuberculosis. In
1884 he revealed the cholera bacillus; Loeffler, that
of diphtheria; Nicolaier, that of lockjaw. In 1911
Flexner obtained an antitoxin for cerebro-spinal men-
ingitis, and two years later it was reported that he
had obtained new knowledge of infantile paralysis.

In a very real sense it may be said that nearly if not quite all natural sciences have been reborn at some date since 1800. Among sciences practically if not wholly new, whose birth is dated as having taken place in our own era, biology has claimed first attention by reason of its significance with reference to all the problems of life, and on account of the striking facts and theories which it has presented to the world. Goethe, Oken, and Erasmus Darwin had advanced certain tentative conceptions of life and of its varied forms, which were brought into more complete statement by Lamarck and Treviranus, who in the same year, 1802, suggested the name "biology" for the general study of living things. They were followed by Geoffrey Saint-Hilaire and others, but it was reserved for Charles Darwin and Alfred Russel Wallace, together with their colaborers and successors, to give its present distinction to this branch of learning.

As has been intimated already, physiology has been transformed by the amazing advances made in knowledge of the human body. Its organs, including the muscles and nerves; its red blood corpuscles and their pigment, hæmoglobin; its white blood corpuscles and its chemical messengers, hormones, discovered and named by E. H. Starling early in the twentieth century; its mysterious glands, its sustentation and care, have been the object of close study resulting in constant and profitable revelations which have both lengthened human life and added to its usefulness and enjoyment. Single items of new information, such as those connected with "vitamins," the recent knowledge of sunlight, and the discovery of insulin by Doctor F. G. Banting and Doctor C. H. Best, in 1923, promise permanent values. The advances made by medicine and surgery have added so greatly to the successes of science that, according to a report of the United States Public Health Service, the average life of American people has been lengthened by fifteen years since 1860 and now stands at fifty-six years. It is reported that in the sixteenth century the human life average was between eighteen and twenty years.

Modern chemistry is said to have been ushered in by the successful explanation of combustion and respiration. This field presents many remarkable illustrations of original work. For instance, Liebig, in 1823, brought to light a very valuable fact of organic chemistry, isomerism, since which time many isomeric compounds have been found to have the same composition and identical molecular weight. Liebig also rendered important service to agricultural chemistry, of which he is called the founder. Another example is the publication by Willard Gibbs, physicist of Yale, in 1876, of a new law of nature of momentous importance and of wide application, called "Phase-Rule." Its presentation was mathematical, and it was ten years before it was applied to chemistry, where it became a most valuable means of classifying systems in equilibrium, and a guide to conditions under which these systems exist. It was of use in investigating origins of salt deposits, and as a means of explaining intricate relations in alloys of carbon and iron.

As a separate and distinct science, psychology begins with the nineteenth century. Before that time, it had been regarded as a department of metaphysics, but now it has many branches of its own. The reform instituted by Pinel, Benjamin Rush and others in the care of the insane led, during the latter part of the eighteenth century, to those epochal studies of the brain and nervous system from which modern psychology arose. Weber's Law was hailed by Fechner as the fundamental principle of psycho-physics. Fechner christened a new science by the phrase "physiological psychology." The first psychological laboratory was established at Leipsic by Wundt in 1879. The laboratory at Johns Hopkins was instituted by Hall two years later. Experimental psychology is therefore as yet merely in its infancy. Psychiatry is both a branch of medical science and of psycho-pathology. This specialty has had a comparatively recent development.

Sociology is a modern outgrowth of the ancient and imperfect philosophy of social relations, and is in close association with and indebted to psychology. The name "sociology," a Greek and Latin hybrid, was invented in 1839 by Auguste Comte, whose conception of a comprehensive social science was bound up with a defective philosophy. Herbert Spencer, in his effort to explain human society in terms of evolution, made an impression upon the scientific mind. Sir Francis Galton, a cousin of Charles Darwin, attempted to apply the principles of another new science, "eugenics," to human conduct and progress, leaving morals out of account as being too difficult. Henry Sidgwick very nearly identified sociology and politics. This narrow conception, as well as the mainly physical one insisted upon by Galton, widened into the better comprehension of organic society based on qualities which contribute to social well-being and efficiency. T. H. Green profoundly remarked that during man's whole history the command "Thou shalt love thy neighbor as thyself" has never varied. Benjamin Kidd acclaims the extended conception of the answer to the question, "Who is my neighbor?" which has resulted from the characteristic doctrines of the Christian religion as being the most powerful evolutionary force which ever acted on society.

Genetics represents biology in its efforts to deal with heredity and variation. The science of eugenics, in its attempt to apply biological theories to the improvement of our race, early divided into two branches, Pearsonian and Mendelian. The latter

presents facts from experiments on individual lines
of inheritance in accordance with the laws of heredity, taught in 1866 by Gregor Mendel, and independently rediscovered by several experimenters in 1900.
Followers of Karl Pearson, or biometricians, impressed by the views of Galton, depend on averages
from large numbers of cases, assuming that traits of
individuals vary from a normal value. Systematic
studies, as those instituted by Thorndike and others,
are slowly making headway for the belief that ultimately, by force of private and public sentiment and
practice, and at length in part at least by aid of law,
degeneration may be lessened and the improvement
of mankind may be greatly accelerated.

Euthenics is a companion science which adds to the
eugenicist's effort to improve heredity the betterment
of mankind by means of environmental changes.
William M. Goldsmith, biologist, "seeing the impossibilities of isolating the effects of environment from
those of heredity," has coined (*Science,* April 16,
1926) the term "eugenothenics," by which man is to
be developed both by breeding and culturing, including
the idea of spiritual development.

Modern anthropology, another science connected
with man, and of which such separate undertakings
as those of anthropometry, ethnology, and anthropog-
raphy are branches, begins in the first half of the
nineteenth century with Blumenbach of Göttingen,
teacher of Humboldt, and his classification of skulls
by form and measurement. With anthropometry the
name of Bertillon, the French investigator, and the
Bertillon system of physical notations are inseparably connected.

The relationship between such branches of science
and religion is quickly apprehended, and the aid to
be given all social investigations and discovered
methods of human betterment by intelligent Christianity has long since been realized and partially

acted upon. The utterances of the religious press and
pulpit, and the studies made by Christian leaders
have brought to the aid of sociology some forces which
otherwise it would have been difficult to reach and
utilize. It is admitted, however, that the task of
social uplift has only begun to be accomplished.

In order further to illustrate the typical character
of this age it is not necessary to list and describe all
new or almost wholly renewed sciences. An addi-
tional word may be said about electricity. This
term, whose present meaning, however ancient the
fact, is almost wholly a nineteenth-century product,
connotes the thought of many new types of investigation and utility. Electro-chemistry, based on the
invention of Volta's pile, was begun by the decomposition of water by Nicholson and Cavendish, and of
potash and soda, discovering the metals potassium
and sodium, by Sir Humphry Davy, in 1806. Electron physics, as Pupin has shown, is studying matter,
gravitation, ether, radiation, and the nature and relations of electricity, magnetism, and heat, with wonderful results, some of which are mentioned elsewhere.
Electro-biology, mechanics, therapeutics are among
departments of electrical knowledge, many of which
are whole sciences in themselves, and have made vast
contributions elsewhere, as in aeronautics, aviation,
telegraphy, telephony, and in many other places.
Important future developments are expected.

Some of the most far-reaching scientific theories of
all time belong to the past one hundred years. The
principle of the conservation of energy is one of these.
It is less obvious than the much older dogma of the
conservation of matter associated with the name of
Lavoisier, founder of modern chemistry.[8] The con-

---

[8] James J. Walsh, physician and physiologist, claims this discovery
for Thomas Aquinas by virtue of his saying: *Nihil omnino in nihilum
redigetur. The Popes and Science*, p. 313. The method of Aquinas
was but partially that of science, however.

servation of energy was perhaps foreseen by Rumford, and, as Tyndall thinks, was dreamed by Carlyle.
Carnot, Joule, and Mayer had well prepared the way
for its formulation by Helmholtz, in 1847, when it
was at once generally accepted. The doctrine of
evolution is commonly associated with the name of
Charles Darwin, who published *The Origin of Species
by Means of Natural Selection,* in 1859. Lamarck,
Lyell, Erasmus Darwin, before; Wallace, Haeckel
and many others after Charles Darwin developed the
general conception or added specific illustrations.
Perhaps no scientific teaching has ever been more
highly lauded or more frequently misunderstood and
misrepresented. The electro-magnetic theory of light
and matter, as we have seen, was a vision of the great
Faraday, scientifically formulated half a century
later, by James Clerk Maxwell, and demonstrated by
Henry and by the Hertz experiments, as announced
to the Berlin University Physical Society in 1887 by
Helmholtz. One of the most impressive developments
of the last three decades has been the result of recent
studies of the structure of matter, made by use of
newly discovered agencies—cathode-rays, X-rays,
radio-activity, ultra-violet light and so on. As the eyes
of the mind peer into the atoms of which the universe
is composed, new phases of atomic theory are being
continuously developed. The work of Sir William
Crookes, Sir Joseph J. Thomson, Sir Ernest Rutherford and Niels Bohr, are outstanding achievements.
Bohr's atom differs from that of Thomson in that
while both have a central nucleus of positive electricity and a number of electrons of negative electricity,
the Bohr electrons are not stationary but revolve
about the nucleus as our earth travels around the sun.
Each atom is, then, a tiny universe similar to our
solar system, if the theory be accepted. When one
recalls our former views of the indivisible units or
"bricks" of which all natural objects were supposed

to consist, is it not amazing to receive instruction concerning "the astronomy of the atom"?

It was in 1901 that Max Planck, physicist, formulated his law of radiation, extended in 1912 to all forms of energy, to the effect that energy is emitted and absorbed in integral multiples of indivisible "quanta," depending on the frequency of the oscillation of electrons. This theory, like others of modern origin, while greatly praised, is not without considerable opposition.

The theory of relativity arose from an effort to explain results obtained in ether-drift experiments by Michelson and Morley in 1887, and by Morley and Miller in 1904-05. It was announced by Einstein in 1905 in a special form, later greatly extended. He described motion and direction as dependent on the observer. Space and time likewise are not real but relative existences dependent on our measures, such as rods and clocks. Newton himself clearly stated the problem to which the theory of relativity has attempted to supply an answer by his distinction between absolute and relative space and motion. Our experience is entirely of relative motions. By the theory of equivalence, gravity is not, as Newton held, a force, but a property of space, which is not Euclidean, as Newton thought. Einstein's theory, which is supported by certain scientific observations and tests, takes us behind space, time, and matter to find an original unity. There are four dimensions of all bodies: length, breadth, thickness—and duration. It was Minkowski, who explained, in 1908, that if we cease to think of space and time as separate entities, and bring the length, breadth and thickness of space into relation with time, we get a four-dimensional continuum which is the same for all observers. The generalized theory of relativity, published about 1916, and said to have been partially confirmed by English astronomers in 1919, has been called by its exponents

probably the profoundest single achievement of the
human mind.   The details are abstruse, and the
effects upon scientific conceptions are being succes-
sively worked out by mathematicians and physicists.
Dayton C. Miller, physicist, one of the early experimenters on whose work the theory was based, has
brought serious criticisms against the hypothesis.
Charles Lane Poor, in his lecture, "Time and Relativity," and in his book, *Gravitation Versus
Relativity*, states the case of opponents of relativism.
In any event it is not to be understood that Einstein's
work overthrows that of Newton.   If correct, he
amends and supplements the latter, whose laws, within
the limits of our solar system, are held by various
authorities to be as valid as ever.   Even as to gravitation, whether regarded as a mere force or as a "warp
in space," it may be said that its effects in case one
falls are precisely the same.

The bare names and the briefest description of such
vaulting conceptions of physical facts and relations
lend distinction to a period characterized by thinking
on planes so high. It will become clear as we further
recall the deeds and notable personalities of scientific history that the attempt to penetrate the recesses
of nature and to comprehend its processes and the
laws by which its affairs are governed not only is not
irreligious but may be so conducted as to elevate the
mind into realms of infinite truth and to bring its
visions into ever closer correspondence with the
Christian conception of the universe.

CHAPTER II

THE HUMAN MINISTRY OF SCIENCE

In former times, when "Christian service" was mentioned, the reference was usually to the ministry of the gospel. Long since it has been very generally acknowledged by religious leaders that men are "called" by the Spirit of God to various careers for which their gifts and experiences adapt them. In harmony with this sensible and scriptural view, it is possible to perform any needed and useful task for which one is fitted by nature and training, or which circumstances seem to devolve upon him, with the consciousness of religious motives and results. Those who practice the arts and apply the principles of science may always be to some degree, as they sometimes are in every sense, "God's fellow workers." It may be well to repeat the statement already made that great numbers of people have a very inadequate conception of the prodigious labors and vast achievements of scientific men. It is for this reason, and in order to prepare the way for more intimate acquaintance with various personalities and religious relationships of scientific history, that this review is now carried into the realm of law in application.

Every great department of human activity, art, religion, commerce, invention, may be pictured clearly before the mind only by considering the broad range of its development. Let us, therefore, attempt at least a bird's-eye view of the realm of applied sciences. We do this with admiration. That the pursuit of science for its own sake, whatever may be the nature of the discoveries made, and without respect to the question of utility, must always be regarded as honorable and important, few are prepared to deny. While this conception, as J. Arthur Thomson has said, "is an autonomy worth fighting for," it is also true, as he adds, that "both scientific inquiry and artistic device are natural and necessary experiences of the evolving human spirit."[1] Bunsen asserted that honor belongs to two classes of men, those who toil at extending the boundaries of knowledge, and those who adapt knowledge to useful ends. It is to be noted, however, that it is really the classes of work, and not the persons engaged in it, which are distinct, since the same investigator is often both discoverer and inventor. Cassius J. Keyser represents all forms of mathesis when he points out the fact that "the pure mathematician and the applied mathematician sometimes may —indeed, they not infrequently do—dwell together harmoniously in a single personality."[2] Lord Kelvin gave a death thrust to a certain type of scientific aristocracy by declaring that there is no greater mistake than that of looking superciliously upon practical applications of science. He called attention to the fact that many of the chief advances from the beginning of human effort to the present time have been made in the ardent desire to turn knowledge of the properties of matter to some purpose of value to mankind.[3] Sensible judges will admit the force of this contention, and will not doubt that an Edison is as necessary to the world as a Tesla; a Wright as a Langley. Kelvin is a splendid example of the combined talents to which Keyser refers. He was equally great in mastery of principles and of their application. It is estimated that a modern ship uses in its

---

[1] *Introduction to Science,* p. 225, Henry Holt and Company. See also his defense of scientific theories as necessary to utilities, p. 236, *et seq.*

[2] *Human Worth of Rigorous Thinking,* p. 36, Columbia University Press.

[3] See quotation in Kelvin lecture of Silvanus P. Thompson, *Journal of the Institute of Electrical Engineers,* vol. xli, London, 1908.

operations some two hundred of his ideas and devices.[4]

If it is impossible, within reasonable limits, even to name all the scientific discoveries of the nineteenth and twentieth centuries, how much more so to list completely or to describe fully their inventions! These are so numerous and valuable that it is little wonder that our period is often called the Age of Invention, though in view of the prompt exploitation of new devices, Gilbert N. Lewis calls it an age of publication and conservation. The results of recent scientific ingenuity have so transformed the processes of manufacture and labor that many insist that we should describe these times as the Age of Industry. It should be kept in mind, however, that industries and the devices which they use are applications and effects of principles whose development is comprised in the general term "science."

The comprehensiveness of the field of scientific investigation is even more impressively displayed by the applied than by the abstract sciences. Practical results are not only more numerous but more evident than are principles. A hundred devices of ingenuity and of profitable use may be instituted in less time also than it takes to formulate and establish a simple law which may be stated in a dozen words. Although it is basic discoveries that make relatively easy and speedy a host of mechanical, chemical, or electrical applications, it must be recognized that one of the most amazing things about the scientific world is the diversity of its inventions. Science follows every train of thought and every human experience. It penetrates every nook and corner of the universe. Its achievements during the first decades of the twentieth century alone have been described in ponderous volumes numbering hundreds of pages.

---

[4]Dayton C. Miller's commencement address, Baldwin-Wallace College, 1927.

In reviewing the "works" of scientists it may be well to follow an order mainly chronological, but not wholly so. In 1802 Murdock, on the basis of former experiments, successfully obtained gas illumination for streets and houses, though general use came slowly. The Lyceum Theatre in London was so lighted in 1803–04 and Westminster Bridge in 1813. Electroplating is said to have been done by Brugnatelli in Italy in 1803. This was made possible by Volta's electric battery of 1800, and by experiments showing that salt solutions can be decomposed by electricity, the acid appearing at one pole and the metal at the other. Gay-Lussac made the first balloon ascension for scientific purposes in 1804, attaining a height of 23,040 feet. Symington, in 1802 in England, following earlier efforts in America, constructed a primitive steamboat. Robert Fulton, who had written on navigation by steam in 1793, in 1803 on the Seine successfully experimented with a small boat. His Clermont, launched on the Hudson in 1807, began the first really successful steamboat transportation for passengers and freight. Sir David Brewster's kaleidoscope, 1814, which was thought to have no other value than that of a beautiful toy, received instant popularity, and because of the variety and novelty of form and color which it presents to the eye became valuable in designing. In July of that year George Stephenson, who had been preceded by Trevithick's primitive work in 1803, ran his "traveling engine," nicknamed "My Lord," between Killingworth colliery and the shipping port, nine miles distant. In 1829 Stephenson's engine, "Rocket," triumphantly won at Rainhill the prize of five hundred pounds offered by the Liverpool and Manchester Railway, after which the name of the inventor became permanently associated with the locomotive.

The wonderful progress made by astronomy in recent times has been due in good part to the improvements made in telescopes and to the establishment of well-equipped observatories in various parts of the world. The first observatory in the southern hemisphere was at Parramatta, New South Wales, established in 1821. The century was nearly half over before an observatory was built in the United States. Prior to 1816 no refracting telescope had been made with an object glass of more than six inches, though Herschel's reflecting telescope of 1801 had a mirror four feet in diameter. Frauenhofer's Dorpat, Russia, object glass of 9.9 inches, made in 1824, was considered a "giant." Alvan Clark became the great maker of telescopes, and between 1844 and the end of the century the Clark firm had produced the Chicago Astronomical Society 18.5-inch, the Washington Naval Observatory 26-inch, the Saint Petersburg 30-inch, the Lick Observatory 36-inch, and the Yerkes 40-inch telescopes. Alvan G. Clark made many discoveries, and received the Lalande medal. Bengt Strömgren, precocious son of the astronomer at Copenhagen, in 1926 applied the photo-electric principle to observations of transits of stars in a meridian instrument. Sensitive wires are used in the focal plane of the instrument so that when light from a star falls on the wire a slight electric current is produced, and this is recorded by a highly sensitive galvanometer.

Turning to other items of interest, it should be remembered that in 1816 Sir Humphry Davy supplied miners with the safety-lamp, thus becoming a lifesaver of the first order. George Stephenson independently devised one at about the same time and Clanny had produced something of the kind three years earlier. The sad connotation with the account of the invention of the stethoscope by Laënnec, about 1816, is that by its aid the maker of it was found to be dying with tuberculosis of the lungs. The value of this instrument in determining conditions which need prophylactic or therapeutic treatment, so that many persons may be saved from speedy death, is well known to physicians and the public. It is of use in making examinations for various purposes, including life insurance.

Among devices for saving the labor and increasing the powers of man which were in use before the middle of the nineteenth century are Babbage's calculating machine, 1822; the electric telegraph, suggested to fellow passengers returning from Europe in 1832 by Samuel F. B. Morse, and later developed by him; the reaping machine, Cyrus H. McCormick, 1834; the automatically played piano, Seytre, 1842; the steam hammer, said to have been designed in a few minutes after the idea occurred to him, by James Nasmyth, 1839; the typewriter, Charles Thurber, 1843—first made practical by Sholes, 1868; and the sewing machine, Elias Howe, 1845. On the basis of some of Faraday's experiments Dewar produced the "thermos bottle," 1823. Walker, 1827, is credited with friction matches. In 1829 Braithwaite and Ericsson, in London, brought out the first portable fire-engine. Ericsson's screw-propeller, 1836, may not have been the first. Babbitt metal came in 1839, and in the same year Goodyear vulcanized rubber by means of sulphur. The Hoe double-cylinder printing press dates from 1845, and the pneumatic tire, R. W. Thompson, from the same year. During the nineteenth century came the twisted link cable, cable-car, and cable-way. Portland cement, which has so marvelously affected building and paving operations the world over, was first made in England in 1824. The first electric locomotive came about the middle of the century, and various experiments in making artificial ice did not come into practical general use until a quarter of a century later.

Many destructive inventions may be named, among which are Colt's revolver, 1836; gun-cotton, made at

Schönbein, Germany, 1846; nitroglycerin, discovered by Sobrero, 1847; Hunt's magazine gun, 1849; Gatling gun, 1862; smokeless powder, 1863; Whitehead torpedo, 1866; dynamite, Nobel, 1868. While it will be claimed that these devices have done much good as well as great evil, one would prefer to have been one of more than one hundred and fifty persons who have taken out American patents on artificial limbs during the past century, to have invented a lifeboat, like Lukin and Greathead, to have devised the apparatus for shooting a rope to a distressed ship, George Manby's "life preserver" of 1808, to have made safety matches with Lundstrom in 1855, to have perfected an automatic car-coupler as did Janney, 1873; or to have produced a pulmotor as did Drager in 1911.

Alfred Nobel, the Swedish chemist, who was first to produce nitroglycerin commercially and who invented dynamite, blasting gelatin, and other explosives, not only aided those who made war, but all who dig tunnels, work mines, sink oil-wells, and engage in many other necessary enterprises. In addition he left his fortune as a fund for the establishment of forty thousand dollar prizes to be given to those whose work in chemistry, physics, medicine, and idealistic literature is most helpful to the cause of world peace. Nobel was an incessant worker, though he was a semi-invalid laboring under limitations during his entire lifetime.

Herman's rock-drill dates from 1853. Sommeiler's reciprocating drill was patented in 1857 and was used in the Mont Cenis tunnel. Sir Henry Bessemer in 1855-56 took out patents on his process of making steel. The Siemens Brothers of London, and Emile and Pierre Martin, 1858–64, perfected the Siemens-Martin open-hearth process of steel making. Basic steel, the Thomas-Gilchrist process, came later; nickel steel was made by James Riley, Glasgow, 1888–89; and Jupiter steel was introduced in 1901

under Lundin's patents. The discoveries of Sir
Robert Hadfield in the development of manganese and
silicon alloys of steel and the strenuous adventures
of the Flannery brothers in finding, reducing, and
marketing vanadium, discovered by Del Rio in 1801,
and an essential of all high-speed tool steel, are epics
of metallurgy well told in *Popular Research Narratives.*

.Here is a variety of wonders: invention and
development of quaternions, Sir William R. Hamilton, 1843; lenticular stereoscope, Brewster, 1849;
gyroscope, Foucault, 1852; Bunsen burner, 1855;
sleeping-car, Woodruff, 1856; coal-tar dye, Perkin,
1856; steam-injector, Gifford, 1858; driven well,
Green, 1861; passenger elevator, Otis, 1861; celluloid,
the Hyatts, 1866; railway airbrake, Westinghouse,
1868; Lyall, positive motion weaving-loom, 1872;
twine-binder, Gorham, and self-binding reaper, Locke
and Wood, 1873; duplex telegraph, Edison, 1873;
cash-carrier, Brown, 1875. In 1876 N. A. Otto, following a long series of experiments by others and by
himself, invented, as Beau de Rochas had done, the
full cycle of operations used in compression gas
engines. He overcame practical difficulties and made
his engine one of world-wide application. Other new
productions were the phonograph and carbon telephone transmitter, Edison, 1877; Faure, primitive
storage battery, 1880; linotype machine, Mergen-
thaler, 1884; electric welding, Elihu Thomson, 1886.
In the same year, Tesla's system of multi-phase electric currents, first used at Niagara, made possible
long distance power transmission. The super-power
plants which have resulted render an ever greater
service. The Kodak camera, Eastman and Walker,
though its name came later, may be dated 1888, when
the first model appeared; kinetograph and kineto-
scope, Edison, 1890; rotary steam turbine, Parsons,
1891; telautograph, Elisha Gray, 1893; thermit proc-

ess of welding, Goldschmidt, 1908; Tungsten light, Hanaman, 1911.

An excellent illustration of inventive history, covering most of our era, is that of photography. The record is carried back by Abney even to the first tanning of the skin by the sun's rays—rather an early incident. In 1802 Thomas Wedgwood published an account of copying paintings on glass and of making profiles by the agency of light. Daguerre and Niepce produced the daguerreotype, and made it public in 1839. The Fox-Talbot printing process dates from the same year. In 1840 for the first time a celestial object, the moon, was photographed by J. W. Draper. In 1845 Foucault and Fizeau photographed the sun. In 1850 came the collodion process, giving great impetus to the art. Dry plates came in 1854 from the efforts of Gaudin, Muirhead, and Taupenot. In 1864 Bollin and Sayce inaugurated the collodion emulsion process, and gelatin was used instead of collodion by Maddox in 1871. Various improvements have succeeded, leading to autochrome or color-photography, imperfectly developed, to photo-engraving, to the production of moving pictures, and to elaborate astro and micro-photography, which are of the greatest benefit to many arts and sciences. The development of astro-photography may be illustrated by the conviction expressed by Edwin B. Frost, director of Yerkes Observatory, that astronomers are now photographing spiral galaxies as remote from the earth as one thousand million light years.[5]

Closely allied with photography, and enabling us to detect the composition of various substances and of the heavenly bodies, is the spectroscope. Gustav

[5]See also article by E. P. Hubble, *Astrophysical Journal,* 1926. In a letter to me, October 20, 1927, Frost stated that "there is now no question that we may regard one million light years as the order of distance of the nearer galaxies, while the most remote ones that can be photographed with our greatest telescopes may well be a thousand times as far away."

Robert Kirchhoff, who, with Robert Wilhelm Eberard
Bunsen, about the middle of the nineteenth century,
brought this instrument to perfection, has been called
"the famous discoverer, formulator, and interpreter
of the science of spectrum analysis, and the founder
of the theory of radiation." Notice will be found
elsewhere of slightly earlier work of Sir G. G. Stokes,
in part anticipatory of the achievements of Kirchhoff, a professor of mathematical physics at the University of Berlin, who made important contributions
to electrical theory.

Rear Admiral Bradley A. Fiske, who patented a
method of controlling the movements of vessels by
radio, reiterates in his book, *Invention,* the statement
that an invention of the highest order must possess
three essentials. It must have a satisfactory conception, an appropriate development, and actual and adequate production. It is surprising to see how many
products of the genius of this age are able to meet
all of these requirements. Some of the most valuable
of them have enriched the public and posterity far
more than they have their authors.

The wide sphere of science is strikingly illustrated
by the variety of its spectacular first events. Never,
during a similar period of human experience, have so
many thrills been enjoyed as have come to human
minds from scientific achievements during the past
century. Perhaps no "watcher of the skies, when a
new planet swims within his ken" ever felt more
elated than was the whole scientific world when
Galle, of Berlin, observed in the heavens the most distant of the known planets, Neptune. The mathematical studies of Adams and LeVerrier, based on the
perturbations of Uranus, had almost exactly fixed the
position of such a body, and it was found on the very
night it was first looked for, the evening of September
23, 1846. Neptune had been seen by Lalande in May,
1795, but it was taken to be a fixed star, and cata-

logued as such, until discovered as a planet. This body, invisible to the eye, is at least 2,629,000,000 miles from the earth, and, of course, farther from the sun. Its mass is nearly seventeen times that of the earth. The international brotherhood and copartnership of science has a beautiful illustration in the joint labors and success of Adams of England, LeVerrier of France, and Galle of Germany.

What a day was that second of September, 1837, when, in a New York University building, Samuel F. B. Morse demonstrated over a circuit of seventeen hundred feet of copper wire his production of the electro-magnetic telegraph. The few friends present were not less enthusiastic than were the many who shared in the revelation of May 24, 1844, when the new line from Baltimore to Washington was first used.

Menlo Park, New Jersey, was the scene of a memorable triumph when, in 1879, in the laboratory of the wizard Edison, the incandescent electric lamp was first exhibited. A year before this a great sensation had occurred in Paris when Paul Jablochkoff's "electric candle," precursor of the modern arc light, was shown to admiring beholders. In these adventures, as improved later, the basic work of Davy in 1810 came to its full meaning, and pushed back from nature much of the darkness which in past ages had limited the progress and diminished the happiness of the race.

The story of the laying of the first Atlantic cable by Cyrus W. Field in 1858 is one of the most popular and exciting tales in the history of modern undertakings. As the initial outcome was not successful, great discouragement resulted. A second cable was laid in 1865, but was broken when it had been paid out for ten hundred and sixty-five miles from Valentia. The following year the Great Eastern sailed again with a lighter, stronger cable of twenty-three hundred

and seventy miles length, and laid it successfully.
She then grappled the lost cable at a depth of two
miles, spliced it, and landed the end at Heart's Content.

Many still living recall the awe and even timidity
with which they spoke into their first telephone. It
was more than a household and business necessity
which was patented by Alexander Graham Bell, a
student of phonetics and electricity, in 1876. This
child of the inventor's brain, as Edwin Markham puts
it,

> "Dispels the distances, shrinks up the spaces,
> Brings back the voices and the vanished faces,
> Holds men together though the feet may roam,
> Makes of each land a little friendly home."[6]

The telephone was shown, as the writer well recalls,
at the Centennial Exposition in Philadelphia. At that
time such an instrument was unbelievable. The report of the judges was exceedingly important to the
inventor, but they paid no attention to his work. On
the final day they were about to pass by without even
testing his apparatus, when Dom Pedro, Emperor of
Brazil, came into the building with a brilliant retinue.
Approaching Mr. Bell, this distinguished visitor recognized and warmly greeted him, as his work in teaching deaf-mutes had brought him the Emperor's
acquaintance and admiration. Of course the new device was then examined. The eager young man went
into another room and spoke into his transmitter,
while Dom Pedro listened at the receiver. The judges
and spectators were startled when the astonished Emperor cried, "My God—it talks!" The instrument
has been talking ever since over multiplying lines
and increasing distances. The impression made on
so great a mind as that of Helmholtz by the telephone

---

[6]Reprinted by permission.

disk, and still more by the phonograph disk, is a capital tribute to the surpassing novelty and interest of invention. In the summer of 1894 a method of high inductance wave transmission occurred to M. I. Pupin, which vastly extended telephone service and saved to the public multiplied millions of expense. He is also the inventor of methods of electrical tuning and rectification used in radio mechanics and in wireless telegraphy. As to wires, their extent in overland and undersea use is constantly increasing. In "A Midsummer Night's Dream," Puck said, "I'll put a girdle about the earth." This has certainly been done. It was reported a quarter century since that the land and cable wires in use would surround the earth more than two hundred and fifty times and would extend in a straight line for more than thirty-three million miles, or a third of the way to the sun. The Bell Telephone Company reported on June 30, 1927, that in the United States alone there were at the time sixty million miles of telephone wire, and that the Bell system wire would reach from the earth to the moon and back about one hundred twenty times.

January 7, 1927, a little more than a half century later than the date of the epochal invention of the telephone, occurred the opening of the first transatlantic commercial telephone service. The formalities observed as New York called London and received a clear response were of general interest, and the event was widely published.

Those who experienced them can well remember the accidents which occurred when they tried to ride the old-time high bicycle, with its oddly assorted wheels. The first trolley car filled one with amazement, but the horseless carriage was a greater wonder, bringing in the more than humorous classification of pedestrians as "quick, or dead." The modern motor car is an assembly of various principles, inventions, and improvements made by many minds. No rapid development followed efforts to drive ordinary road vehicles by mechanical power until Daimler's petrol-motor of 1886 made this possible. The Elwood Haynes horseless carriage of 1893-94 is exhibited at the Smithsonian Institution, Washington, and great credit is due Haynes, chemist and inventor, for the development of a practical automobile.

In 1913 Lloyd George stated that England had 220,000 motor vehicles, double those of any other country, except the United States, which, thanks to the industry and ability of Henry Ford, had more than three times as many as England possessed. About the middle of 1924, when the Ford factory turned out its ten millionth car, it was calculated that Mr. Ford's genius as an organizer had made available motors with a total of 220,000,000 horse-power, seventy-six times the estimated power of Niagara Falls, ten times the total hydro-electric power which had been developed on earth, twenty-five times the available electric power of the United States. The coming of the automobile has required vast changes, has resulted in great improvements in road-making, and has introduced truck and motorbus services which have revolutionized systems of transportation.

A sensation which can never be forgotten was made upon my own mind when, in mid-Atlantic, our steamship received information by wireless that the first human being to do so had flown across the British Channel. Here were three marvels in one, the steamboat, which alleged scientific demonstrations were once supposed to have proven could never be made to cross the Atlantic, wireless telegraphy, and successful aviation. The first practical installation for wireless telegraphy was made by the young Italian, Marconi, in 1896. Previously Sir Oliver Lodge and Sir William Preece had each independently transmitted messages between stations unconnected by wires, employing the induction currents discovered by Faraday in 1832. Preece was consulted by Marconi and gave him aid. Branly's coherer, 1891, followed by Marconi's magnetic detector, of 1901, and since 1906, by devices for storing up the effect of successive trains of waves and giving them more vigorous discharges to the telephone, made possible the recognition and interpretation at their destination of impulses across space. Signals were sent over Salisbury Plain, a mile and three fourths, early in 1896. The distance was increased to four miles in March, eight in May, eighteen in December. By 1901 the distance had increased to eighteen hundred miles. The two stations were at Saint John's, Newfoundland, and Poldhu, Cornwall. Marconi had put a bridge between England and America, and the new century was opened by this thrilling event, auspiciously linking the old world and the new. The use of the wireless in broadcasting concerts and speeches, in communicating with ships, aeroplanes, dirigibles, and railway trains in motion is a commonplace, the result being not only pleasure but convenience and added safety in travel. One of the most astonishing marvels is that of the transmission of pictures by wireless, a feat made possible by the devices of Radio Corporation engineers, headed by Captain Richard H. Ranger, and by the work of C. F. Jenkins, of Washington, D. C. Picture transmission over wires was accomplished at about the same time, the labors of those who solved these problems culminating in the successful experiments of 1923 and 1924. April 7, 1927, three months after telephonic communication occurred between New York and London, television enabled Secretary Hoover and others, speaking in Washington, to be seen as well as heard in New York.

Could anything be more exciting than the developments which have given to science mastery of the air? Thrilling events in this realm of experimentation have followed one another with increasing frequency, and their spectacular character has attracted the attention, not only of multiplied thousands of beholders, but of practically the entire world. As in case of other inventions of the first class, the dirigible and the aeroplane are attainments in a struggle lasting hundreds of years—from the earliest kite experiments to the last flight around the world. In 1784, the French physicist, Charles, illustrated the principle of Montgolfier's balloon, and constructed the first balloon filled with the light gas, hydrogen, which Cavendish had recently discovered. Sir George Cayley, in 1809, stated the essential principles of locomotion with a heavier than air machine. In 1852 Gifford, inventor of an injector, fitted a balloon with a steam-engine and propeller, and drove it five or six miles an hour. Lilienthal, about 1871, studied the flight of birds, kites, and gliding, but met with a fatal accident in 1896. S. P. Langley, of the Smithsonian Institution, Washington, inventor of the bolometer, made many studies and efforts. The first recorded motor-driven aeroplane flight was made in 1896 by a machine devised by Langley; but later experiments were disappointing. It was the gasoline motor which made possible present-day aviation. The first successful aeroplane demonstration was that of the machine built by the Wright brothers, in which Orville Wright flew for twelve seconds, and later, eight hundred fifty-two feet in fifty-nine seconds, December 17, 1903. In 1906 in France Santos-Dumont flew two hundred yards, and others extended the distance. It was a great day when Wilbur Wright, having crossed the Atlantic to give a demonstration, flew for more than two hours, carrying passengers at a height of four hundred feet. He had some difficulty getting his machine to work. The skeptics began to scoff, and the situation looked unpleasant, but when the flight started all criticism was dispelled. The performance was very successful. Within less than twenty years from the first flight of the Wrights, trips were made across the Atlantic and to Australia and South America. Engines of more than fifteen hundred horsepower were soon driving air machines at speeds of more than two hundred miles an hour. The necessities of the World War gave impetus to the early efforts of fliers. Modern mail and passenger service and the attainments of great dirigibles brought into existence the present elaborate air vehicles. As the items which are being considered indicate, there have been so many "first nights," or days, in the world's theatre that little excitement was caused when those adventurous spirits of 1924 traveled around the globe or when the great Z-R 3 arrived in America from Germany, having carried thirty-two men safely over five thousand and sixty-six miles of land and sea in eighty-one hours and twenty-five minutes. Rear Admiral Robinson thought that the world flight, though largely a feat, was justified. "Other men," he said, "will fly around the earth, but never again will anybody fly around it for the first time." The disastrous loss of the Shenandoah in 1925, while it was a shocking accident, served to teach valuable lessons of workmanship and wise administration. New devices of manufacture and control, and world records for distance, height, and speed follow each other with great rapidity, and "the highways of the skies" are being traveled by increasing numbers on diverse errands of adventure and usefulness.

The flight from New York to Paris of Charles Augustus Lindbergh, who reached the French capital May 28, 1927, in his monoplane, Spirit of St. Louis, stirred the imagination and elicited the admiration of the world, and was followed by the remarkable exploits of Clarence Chamberlin, Richard E. Byrd, Francisco de Pinedo, and others. The Smithsonian Institution handbook of 1927 presented a concise history of aeronautics from the flying toy of the fourth century before Christ and the wooden bird of Archytas down to the first sound principles of Leonardo Da Vinci, and the steam models of Henson and String-fellow, and on to the modern successes of Langley, the Wrights and their followers.

Electric storage is one of the partially solved undertakings of our time. The principle of the electric storage battery was made known by Gautherot in 1801. In 1842 Sir William Grove constructed a gas battery. These efforts were not practical, however, and it was reserved for Planté, 1860, and Faure and Brush, about 1881, to perfect successful batteries of the storage type. Their work, and the Edison accumulator of 1904, have led to a multitude of devices for lighting, starting, and running various machines and factories. In some future day the storage battery may do away with the smoke and dirt of the present locomotive and factory, and may perform undreamed wonders of service to humanity. In general, the tendency of electricity to overpower all its competitors is illustrated by a unique tug of war contest at Erie, Pennsylvania, December 4, 1923, which must have given great entertainment to beholders. The New York Central Railroad furnished a Mikado type unit, equipped with booster, superheater, and other improvements, operated by a picked crew for a pulling match against an electric locomotive designed for the Chicago, Milwaukee and Saint Paul lines. The steam monster was allowed to get a start, and then the electric's engineer gradually threw on his power. Slowly the steam engine was brought to a stop, and then with throttles open was pulled backward despite its utmost struggles. The development of the gas-electric locomotive furnishes another illustration of inventive progress. In 1927 one of these machines covered the three hundred thirty-four miles between Montreal and Toronto, Canada, in five hours and a half, giving promise of greater achievements in future.

Thus comes the new day in competition with the old! After this fashion is science improving the past, and bringing on the day of added information and of greater power to achieve good ends.

During the latter portion of 1924 and the earlier part of 1925, a sensation was created by the news that from the wharves of Kiel, Germany, a two thousand-ton ship had put out to sea without sails or steam. The beholders of the exploit saw a sailing vessel, which had formerly required five hundred yards of canvas to propel her, move off mysteriously after having been deprived of sails, masts, and rigging. Two great cylinders, resembling gigantic smoke-stacks lifted themselves above the deck, but there was no smoke, no sound of engines, and no churning of screws. Nevertheless, the boat made its way through the Baltic waves at almost twice its former speed. The schooner was the Buckau, equipped with a new invention called a rotor, devised by the director of the Institute of Aerodynamics at Amsterdam, Holland, Anton Flettner. The huge cylinders of the Buckau were spun by a small engine, and their surfaces presented to the wind afforded the means by which the craft was propelled. Flettner's invention was based on the Magnus Law, a principle known for the greater part of a century, and simply illustrated by the curves made by a spinning baseball when hurled by a skilled pitcher. Some steamship officials gave the Flettner rotor immediate approval, and the Hamburg American Company took steps to use it on new freighters for its East Asia route. Albert Einstein asserted that the rotor principle is one of great practical importance. Flettner, who had formerly produced a widely used automatic rudder, and whose work in marine invention is well known, had successfully demonstrated an idea which he thought would ultimately enable ocean vessels greatly to reduce the size of crews and to save the larger part of their fuel.

Later, the rotor-driven Rotterdam crossed the Atlantic. It has been suggested that possibly rotors may prove able to store electric energy for the propulsion of various kinds of machinery in industrial plants, but this notion is declared by good authority to be inconceivable and some physicists think that the rotor, however interesting, will not prove to be of great practical value.

The marvelous recent progress of both the abstract and applied sciences has been due in part to the organization of scientific societies, the establishment of helpful funds and foundations, and the inducements made by suitable recognitions of success—degrees, honors, medals, prizes. These are the natural concomitants of such a time and of the undertakings which have given it distinction. Learned societies had previously existed. The Royal Society of London dates from 1660. The French Academy of Sciences began work in 1666. Similar institutions were established in Germany, 1700; Russia, 1725; Sweden, 1739; Denmark, 1743. The Royal Institution of Great Britain was founded in 1799 and was incorporated in 1800 by Count Rumford, Sir Joseph Banks, and others, for the promotion of scientific and literary research, the teaching of experimental science, the exhibition of its applications, and the presentation of opportunities for study. In the laboratories of this institution many distinguished chemists and physicists have conducted their experiments. In America the Philosophical Society dates from 1743, the Academy of Arts and Sciences from 1780, the Association for the Advancement of Science from 1848, the Society of Civil Engineers from 1852, the National Academy of Science from 1863, Society of Electrical Engineers from 1884, Mathematical Society, a successor of an organization of 1888, from 1894. The American Physical Society was started by physicists from various American colleges at Columbia, 1899. In 1916

the National Research Council was called into
existence as a war measure for the study of
the mathematical, physical, and biological sciences
with reference to the arts and problems connected
with national defense. The National Academy of
Science and the National Research Council are mag-
nificently housed near the Lincoln Memorial at Washington. Contrast the energies and achievements of
these great aids to investigation with early poverty
and disparagement of activity in scientific research.
Add the great funds contributed by the Swasey, Carnegie, Rockefeller, Eastman, and other foundations,
the various scientific prizes and medals, the vast laboratories of the largest industrial corporations, where
thousands of young men are trained, and the technical schools and colleges of to-day. The sum total
is beyond calculation as to present value and future
achievement.

Of similar importance to natural studies has been
the service of scholarly and of popular journals and
magazines of science. Some of the oldest publications
of the former type, and their dates of establishment,
may be named here: *Journal de Physique,* Paris,
1771; *Journal der Physik,* Halle, 1790; *Journal
of Natural Philosophy, Chemistry and Arts,* London,
1799; *Journal of Science and the Arts,* London, 1816;
American Journal of Science and Arts, 1818. Among
important scientific publications are *Der Annalen,
The Philosophical Magazine,* the *Astrophysical Journal,* and the proceedings of such foundations as the
Royal Institution, the Physical Society of London, the
Smithsonian Institution, and others. Reviews of
special sciences and the more popular periodicals are
well known, and are increasingly successful.

Such facts as the foregoing cannot be too often nor
too fully published. It is the present purpose to
claim them as abundant evidence that men of science
have obeyed the teaching of Jesus in his great parable

of the talents. They have used their powers in a manner profitable to Him who gave them ability and opportunity. That this has frequently been done in the full recognition of his precepts as being authoritative and binding is beyond all doubt. The emphasis which Christianity places upon usefulness brings within the circle of divine service the most practical deeds. In his vision of the Judgment it is taught that Christ accepts as done for himself the simplest acts of ministry to the needs and limitations of humanity. Who is disposed to shut out of this approval and appreciation the valuable applications of scientific invention? Their devising has cost labor and pain, and many scientists have toiled as unselfishly as have the best of those who have followed other callings.

The reviews which have occupied the first chapters of this book represent the scope of scientific adventure and achievement. The wide range which science takes may also be seen in various attempts at classification of the branches to which its attention is given. The ancient Greeks had relatively few sciences. The Platonists studied dialectics, physics, and ethics. Aristotle discussed theoretical, practical, and poetical branches: the practical included politics and ethics, while the poetical or technical were useful or imitative. Sir Francis Bacon, 1605, based his classification on the human faculties—memory, imagination, and reason. The result is history, poesy, and philosophy. The latter contains divine, natural, and human branches. Natural science is physics and metaphysics. These are again subdivided, producing under metaphysics pure and mixed mathematics, which are, on the one hand, geometry and arithmetic and, on the other hand, perspective, music, astronomy, cosmography, architecture, enginery, and divers others. Hobbes used "knowledge of consequences" as a principle of subdivision. Bentham and Ampère produced a highly artificial and complex arrangement with a harsh Greek nomenclature. Comte divided sciences by hierarchical order, and not by genus and species. The true order turns out to be mathematics, astronomy, physics, chemistry, physiology, and social physics, which, as has been seen, Comte denominated "sociology." Herbert Spencer, on the basis of abstractness, produces abstract, abstract-concrete and concrete sciences. Wundt distinguishes by the conceptional viewpoints. One must find the scheme in the facts. The progress of knowledge has produced so many facts and relations of facts that sciences are multiplied, although they may be grouped variously in accordance with the particular principle chosen for the purpose.

One of the latest discussions divides sciences into abstract, general, special, combined, and applied.[7] Abstract sciences are metaphysics, logic, statistics, graphs and mathematics. General sciences are sociology, psychology, biology, physics, and chemistry.

Is there any limitation of the sphere of science? Its wonderful activities are pressing forward in every direction, but L. T. More thinks that "there are other fields of knowledge in which science is not concerned," a view which manifestly depends upon his definition of science, and especially upon the reservations made. He says that "as long as men of science restrict their endeavor to the world of material substance and material force, they will find that their field is practically without limit, so vast and so numerous are the problems to be solved."[8] But are not the events which are taking place in thought and research fast pushing science beyond the boundaries of material substance and force, in the sense previously understood, and is

[7]*The Outline of Science*, J. Arthur Thomson, editor, fourth vol., p. 1171.
[8]*The Limitations of Science*, L. T. More, Henry Holt and Company, publishers, New York, p. 260.

not the scientific method more and more penetrating interstellar spaces and to the full extent of the universes? Shall we not have to admit, as the next chapter intimates, that science is limited only by the knowable, and by the logic of that which comes to be known, as it impinges upon the deeps of the unknown and the future, tending toward a vast and as yet undemonstrated unity? Proceeding upon the assumption that nature and the laws of nature are intelligible and reasonable and that the problems which they present are solvable, scientists will ever undertake the profoundest investigations, utilizing the most refined instruments with all available skill. Not only with microscopes, ultramicroscopes, telescopes, spectroscopes, micro and stellar photography and penetrating rays will they contrive to seek that which may possibly be revealed concerning the products of Infinite Wisdom and Power; but the wisest of them will employ their faculties of mind and spirit to bring them into contact and co-operation with the Infinite Love and Purpose to which each form of knowledge after its own nature gives some degree of testimony, and in which are the ultimate hope and promise of mankind. Oersted went further than this in his thinking and believed that the highest motivation of scientific knowledge lies in its relation to the advancement of the interests and program of Christianity. He told his students that the conviction that when you diffuse knowledge you are instrumental in the consolidation of God's kingdom on earth can alone give a true and unalloyed desire to lead those around you toward a higher light and higher knowledge.

CHAPTER III

THE LOGIC OF SCIENCE

BEFORE reviewing contributions made by scientists to departments of knowledge which are closely related to Christianity it may be profitable to consider the general question, What is the logic of science? The term "logic" is here employed, not with the philosopher's technical connotations, but in its hard-sense significance of something taught or implied. Scientific investigations and judgments cannot, of course, be confined within the walls of formal methods. They deal with facts which are intimate and vital, and which are often too profound for artificial terms or dialectics. "Syllogistic reasoning," as Bacon declares, "is utterly inadequate to the subtlety of nature." Nevertheless, the processes of science are not illogical, and its results are far from meaningless. Nature is infinitely more than a mere congeries of phenomena and incidents. It is vastly greater than empty laws and unintelligible systems. If this were not the case, and if knowledge and life were bound up with a witless aggregation of bodies and forces, thought and service would be vain, and it would be better to eat, drink, and be merry than to bother at all with scientific or other difficult undertakings. What, then, is the deepest meaning and message of science? Is its teaching merely mechanistic and materialistic, or does it manifest wisdom beyond that which is confined to physical objects and powers? Does it deny or does it reveal to intelligent reflection a spiritual conception of the universe? Are its implications anti-Christian or Christian?

It may be well, as we consider these questions, first

77

of all to direct our attention to the depth and the far-reaching value of knowledge. It is easy to underestimate this. Even so great a teacher as Henry Adams thought that in education nothing is so astonishing as the mass of ignorance it gathers in the form of inert facts. For facts as such he indicated profound contempt. There is a relative and temporary, and a theoretical permanent truth in this judgment. When one thinks of it, what could be the value of meaningless knowledge? Is not inert information as dead as are all other forms of inertia? Conceivably, and to all high purposes, actually, one may know a hundred physical laws or may own an intellectual field containing thousands of matter-of-fact cobbles and bowlders, and even of ledges full of treasure-bearing veins, and may be little the richer or more valuable to society for either the one or the other of these possessions. The same is true of knowledge as a whole. If science had not imports worthy of its vast costs in time, energy, and resources, and of the personal sacrifices which are often made in its behalf, if these values were undiscoverable, or if they were ignored or neglected, its attainments and accumulations would be relatively worthless, and the life to which such learning ministers would surely be slightly better than "a tale told by an idiot, full of sound and fury, signifying nothing."

But what is the case? As we look more closely into this subject, it becomes evident that however imperfectly individuals, or even generations, may scrutinize or comprehend natural phenomena and make use of them, later and more careful examination may disclose therein and profit by unexpected properties, relations, and values. "There is a question in my mind," writes Arthur L. Foley, physicist, "whether any facts are inert. They may be inert for a few years, possibly a few centuries. Sooner or later comes a man who uses these 'inert facts' to generalize and to

discover far-reaching principles and laws. Let me
give an illustration," he adds: "Sir William Crookes
worked with vacuum tubes more than a half century
ago and predicted that some of the greatest advances
of the future would be made in the domain of high
vacua. He was laughed at. I myself heard a professor of physics in my boyhood days say that a man is a
fool to try to make something out of nothing—and
that when he experimented he wanted to experiment
with *something*. Vacuum tubes were in disrepute until Röntgen's discovery in 1895. To-day there is no
other piece of physics equipment that is being studied
more than is the vacuum tube. All that some of us
can do is to accumulate facts upon which somebody,
some day, may be able to generalize."[1] Is not such a
statement illuminating? Is it not significant that, in
harmony with the truth that nature is profoundly
meaningful, generalizations of an increasingly interesting and far-reaching character attend the history
of science, revealing the universe as filled with system
and moment?

"All's law," cries the poet. "All's law," asserts the
man of science. He goes further, this eager, insistent,
patient investigator. He seeks for laws until he finds
and, as far as possible, proves them. Everywhere in
nature he sees order and system, and this is what his
labors are teaching the world. But if, as we have just
seen, there must be more in facts than their simple
existence, or they are relatively, if not absolutely,
valueless, so the recognition that the universe in which
we live, and, therefore, doubtless all natural realms,
is schematic and orderly, implies something beyond
itself, namely, the idea of universal intelligence, reason, mind. In nature, as an organism of related parts
and functions, is a magma and principle deeper than
its manifestations. Nature is not self-contained and

---

[1]Contributed for this book.

self-sufficient. It cannot fully explain or account for itself. It reveals infinitely more than the bones, muscles, and nerves of its own body. If this be true, it follows that the attempt to interpret nature by its clothing or cuticle, by its inferior or vestigial organs, or even by its necessary parts, must result in partial, misleading, and false conclusions. The case is just the same, whether the effort and end of such a judgment be that of scientist, philosopher, or theologian. Each of these may furnish illustrations of adequate and inadequate logic with reference to the constitution, phenomena, and meaning of nature. It is sufficient to the present statement to point out that abundant instances are found among the greatest intellects of scientific history of those who have not only discovered law, system, and significance in the physical universe, but have on this basis founded conceptions of a ground and background of pure intelligence, which alone can account, as they have believed, for observed and established scientific facts and principles.[2] If at this or any other particular moment another tendency is represented as being that of scientists in general, it may be confidently assumed and believed on the basis of experience that this attitude is misrepresented or temporary. Winds of materialistic dogmatism frequently sweep over the scientific world, but they leave most of the sound trees standing. A self-constituted exponent of science, not himself recognized as an authority in any of the departments for which he speaks, says that just at this time pure naturalism seems to be rising everywhere. Even if this be the case—and the statement is not without question, and even denial, by observers more competent than is the maker of it—that is far from proving

_____

[2] Vide *Science and Religion*, J. Arthur Thomson, p. 240. For a clear putting of the significance of the order, unity, progress and purpose in nature, see E. G. Conklin's "Biology and Religion," in the Princeton *Alumni Weekly*, March 18, 1925.

that naturalism, pure or impure, will now or ever
destroy or seriously affect the primacy of mind in the
universal order, or the sway of intelligence over the
affairs of nature.

This lesson is further emphasized by another illustration. It might have been expected, and not absurd-
ly, that the discovery by men of science of such vast
numbers of new facts and laws as have recently come
to light would throw into confusion our ideas as to
the very constitution of the universe. This is not the
case. Not only does nature disclose law and system,
but everything in appropriate relations. In biology,
for instance, the central truth witnessed is that of
the unity and harmony of all nature. Another impressive fact is that of the essential unity of the various physical sciences, which has been shown by the
discovery that the same kind of units and particles are
identical to matter in every form. These and other
unifying principles appear to many as if one intelligence had given nature its substances and relations,
and was supplying meaning and direction to the affairs of the cosmos as a whole. The logic of unity in
diversity certainly gives little support to any dogma
of heterogeneity and chance. The most impressive
form of unity is personality, a subject too long ignored, and now but beginning to reveal depths of
meaning which cannot fail in the not distant future
to enrich both anthropology and the science of religion.

The relation of science to reality is discussed in another connection. In this place, however, it should
be noted not only that the logic of science is not un-
reality, but that science itself is exceedingly prominent among the agencies which are giving mankind
the conviction that we do not dwell in the midst of an
impenetrable and everlasting mirage. Science posits
physical and intellectual objects, and demonstrable
qualities and relations of facts and forces. This, in-

deed, is what seems to be implied in the very character as well as in the activities of the scientific state.

Whatever else science may establish, it certainly assures the worth-whileness of knowledge. This is demonstrated to the man in the street by the practical uses to which scientific teachings may be put, and for which many of them are certain to be employed. He can be better convinced as to the value of science by such a list of ingenious devices, adding to human wealth and well-being, as is given in the preceding chapter than by all the treatises on abstract principles which the world contains. For this reason, among others, some account of modern inventions has been included here. Even such a fragmentary list as can be at all profitably brought within the compass of this discussion helps those who are inexperienced in the lore of scientific history partially to realize our indebtedness to the student's closet and laboratory. What transformations have taken place, even within a brief period, in the arts and experiences of living, in the methods and results of industry, in the development of the means of human comfort, safety, and pleasure! The luxuries of the recent past are the commonplaces of to-day. Ordinary laborers now enjoy conveniences and opportunities which were once unknown to kings. To some extent those who profit daily from the toil and success of scientific effort recognize the source of these benefits, and anticipate others to come. However, it is the scientist himself who is most fully aware that the slightest added item of information which may be obtained by him may lead to events of the greatest utility. This confidence inspired the reply of Faraday to a woman who after witnessing one of his simple and significant experiments inquired, "What is the use of it?"

"Madam," was the laconic answer, "what is the use of a new-born child?"

It is said that Mr. Gladstone, who certainly knew better, once asked him a similar question. The rejoinder was, "Why, sir, there is every probability that you will soon be able to tax it."

The scientist, however, has a higher regard for knowledge than that which is based merely on what may be drawn out of it in the way of immediate and practical results. He, at least, who belongs to the loftiest rank of investigators, while, as we have seen, he is not disposed to discount the arts, loves nature and truth for their own qualities far more than for any dividends which their development and application may pay. This attitude, when associated with the modesty which is its normal accompaniment, is one of the most valuable human assets. It ennobles its possessor, lifting his mind into the realm of the infinite and eternal, and crowning his temples with the laurels of intellectual and spiritual majesty. Such a character is a mountain peak, whose gleaming summit fills the beholder with joy, and whose slopes pour down verdure to the plains. He is a sun of wisdom and reverence, teaching the simplicity and naturalness, the sublimity and beauty of truth. The epochs of history which have contained such personalities have always been the better for their presence. From their lives have come influences which have tended to lift the generations to new levels of thinking and behavior. They teach anew the lesson that men are greater than their deeds—that the best service which it is possible for one to render is to be at his best, and to seek the highest.

The teaching of the opening chapters of this book is that of scientific progress. To those who can read the signs of the times, and who can comprehend that which is taking place, what is it that is being so impressively taught by the amazing advancement which, after the long centuries have passed, science continues to make? Is its task finished, or is it nearing completion? Is the "Riddle of the Universe" now wholly or almost solved? Is knowledge approaching its limit of achievement, and are investigators coming to the end of the road of discovery? Are the final secrets of nature about to be revealed? Is the *ultima thule* of wisdom to be attained within a few centuries, or in the twentieth century, or, mayhap, in 1975? Occasionally someone speaks as if something like this were the situation, but he is not a scientist. The man who is spending his life in pursuit of knowledge is too familiar with unsolved problems, and with the existence of vast deeps and unexplored regions, to be deceived into the notion that his task and that of his successors will soon be over. In the familiar figure of Newton he is forever a child, full of interest and wonder; he still is, and always will be, picking up on the shores of his time and opportunity new pebbles, fossils, shells, and seaweeds; above and before him now and forever are the heavenly bodies with their glories, and the sea with wide and boundless spaces and depths, and with far off harbors which he will never reach.

Illustrative evidence of this attitude on the part of those who have a right to speak is not difficult to find. The title of Essay X, Vol. III, *Works of Robert Boyle,* quaintly is "Of Man's Great Ignorance of the Uses of Natural Things, or That There Is no One Thing in Nature whereof the Uses to Human Life Are Yet Thoroughly Understood." John Tyndall thought that when science has finished its mission on earth, the known finite will still be embraced by the unknown infinite. Charles A. Young closed his book, *The Sun,* with a list of problems, the solving of which he thought might be a future achievement, and with the statement: "Not, of course, that we are to suppose that even their solution would bring us in sight of the end or limit of knowledge. Each onward step only opens before us a new, wider, and more magnificent horizon, with infinity beyond it."[3] Dubois-Reymond similarly lists unsolved problems in the physical universe—seven major puzzles with which science will long be occupied. A striking utterance of Fabre is as follows: "Life has many unfathomable secrets. Human knowledge will be erased from the world's archives before we know the last word concerning a gnat."[4]

"As to whether or not investigators are coming to the end of the road of discovery," says Professor Foley, "I might remark that most physicists, possibly all of them, feel that we are simply on the borderland. A celebrated French statesman, just after the discoveries of Volta and Ampère, made the statement that it appeared that all of the facts in electricity had been discovered and that men of science would thereafter need to study in some other field. Even so noted a scientist as Professor Michelson, of Chicago University, made the statement at a Chicago University Convention in 1894 (at which I was present) and in the annual catalogue of the university, that the future discoveries in physics would be made in the fifth or sixth decimal place. Within a few months came the announcement of the discovery of X-rays and we have had a perfect torrent of discoveries ever since."[5]

A. S. Eddington, astronomer and experimental philosopher, and expounder of Einstein's views, in *Space, Time and Gravitation,* says: "The theory of relativity has passed in review the whole subject matter of physics. It has unified the great laws, which by the precision of their formulation and the exactness of their application have won the proud place in human knowledge which physical knowledge has to-day. And yet, in regard to the nature of things,

---

[3] P. 343. D. Appleton and Company.
[4] *The Life of Jean Henri Fabre,* Augustin Fabre, p. 379.
[5] Contributed.

this knowledge is only an empty shell—a form of symbols. It is knowledge of structural form, and not knowledge of content. All through the physical world runs that unknown content which must surely be the stuff of our consciousness. Here is a hint of aspects deep within the world of physics, and yet unattainable by the methods of physics."[6]

Of course, as has been shown, there is nothing new in the conception of knowledge as vast, both in expanse and in penetration. Ancients thought this, and mediæval thinkers and seers so believed. The added wonder is the positive experience that each modern discovery, instead of reaching finality, actually opens new worlds beyond itself, to be explored and exploited. What a glorious surprise and what a heavenly revelation was that which came to Herschel when first he turned to the skies the far-reaching orb of vision, gigantic for that day, which his own hands had so laboriously constructed. With his enlarged and powerful instrument he entered the very precincts of celestial grandeur. Dark spaces flashed into radiance. Unknown bodies, which terrestrial eyes had never before perceived, gleamed before his entranced gaze like brilliant gems. Nebulous masses, the star-dust of the universe, resolved themselves into widely separated individual bodies. Beyond these were other unresolved groups and systems. Literally Herschel beheld "new heavens," filled with sublimity and beauty, but he did not see the end of the heavens nor find the center of the system of sidereal spaces and bodies. Moreover, after his day, better equipped telescopes not only revealed greater wonders in stellar depths but added to the evidence that there was immeasurably more to see. What would the astronomers of former generations say if they could return to earth and by the use of modern instruments behold celestial

[6]Page 200. The Macmillan Company.

objects almost inconceivably remote? Would they not
approve the judgment of Edwin B. Frost when he says,
"I am definitely of the opinion that proper estimates
of vastness of the material universe lead to a more
spiritual conception of the Creator behind and
throughout this whole material universe"?[7]

The lesson of objects and beings invisibly minute is
being most carefully considered and it is certainly
not less impressive than is that of the invisibly distant. Some would say that they are even more profoundly moved by the marvels revealed by microscopy
than by the thought of limitless magnitudes and by the
sight of far-off, well-nigh undiscoverable worlds. A
little time with an achromatic, and a bit of instruction
from one trained in the lore of bacteriology, of tissues
and of the constitution of matter, are enough certainly
to expand one's universe intensively by as many
measures and diameters as it may be increased by any
type of knowledge. A very beautiful illustration is
found in the celebrated collection of glass flowers at
Harvard University. Not only has genius so precisely imitated the forms and tints of the most deli-
cate and complicated floral objects, stems, leaves,
intricate blossoms and all that it would be utterly
impossible at a little distance for the eye to decide between natural and artificial objects, but the tiny parts
of floral structures—stamens, pistils, ovaries, and the
florets of the compositæ—are faithfully reproduced.
No one who has not beheld in this way, or by the
use of a lens, such recondite and elaborate structures,
has any sort of conception of the architectural variety, of the artistic coloring, and of the elaborate and
perfect mechanism to be found in this realm of nature.
The study, under the microscope, of the blood and
of various tissues, elements and substances constantly
enlarges the periphery of known and the expectancy

of unknown forms, qualities, relationships, and values.

Every successful adventure and event in the history of scientific exploration has opened altogether new vistas and treasure-stores of information. It has often been observed, as Sir John F. W. Herschel once declared, that "every new discovery in science brings into view whole classes of facts which would never otherwise have fallen under our notice at all."[8] For example, John Dalton, 1809, found that the measurements of the relative weights in which chemical elements combine give the relative weights of their constituent atoms. Gay-Lussac was thereby enabled to make important discoveries as to the combination of gases, which Avogadro used to show that equal volumes of all gases contain the same number of molecules. Mendeléeff followed, 1869, with his periodic law of chemical elements. In 1913, Henry Moseley, an Englishman but twenty-six years of age, found a way to analyze the elements by the reflection of X-rays from their atoms. The result has been called "the most important generalization in the history of chemistry since Mendeléeff's Periodic Law," namely that chemical properties of an element depend on the number of free charges of electricity upon its nucleus. Ninety-two elements, from hydrogen, the lightest, to uranium, the heaviest, were indicated, all of which, save four, have been actually discovered.[9] Moseley, killed at Gallipoli, was one of the unjustifiable sacrifices said to have been due to blundering strategy in the European war.

To take another starting point, Faraday determined the fact that a definite and invariable quan-

---

[8] *Preliminary Discourse on the Study of Natural Philosophy*, p. 358.

[9] R. A. Millikan, in a letter to the writer, says of these elements: "I think they have all (ninety-two) been identified except two or three which are in the radio-active group and therefore very short-lived, perhaps too short to make this direct identification possible."

tity of electricity is attached to each valency of an atom or molecule. What of this? Glance through the brief sketch of inventions in the preceding chapter, and find the answer partially given. Improved facilities in lighting and heating the abodes of man, better methods of travel and of communication throughout the earth, the famous exploits of electrochemistry, are some of the results of Faraday's thought. From his work has sprung the whole science of electro-magnetism, which, under the direction of minds like Maxwell, Hertz, Pupin, and others, has transformed our ideas of the environment in which we live, and has enriched the experience of life itself. Another striking example of the fruitfulness of a single scientific discovery is furnished by Kirchhoff. His spectrum analysis not only opens but magnifies the secrets of the earth and of the heavens, making fresh demands on intelligence, and particularly upon the reasoning faculties. Incidentally, the invention of the spectroscope made various additions to knowledge immediately possible, and they occurred; as, for instance, Sir William Crookes' discovery of thallium in 1861.

In view of such instances as have been named, and of many others of a similar character, should it not be clearly understood that the progress of science is constantly making room for and demanding the Infinite? Narrow and trivial explanations of the universe are no longer rational. It should be impossible to deceive intelligent students with partial and irresponsible interpretations of nature. If increasing knowledge were shrinking the dimensions of space and the number and variety of its known contents and principles, if the secrets of far-off worlds, of our planet, or even of our own bodies, were being exhausted, it might be thought that at last all intelligence may be reduced to the thumb-rule, and physical nature be found to be its own *raison d'être*. The day

of wonder and of wonders has not passed. Scientific
man, however sophisticated, is faced by greater marvels and mysteries than ever terrified the savage. The
more we know, the more there is which we do not
comprehend. Intelligence is everywhere, and is invincible, recalling the aphorism of Tertullian, "Nature
is the rational work of God." Mind is greater than
matter, and the more evidently so as physical realms
and objects cry aloud the doctrine of the depth and
vastness of wisdom and of infinities of development
and meaning. It is not too much to say that the very
limitlessness and intricacy of the universe as revealed
to us by science, tending to the expectation and ap-
propriateness of still other revelations and forms of
revelation, make necessary the conception of a universal purpose and a final event worthy of the system
and cause of nature.[10]

It is especially worth noting in this connection that
Cassius J. Keyser, mathematician, not only believes
that Bernhard Bolzano dispelled the clouds from the
notion of infinitude, but that mathematics reveals infinity in such a manner as to confirm theology:
"Whereas, in former times, the Infinite betrayed its
presence not, indeed, to the faculties of Logic only
but to the spiritual Imagination and Sensibility,
mathematics has shown—and the achievement marks
an epoch in the history of man—that the structure of
Transfinite Being is open to exploration by the organon of Thought. Again, it is in the mathematical
doctrine of Invariance, the realm wherein are sought
and found configurations and types of being that,
amid the swirl and stress of countless hosts of transformations, remain immutable, and the spirit dwells
in contemplation of the serene and eternal reign of
the subtile law of Form, it is there that theology may

---

[10]These statements have not been made without consideration of
relativist conceptions.

find, if she will, the clearest conceptions, the noblest symbols, the most inspiring intimations, the most illuminating illustrations, and the surest guarantees of the object of her teaching and her quest, an Eternal Being, unchanging in the midst of the universal flux."[11] A majestic passage, lighting to its conclusion a sublime thought!

It may be as well to pass over, for the present, the implications of some of the outstanding theories of science. Reference is made elsewhere to the doctrines of evolution, of the conservation of energy, of relativity. Each of these may here be said to have its meaning for human thought and its fitting interpretation. Each of these declared principles, to the degree of its reasonable comprehension and acceptance, adds to the sense of wonder with which, as never before, nature must be viewed, and to the argument for the spiritual background which is to be found behind all physical objects, laws and forces, giving to history fundamental consistency, continuity and value.

Another very significant, not to say gratifying, lesson is being taught by modern science. Its whole message is not given when it has represented nature as an orderly process and system and when it has established its greatness and its necessary relationship with infinity. We are also assured by the latest and best authorities that not matter but force controls the universe. Old notions of matter are pretty badly shattered. Its various forms, and even the ether, are no longer regarded as dead and inert. The terms "atom" and "molecule" are still used, but twentieth-century atoms and molecules are wholly different in constitution from those which figured in the old atomistic and molecular theories and dogmas.

---

[11]*The Human Worth of Rigorous Thinking,* first edition. Columbia University Press, p. 312. Bolzano wrote *Athanasia, or Proofs of the Immortality of the Soul.*

They are composed of units and centers of force. The ultimate entities are seen to be positive and negative electrons, packed into nuclei and held about these in mutual relations. In the invisible atoms are locked up powers vastly greater than those to which man has hitherto been accustomed, and has employed. It has been suggested that perhaps the world is not yet good enough to be trusted with full knowledge of atomic energy, which, as Sir William Bragg believes, may some day be so utilized as to supply the needs of humanity.[12]

It was Röntgen's X-rays which enabled Sir J. J. Thomson, 1897, to examine the electrical properties of gases, and to realize the vision of the ancient Greeks and mediæval alchemists of a common basis for matter. He found the electron, so named by others, of negative or cathode rays. His electron is a negative unit of electricity, and if it is part of a neutral atom, that atom must contain equivalent positive electricity. The deflexion or scattering of alpha particles from radio-active substances by collision with atoms indicates that this positive electricity exists as a very minute central nucleus able to exert very intense forces on "a" particles. An ejected alpha particle, because of its enormous velocity, is a most intense concentration of energy, and can do what radio-activity does spontaneously, namely, break up atoms. In some cases—and it is hoped some time in all—man can direct this process and so transmute elements at will. At present we know little about artificial rebuilding.

What fascinating studies are these, filling the universe with energy and witnessing the display of forces, measurable by science, but as far off as ever as to causes which may be determined by the scien-

[12]See *The Outline of Science*, Thomson, vol. i, p. 268, and *The Electron*, R. A. Millikan.

tific method! So astounding are these discoveries, and so portentous is their teaching, that it is small wonder that those who cling to materialistic conceptions hasten to explain that the new physics really does not imply any change of attitude on the part of scientists with reference to the deeper problems of the universe and of human life. Of one who has been most instant and insistent in this assertion, it suffices to say, "He doth protest too much." Another voluble defender of mechanism as the true interpretation of nature "spinneth out the web of his verbosity finer than the staple of his argument." The genuine man of science is not so hasty and garrulous either in affirming or denying the implications of assured facts. Nor is the thoroughly scientific mind prejudiced against inferences which may be drawn from its discoveries, provided they can be shown to be logical results of known facts. A generation or two ago Poincaré, in *Science and Hypothesis,* exclaimed: "Matter seems on the point of losing its mass, its solidest attribute and resolving itself into electrons. Mechanics must then give place to a broader conception which will explain it, but which it will not explain."[13] In the light of what has occurred in recent investigations, it seems but fitting that men of wisdom give themselves to the "broader conception" which alone can do justice to both nature and life.

A bulletin of Edwin E. Slosson, director of Science Service at Washington, gave the following account of a presidential address of William McDougall before the psychology division of the British Association for the Advancement of Science.[14] The session was held at Toronto, Canada, in July of 1924. The successor of William James is represented as saying: "In the days of Spencer, Huxley, Tyndall, and Weis-

---

[13]Preface, XIII, Science Service.
[14]Also published in *Science,* November, 1924, under the title, "Purposive Activity the Fundamental Category of Psychology."

mann it was held that life and mind as well as the inanimate world could be completely accounted for on the physical principles that determine the action of a machine.   Every atom of the brain then was supposed to pursue its predetermined course impelled by physical forces.   But if the mind could not exert any influence on the operations of the brain without violating the law of the conservation of energy, consciousness, which seems all important to us, must be an idle and superfluous accompaniment to chemical processes.   But the modern view of the physical universe, as set forth by Einstein, Eddington, and Soddy, is very different from and less embarrassing than the old mechanical conception."   As the speaker said, "The atoms are gone, matter has resolved itself into energy, and what energy is no man can tell, beyond saying it is the possibility of change, of further evolution."   Charles Nordman, Paris Observatory astronomer, holds that the external universe contains nothing but energy, and thinks this conception of modern physics a nearly spiritual attitude.[15]   J. S. Haldane, physiologist, author of *Mechanism, Life and Personality,* disposes of the conception of a dead universe as follows: "The material world, which has been taken for a world of blind mechanism, is in reality the spiritual world seen very partially."[16]

A man who is competent and has a right to speak with authority has gone just a little further in this discussion.   M. I. Pupin, a former president of the American Association for the Advancement of Science, in one of his Columbia lectures, told his audience that no electrical generator generates electricity, "because electricity was made by God, and, according to Faraday, its quantity in the universe is con-

---

[15]Vide *Einstein and the Universe,* p. 115, Henry Holt and Company.

[16]Article, "Natural Science and Religion," *Hibbert Journal,* April, 1923, p. 418.

stant."[17]   This gets on with right and clear thinking.
Mankind now seems to be inhabiting a new world.
The universe of mud and muck and the science of
lifeless and meaningless substance may be passing.
With the new conceptions of all entities which have
arrived and are growing in clearness, it should no
longer be possible for any to retain the crude forms
of error which long influenced philosophy and misrepresented science.   "No scientist to-day," reports
Principal H. B. Workman, London, "believes in the
old materialism, for matter itself, if I may so put it,
is non-material."   Therefore he thinks that in Great
Britain "Every scientist feels that there is a spiritual
basis of the universe."[18]   Insofar as this is the case
it represents a definite change in affairs from the
time when Mrs. Browning could exclaim:

> "We're filled up to the throat with clay,
>   And grow the grimy color of the ground
> On which we are feeding.   Ay, materialist
>   The age's name is."[19]

In view of modern developments, it is not surprising that friends of science should issue such warnings as that of Garrett P. Serviss: "Foolish, indeed,
are those who try to tie science to the chariot wheels
of dust-choked materialism."[20]   Archibald Vivian
Hill, physiologist, closes his account of *Living Machinery* with a pronouncement against materialistic
dogmas, which he regards as being as false as mediæval theology.   He opposes "vital force" but de-
clines to accept mechanism as an explanation of life
phenomena.   He recognizes the fact that we can be too

---

[17]From *Immigrant to Inventor*, p. 281, Charles Scribner's Sons.
[18]Contributed.
[19]From *Aurora Leigh*, Eighth Book, p. 388, Houghton Mifflin Company.
[20]International Feature Service Bulletin, New York.

busy in a scientific laboratory to see more than a little corner of the universe or to reflect on the bigger things in life.[21] Bettex, in *Science and Christianity,* illustrates the tragedy which even outwardly often comes to individual lives through trusting to materialistic assumptions.

The present is the most evidently vital environment which humanity has ever known. The universe is alive, not dead; developing, not static. "No one realizes this," says an undoubted authority, "more forcibly than the student of science. One need study nothing more than a single crystal of snow to be impressed with the fact that he is face to face with forces, a growth, with an evolution, if you please, that he is absolutely at a loss to explain." The stubborn rocks, as they are now known, appear as centers of forces; the very elements are awaking to intensely powerful and useful activities. With it all, the reach and control of the human mind and will are lengthened and strengthened. In view of this, what shall man think of himself? Is not the logic of the age of science and of the judgment of its best representatives the renewed and deepened consciousness that he who is exploring the wide expanses and the inmost recesses of nature, and who is becoming acquainted with its profoundest secrets, is spirit and power, both in essence and origin, and is related to all other spiritual beings? Nature is force and man is spirit! If in any sense nature creates, McDougall is wholly correct in asserting that men create new things in art, science, and literature. If nature has in it any degree of self-determination, he is right in insisting that psychology should assert self-determination for man. When the sciences which relate to being have assimilated the latest physical revelations and have come into their own fullness, will they not give us still

---

[21] *Op. cit.,* especially pp. 294, 295, 299, 300.

clearer conceptions of truth and positively disclose the
fact that human life and destiny are not confined to
elements and activities which are earthly and physical, but are intimately related to the spiritual and
the divine?

It is not, of course, nor will it ever be, the function
of science to demonstrate by physical processes the
inner facts, laws, and destiny of spiritual existence.
These data, however natural, are personal and transcendent. Religion—and Christianity more definitely
than any other religious doctrine or system—is
closely related to science, but it is supported as science is by its own foundation; it observes its own
phenomena, makes its own generalizations, develops
according to its own nature, and must be judged by
its own criteria. We shall see that the scientific
method, so called, by no means belongs exclusively
to the study of nature, either as to its origin or use,
but may be and is being applied to Christian knowledge, experience, and practice. Procedure in determining truth is similar, however widely the
phenomena considered may differ. It is an error to
assert that modern science has rendered Christianity
unintelligible and unacceptable. If this were the
case, it would be unfortunate for both of these activities, and it is freely admitted that Christianity
would be destroyed if science could prove it to be
baseless and false. This is far from being the situation, however ardently a few individuals may wish
this were the case. Though some stridently assert,
and others subtly insinuate, that the logic of science
is away from God, from the teachings of Jesus Christ,
from the Christian conception and horizon, many believe that the trend of new discoveries and of eternal
truth is in the other direction. Those who can read
aright the revelations which nature is gradually
making of its own transcendent depth and meaning,
and of its order, unity, development, and inherent

purpose are strengthened in their faith in the spiritual ground and atmosphere of the universe and in the conformity therewith of the one religion which can be reasonably associated with science in world-development and progress. In its profound meaning and testimony science is more Christian than in any former period of history. Religious certainty may be more easily and fully attained in our day than formerly.

CHAPTER IV

SCIENCE AND TRUTH

A LECTURER against Christianity at one time made considerable capital with ignorant hearers by declaring that no great religious founder ever taught his disciples to think. What kind of ethics did he have? Not the highest certainly, for he well knew the record of One who taught that we should love the Lord our God "with all the mind," who said to his pupils and followers, "Ye shall know the truth" and "If any man will do his will, he shall know of the doctrine (teaching)" and who also said of his representative on the earth, "When he, the Spirit of truth, is come, he will guide you into all truth." If anyone claims that these words apply merely to the truth about Christ himself, or even to the truths which he personally taught, let it be asked, On what authority is this assertion based? Who has a right to limit the thought and inspiring purpose of the Master? We prefer to think that Jesus put the seal of his approval on all worth-while knowledge, as well as upon that highest wisdom which is indicated by his saying, "I am the truth." Therefore his disciples should eagerly and courageously push into all regions of investigation. They may also joyously welcome, not, indeed, every doctrine vaunted in the name of science, philosophy, or theology, since loudly advertised discoveries are often will-o'-the-wisps whose light is soon quenched, but every attainable scrap of information and every thorough going and verifiable principle by which the various items of human knowledge may be brought together and systematized. "The philosophy

99

of Jesus contains no attack on science or on speculation."[1]

He who seeks truth in any realm becomes thereby,
even though unconsciously, at least a far-off worshiper of the God of Truth. Is he not also to some
degree a disciple of Him whose directions and promises concerning truth have been partially stated? It
is characteristic of intelligent Christians that they
respect whatever is believed by them to be reliably
accredited as fact. If unintelligent believers are hostile to any well-certified truth or system of knowledge, investigation will show that, as a rule, even
their opposition is based on misrepresentations made
to them as to what is the truth and not to truth as
such. There is ultimately no respectable rejection of
facts presented by investigators who keep clearly
before them the duty so well indicated by Virchow in
Einheitsbestrebungen: "It is not the object of science
to destroy faith, but to define the boundaries to which
knowledge extends, and within these to establish a
uniform system."[2]

A form of pessimism as to the attitude of people in
general concerning new teaching occasionally finds
its way into print. "Without going more deeply into
this matter," begins such a statement, leading one to
wonder why the writer did not dig a little further,
"I think that we may safely assume that, in order to
gain currency, a new idea must seem 'good,' and mayhap noble, beautiful and useful, and that it must fit
in pretty well with existing notions; or at least must
not threaten violently to dislocate the accepted
scheme of things. If it is ugly, wicked, discouraging,
humiliating, or seriously disturbing to the received

---

[1]Herman Harrell Horne, Educational Philosopher, *Jesus as a
Philosopher,* p. 38, The Abingdon Press. Dr. Horne has also written
on *Christ in Man-Making,* The Abingdon Press.

[2]A keen appreciation of the scientific work of Rudolph Virchow, by
Oscar Israel, may be found in the *Smithsonian Report* for 1902.

plan of life, it is likely to be shown the door. Ideas,
like kisses, go by favor. The truth of a new idea proposed for acceptance plays an altogether secondary
rôle. We rank the Good, True and Beautiful together,
but it is shocking to observe how little does the success of a new observation depend upon its scientific
or historical credentials. In almost all we hear, read,
say, and come to believe, truth, in the scientific sense
of the term, is a matter of almost complete indifference."[3] Comment is hardly necessary. Suffice it to
say that this is a perfectly fine illustration of *non
sequitur*. It is precisely because truth is not a matter
of complete indifference, that new presentations
which make what is claimed to be True incompatible
with the Good and the Beautiful, which show truth
as ugly, wicked, discouraging, disturbing to life,
threatening the wisest scheme of things, and not fitting in, are unpalatable to sane people, and are not
to be accepted until established past peradventure.
Ugly is not only, as J. A. Thomson thinks, but half
way to anything: it is its caricature, or worse. The
man who has a false or mean idea or an unworkable
plan is always dismayed and angry with conserva-
tism. What he must and does have to reckon with,
however, is the instinct of self-preservation, and belief in the profound law of unity—that "All things
work together for good." Men wish and will continue
to accept, as Aristotle indicated, not alone ζῆν, but
εὖ ζῆν, in every sense of the term.

In this connection it may not be unprofitable to call
attention to a great declaration of Le Conte in
Evolution: "Some will say—because it is the fashion
now to say—that as simple honest truthseekers we
have nothing to do with the effect on religion and on
life. They say we must follow Truth wherever she

---

[3] *The Humanizing of Knowledge,* J. H. Robinson, pp. 19-20. George
H. Doran Company.

leads, utterly regardless of what may seem to us moral consequences. This I believe is a great mistake, the result of a reaction, and on the whole a wholesome and noble reaction, against the far more common mistake of sacrificing truth to a supposed good. But the reaction, as in most other cases, has gone too far. There is a true philosophic ground of justification for the reluctance with which even honest truth-seekers accept a doctrine which seems harmful to society. Effect on life is, and ought to be, an important element in our estimate of the truth of any doctrine . . . man's good cannot be in conflict with the laws of nature. Also, whatever in the long run and in the final outcome tends to the bad in human conduct ought to be received, even by the honest truth-seeker, with distrust as containing essential error."[4] It is no slight service to religion that science has evidenced so clear a sense of the value of truth. This testimony, together with that of fidelity to truth, accredited as such, at whatever cost, has been a definite contribution both to religious thinking and life. God's orthodoxy is truth, as Charles Kingsley affirmed. The Teacher who furnished men the highest knowledge of God uttered the instructive saying, "They that worship him must worship him in spirit and in truth."

This may be the place to note that neither science, philosophy, nor religion has been free from error. Anyone interested in scientific vagaries will find D. W. Hering's *Foibles and Fallacies of Science* an interesting description. Very often error has been honest failure, despite ardent endeavors to apprehend correctly the facts and laws for which search was being made. The Ptolemaic Theory of Hipparchus, as published by Ptolemy about 140 A. D., which kept the world thinking that the earth was the

---

[4] *Evolution*, Joseph Le Conte, pp. 276-77, D. Appleton and Company.

center of the solar system until in the sixteenth century it was replaced by the Copernican or heliocentric theory, is simply an example of error traveling a long, slow road toward the truth. "Phlogiston" is not a pleasant word in scientific history, because it represents the ignorance which long concealed the facts connected with combustion. Nevertheless, Becher and Stahl, in their advocacy of a mythical principle which they supposed to reside in combustible bodies, and to be given off when they were burned, were doubtless as sincere seekers of truth as was Lavoisier, when he overthrew this fiction. Newton and Boyle believed in the atomic theory of the Greeks. Why? Because it was the best explanation of matter then to be had. Newton's theory of gravitation, held to be a scientific gospel, while not destroyed, has received what many hold to be important amendments by the theory of relativity. The corpuscular theory of light taught by the same great physicist, and afterward removed from public confidence by the undulatory theory, in view of certain discoveries in electricity, has of late been mentioned with more respect. The comment in *Science and the Modern World*, A. N. Whitehead, on the theories of Huygens and Newton is important here.[5] Sir William Bragg and Robert A. Millikan affirm the necessary use of both theories in our present state of knowledge. The studies of C. T. R. Wilson and Arthur H. Compton in the field of radio-activity and X-rays have served to emphasize the paradox that light and X-ray radiations give evidence that they consist of waves and also of corpuscles.

Edwin E. Slosson, chemist, once drew attention to what is the bane of his profession, namely, that each new discovery starts a pseudo-science. He mentioned "animal magnetism," "telepathy," and

---

[5] Page 256.

"electronic cures." This reminds one that the New Testament contains a warning against science or knowledge "falsely so called, which some, professing, have erred concerning the faith." Every good thing, whether in science or in religion, has its spurious by-products or counterfeits. Medical science has been particularly afflicted in this way. The name of these evils is legion, and the business of the Spirit of Truth is to drive them out.

Of the so-called "Seven Follies of Science," the quadrature of the circle, the duplication of the cube, the trisection of an angle, perpetual motion, the transmutation of metals, the fixation of mercury, and the elixir of life, one, the fixation of mercury, is easily accomplished, but not in the original or alchemical sense; and another, the transmutation of metals, is now considered to have been restored by radio-activity to the realm of scientific discovery and research. Transmutation, as we have seen, is said to be a natural process in the case of radio-active elements. It is very incompetent criticism which would altogether disparage the spirit which seeks to do the impossible, as, for example, to square the circle or to initiate perpetual motion. In some instances labor on "follies of science" has strengthened the powers of those who did this otherwise useless work, and has enabled them to accomplish other things. It has been asserted that the "second law of thermo-dynamics" is the result of the inability of science to construct a perpetual motion machine; that "relativity" is the outcome of failure by experiment to reveal our motion through ether, and that Lavoisier's error concerning a binary theory of compounds led to important discoveries by Sir Humphry Davy and others. Brandt, in 1667, when seeking the "philosopher's stone," discovered phosphorus. To return to an earlier date for an example, it may be shown that even stupid and stubborn errors may result in discovery of truth. "Vegetative force," another humiliating memory—the unsubstantiated principle with which Needham befooled Count Buffon, and with which both of them made buffoons of scientific societies—spurred Lazzaro Spallanzani to the splendid demonstrations by which he determined the development and life history of microbes.

Science has taught religion not to be dismayed by its mistakes and shortcomings, but to learn by them, and above all to be obedient to the suggestion of Saint Paul—"forgetting the things which are behind, and stretching forward to the things which are before," to "press toward the goal unto the prize of the high calling." Observers and experimenters with nature have been tried almost beyond patience by their own and by others' blunders. They are also often distressed because ascertained facts stubbornly refuse to yield their meanings or to fall into classes. Nothing but a passion for truth, together with a will set on resolving whatever difficulties may arise, has kept many a student at his task until success or failure resulted. What Huxley meant by references to the divine in science is of little consequence as compared with the spirit which is acclaimed and which many suppose to be the effective product of the Eternal Spirit. It was the opinion of this biologist that no matter what their abilities, no great scientific achievement had ever been accomplished by those who did not possess the truth-seeker's divine afflatus.

Science is perfectly correct in insisting that religion shall put positive emphasis upon truth. T. G. Bonney was within his rights, especially considering his ordination in the church, and provided that local conditions required and justified the warning, in his oft-quoted advice to ecclesiastics to remember that facts are stubborn things, and that, while they may speak with the confidence of experts who have carefully studied difficult questions, when it comes to those which lie outside of the range of their knowledge they have neither the right nor power to claim authority. It does not in the least lessen the impact and wholesomeness of this declaration to call attention to the fact that the same law applies as fully to scientific as to religious statements. Newton so held and so expressed himself when he said to Halley: "Sir, you have never studied these [religious] subjects. Do not disgrace yourself as a philosopher by presuming to judge on questions which you have never examined."[6] To the same effect a modern physicist, Louis T. More, addresses those who in the name of science forsake its first principles: "It seems a bit presumptuous for biologists to insist on great technical training and ability in anyone who dares to criticize the deductions of biology, and then to apply their theories to the far more difficult and complex fields of sociology and religion in which their own study and training is perhaps not thorough and first-hand."[7] The method of science, then, is not a norm to be adhered to in one realm, and to be replaced by guesswork or hasty generalization elsewhere. The occasional descent of individuals into stubborn prejudice is the inversion of scientific canons, but is attested by such instances as that described by Gilbert N. Lewis, chemist, in *The Anatomy of Science*. A geneticist was asked what he would say if a suggested experiment should yield positive results. This man replied that he would call the experiment in question as badly done. He was pressed as to his conclusion in case the work were his own, and replied that he would not accept the testimony of his own eyes.[8] It is a matter of record that Bouillaud vehe-

---

[6] Sir David Brewster, in his *Memoirs of the Life, Writings and Discoveries of Sir Isaac Newton*, p. 339, gives details of various discussions on this subject between the two men.

[7] *The Dogma of Evolution*, Princeton University Press, p. 32.

[8] *Op. cit.*, p. 212.

mently attacked the exhibitor of the new phonograph to the Academy of Science in Paris as a ventriloquial impostor, and for months declared the machine an acoustical illusion.

It should be kept in mind in connection with the idea of fidelity to its claims, that truth exists, not independently, but in relations with other forms of knowledge. Is it not evident that by confining his interest within too narrow boundaries even a competent scholar may do great injustice to the class of knowledge to which he is devoted? William Emerson Ritter put his finger on an unreliable pulse when he reported, with consternation, that a biological confrere, when asked by sociologists, economists, and educators what his science had to do with their problems, replied, "Biology has nothing to say about such matters." Such an attitude is a complete repudiation of Jacobi's well-known apothegm, "The unique end of science is the honor of the human spirit." Ritter very properly resented the notion that a science which takes extreme care to understand the behavior of sea anemones, earthworms, crabs, and mice should express practical unconcern with the behavior of the species of animal who calls himself Man.[9] Some one might comment, however, that it would seem that there are men who are near enough like crabs and groundhogs to be considered, even under the classification admitted by the unwise biologist mentioned, as coming within the sphere of his specialty. Andrew J. Bigney, zo-ologist, in an address on "A Century of Progress in Scientific Thought," asserts: "Man must more and more be considered the most important creature. He can and must be developed as a symmetrical being."[10] Ritter is very emphatic in his criticism of a science which ignores or is unjust to

---

[9]*The Higher Usefulness of Science*, p. 55, Badger, Gorham.

[10]Address of the president, Indiana Academy of Science, December, 1916.

humanity. His statement must be answered by those who thus narrow the sphere of their studies. "The greatest defect," he says, "in natural science is, I am quite sure, its failure clearly to recognize that its conception of nature must be comprehensive enough to include man in the fullness of his being."[11]

Truth is a unity. The disseverance of any portion of the body of knowledge maims the whole. Religion also must recognize that this is the correct view, and must welcome from every source, and especially from trained observers and good minds, both knowledge of the *ipsissima vestigia* of nature, and opinions, due to inferences, or possibly conjectures. The former may be verified, if this be practicable, or may be taken on authority. Opinions are to be accepted, rejected, or reserved for future attention in accordance with various conditions, including that of the degree of probability which seems to justify them when compared with knowledge from other sources. This is in accordance not only with the Pauline injunction to "prove all things; hold fast that which is good," but also with scientific method, of which the apostolic expression is one of the clearest statements.

Ismar J. Peritz, Hebraist, calls attention to biblical confirmations of the thesis that truth is a unity. "There are many passages in the Scripture," he says, "which might be cited as teaching that observation or study of nature is a source of divine revelation." As an example, he quotes Amos 5. 8.

"Seek him that maketh the Pleiades, and Orion, and turneth the shadow of death into the morning, and maketh the day dark with night; that calleth for the waters of the sea, and poureth them out upon the face of the earth; The Lord Jehovah is his name."

"The distinction between 'natural' and 'supernat-

---

[11] *Ut supra*, p. 103.

ural,'" adds Peritz, "is foreign to the Scripture, which regards God as back of both."[12]

Religion may be regarded as having three primary sources of knowledge—physical nature, human nature, including mind, and divine nature. There are various avenues of approach. Among those which have been suggested are consciousness, intuition, observation, experience, reason, feeling, revelation. As the scientist is often a naturalist, a philosopher and a religious man, it is evident that he may be able—as, indeed, has been the case in various instances—to make contributions to spiritual reality from each possible angle of incidence. Particular honor to him who seeks truth by every definite method, and who conscientiously endeavors to preserve such a balance of teaching as prevents loss of any verity! A letter from a Christian psychologist indicates, not infidelity to the least part of scientific method, but that adherence to the totality and symmetry of truth which characterizes the loftiest conception of a teacher's duty. "I have tried," he says, "to offer analysis of the more normal forms of religious experience as we find it in our churches (not in monastic cells or in psychopathic wards) and I know this can be done with no sacrifice of scientific accuracy. In the interpretations," he adds—and the statement proves the breadth of his mind and his human sympathy, as well as his comprehension of the higher wisdom— "I have sought to conserve, as far as the psychological method will allow, the values of religion as a personal experience." It is to be confessed that certain individuals are willing, or even eager, as far as the psychological, biological, philosophical, or what-not method will allow, to tear down the values of forms of knowledge and experience concerning which they are

[12]Contributed for this use. See discussion of "supernatural" elsewhere in this volume.

uninformed or unsympathetic. This may account for the astonishment of a "foremost biologist," noted by J. H. Robinson in *The Humanizing of Knowledge,* that "when the general story of man's knowledge of nature has been so frequently and so clearly explained there are still men of letters like G. K. Chesterton, who declares that science is 'a thing on the outskirts of human life,' that 'it has nothing to do with the center of human life at all.' "[13] The truth is, the world does not want one-sided, imperfect, partial science. Such science will forever be on the outskirts, and afar from the center of human life.

A consideration which is advanced in other portions of this book as representing the views of many thoughtful men should be borne in mind at this point also, namely, that truth depends not merely upon the experiences which come by observation and reasoning, but also on those which arise from the heart of man. This thought is profoundly stated by Blaise Pascal. "We acquire knowledge," he says, "not only by the force of reason, but by our feelings (*le coeur*); and it is of the latter sort that we have the first principles in ourselves; and it is these which reason vainly tries to combat, seeing she has, in fact, nothing to do with them." Pascal further affirms: "Principles are felt, propositions are believed, and in both we arrive at certainty, although by different paths. And it is equally absurd for reason to require the senses to furnish proofs of their first principles before they can be admitted as for the senses to require of reason a feeling of all her propositions before they should be received. This kind of imperfection ought, then, only to have the effect of inculcating humility upon the reasoning powers in their pretensions to apprehend all things, but not to invalidate our certainty of conviction, as if reason alone could be our

[13]Pp. 79-80.   George H. Doran Company.

instructress."[14] One who has not as yet arrived at the
conviction of Pascal, with respect to a feeling-origin
for truth, may well ask himself whether he can afford
to foster intellectual pride by asserting that truth
is merely a product of brain cells, or of a logic-
machine, and whether he can wisely depend upon
such an output alone for the settlement of the supreme issues of life. Of the conventional method of
science, C. J. Keyser remarks, "Life is so rich as to
have many precious interests and the world much
truth beyond the reach of that method."[15]

Is not this an appropriate point at which to call
attention to the fact of the evident parallelism between science and poetry? Robert Hunt sought to
explain and immortalize this relationship in *The
Poetry of Science,* and Richard A. Proctor discussed
The Poetry of Astronomy. But has its implication
been fully realized by anyone? It certainly means
something that Goethe, Wordsworth, and Tennyson
were profoundly moved by science and have exercised
so strong an influence upon the minds of scientific
men. It is not simply that poets are nature-lovers,
and that they are often close observers of its forms,
describing accurately what they have seen during
their excursions afield; it is also that scientists are,
like the rest of humanity, emotional beings, possessed
of many more senses than five, and their higher
complexes demand some kind of appropriate discharge. But if the scientist is often a poet, and
something of a mystic as well, even in his passion
for truth and for abstractions, as many of his writings indicate, it will never do for him to condemn
religion for the possession of a feeling-content. The
judgment of the bystander is against a science so
inconsistent as this.

---

[14]*Thoughts on Religion,* p. 109, Longmans, Green & Co., Ltd.
[15]*The Human Worth of Rigorous Thinking,* p. 14, Columbia University Press.

Various sciences, such, for instance, as history, archæology, psychology, anthropology, and comparative religions, furnish valuable confirmations of religious history and teachings. They also by their very nature acquire large bodies of exact information which contribute not only to the philosophy of religion and to some phases of theology, but to religious practice and service. Of this, more later.

Another great contribution to the religion of truth is the banishment by scientific knowledge and action of masses of superstition which for centuries hung like a black cloud over the minds of men, obscuring the light of the Sun of Righteousness. The history of superstition is voluminous and makes painful reading. One of the most unpleasant features of it has been its admixture with religion, and, to use another figure, the difficulty with which theology has separated its superlative gold from the association of base alloys. Science itself has been afflicted in the same way, but it has been more independent of influence in its efforts to overcome the irrational, and to destroy what it regarded as being untrue and injurious to humanity. On the other hand, in its destructive work, it has not always been careful to preserve necessary values. It is the fashion with some of its professors to disparage whatever they cannot fathom. It was this class of thinkers whom Edward Forbes rebuked: "I cannot resolve in my mind," he exclaimed, "the many queries which the consideration of the most insignificant of organic creatures, whether animal or vegetable, suggests without feeling that the rejection of a mystery because it is a mystery is the most besotted form of human pride." Science of the type which this naturalist condemned has spurned light when claiming to dispel darkness. It has not only banished the mythological, but it has sometimes resolved history into myth. In showing the door to fancy, extrava-

gance, gnostic and supernatural follies, it has denied
sane mysticism, spirituality, and even divine power
their rights in the experience and respect of men. Of
course, science as a whole has never done this. Rather,
as indicated, individual practitioners have operated
upon the minds of men in the spirit of the surgeon
who was filled with admiration of the brilliancy of
his operation, unmindful of the incidental loss of the
patient's life.

It is the glory of religion that it has devoted itself
so largely to the saving of life. Never mind the little
criticism about saving "souls." The word does not
matter. The church, religion, Christianity, despite
all failures, have no reason to be ashamed of the work
they have done for humanity. This work has had
to be accomplished, not by individuals or small com-
panies of highly trained specialists, as in the case of
scientific undertakings, but by "all sorts and conditions of men," including "the halt, the maimed, the
lame, the blind." The poor also have been ever with
us. Some religious groups and leaders have hurt the
cause more than their zeal and devotion have helped.
Science has lent valuable aid. It has destroyed
various errors, overwhelmed false credulity, slain
ignoble fear, broken the power of omens, charms, and
signs, and has limited the regions in which religious
charlatans and impostors are able successfully to ply
their trade. Its services in this respect have not
ended, for superstition not only dies hard, but seems
to be able to throw its torch to succeeding generations. Huxley's impression that the birth of science
effects the death of superstition expresses an ideal
which has been but partially realized. It is because
of its helpfulness in such issues, however, that the
claim of Sir David Brewster is justified, that science
always has been, and must ever be, the safeguard
of religion.

The sayings and deeds of those who study nature

have furnished to teachers of religion, for use in their own work of instruction, a very excellent volume and quality of illustrative and suggestive material. The profound effect of scientific facts, symbols, and implications upon minds like those—to make a selection—of Albertus Magnus, Butler, Wesley, Bushnell, Bishop Christopher Wordsworth, Kingsley, Beecher, Chalmers, Martineau, Matheson, Drummond, McCosh, Bishop Henry White Warren, Griffith-Jones, is not only well known, but typical of a far wider circle. John T. Gulick, missionary in China and Japan, wrote much on natural history, and acquired added influence by means of his scientific accuracy. C. H. Robertson made extensive use of lectures in attempts to teach the Christian religion to Chinese students. Large collections of natural analogies of spiritual teachings have been compiled for the use of teachers and preachers. If these are not always thoroughly scientific, at least some of them have been prepared by men who have had the training of the best institutions and have done considerable scientific work. Charles H. Tyndall's *Electricity and Its Similitudes* is a book of this character. Many nature books, written probably without the least idea that they will be used in the pulpit or in religious classrooms, lend themselves to such purposes. Works like Wheeler's *Social Life Among the Insects,* Towers' *Masters of Space,* Williams' *Miracles of Science,* Fabre's *Insect Adventures,* and *The Outline of Science,* edited by J. Arthur Thomson, may be cited.

Whatever may be said with reference to alleged reading into nature (may it not be, rather, reading *out of nature?*) of ethical and religious meanings, two facts are indisputable. One is that many speakers and instructors make what they regard as being very valuable use of such material, whether found in collections, or drawn from original sources. The other certainty is that the profoundest minds in art, poetry and science have been impressed by natural analogies, and have taught others to be so influenced. A better and surer source of such comparisons than that of books or teachers must be kept in mind, for, to speak most truly, science is not really in books or in the minds of men; it is in that of which they treat. If one would comprehend and discover the esoteric meanings and revelations of science, he may, as Bryant urged,

> "Go forth under the open sky, and list
> To Nature's teachings."

In its precise definitions, its reservations and disclosures, and particularly in the application of its critical method, scientific energy has done much to clear the ground for buildings of religious verity. God's temple is a Temple of Truth, and it stands on firm foundations. Sometimes, however, as in case of a few cathedrals in Europe, poorly established additions are made, whose ugliness and insecurity take away from the glory and attractiveness of the sanctuary. The sooner and more completely these are fixed to the rock of reality, or torn down, the better for the worshipers. Why should not the scientists' service to this purpose be invited, not as a technical or professional exercise, but for religious ends; not to be accepted without proper terms nor to be taken on suspicion, but in the spirit of the thought of Theodore Parker, that science is the natural ally of religion? I know the question that will be asked here, but the answer is that the scientist must, of course, come and be welcomed as an associate and not as a religious expert or dictator. He who approaches as friend and helper of religion, accredited as one who loves nature, cannot fail to give valuable aid to the thinking and undertakings of the church and kingdom of God. All sincere Christians should, and most of them do, welcome the support of men who are sincerely devoted to what Wordsworth called

> "Those obstinate questionings
> Of Sense and outward things."[16]

Whether or not mankind has been improved by the achievements of scientific progress is a subject which has been variously discussed and which must be considered somewhat apart from the question of ethics, as this theme is treated in the next chapter. If man has been developed in his higher qualities, he should be a better subject of the Kingdom of Faith, in which case religion owes another debt of gratitude to whatever forces have aided its efforts in this direction. For the improvement of humanity on earth, as well as the transportation of man to a sphere of permanent bliss elsewhere, is the very business of religious leadership and effort. Bertrand Russell thinks J. B. S. Haldane has set forth "an attractive picture of the future as it may become through the use of scientific discoveries to promote human happiness." An examination of the essay on which this judgment is based yields, among other things, a hint of shocks to come from future scientific revelations which will not be immediately disastrous, because, owing to man's fortunate capacity for thinking in water-tight (or rather idea-tight) compartments, they will probably not have immediate and disruptive effects upon society. It seems, then, that Mr. Haldane's "attractive picture" is not that of re-creation, but of disruption of society. It is not evolution, he thinks, but revolution to which scientific truth is carrying us. As for himself, Mr. Russell is somewhat skeptical as to the direction in which we are going. "The changes that have been brought

[16]Reprinted by permission of The Macmillan Company.

about," he says, "have been partly good, partly bad; whether in the end science will prove to have been a blessing or a curse to mankind is to my mind still a doubtful question."[17]

Robert A. Millikan indicates two real perils—religion minus science and science unrelated to religion. "It is, of course, true," he asserts, "that the scientific and religious sides of life often come into contact and mutually support each other. Science without religion obviously may become a curse rather than a blessing to mankind, but science dominated by the spirit of religion is the key to progress and the hope of the future. On the other hand, history has shown that religion without science breeds dogmatism, bigotry, persecution, religious wars, and all the other disasters which in the past have been heaped upon mankind in the name of religion."[18] This statement illustrates the fact that it is not contended by the best opinion that the world can afford to trust to scientific information and intelligence alone for the instruction and improvement of the race.

Many leaders in the realm of science have themselves shown that there are higher forms of truth than those which come from the observation of nature, from the laboratory, or from reflecting upon physical phenomena, however certainly these agencies may, and as we believe often do, lead upward. Nevertheless, for one, I cannot subscribe to Russell's summary of "Icarus": "Science has not given men more self-control, more kindliness, or more power of discounting their passions," unless he would say that science, unaided by reason and religion, has not done this. Nor ought one to accept easily his view, even in the face of disconcerting incidents and tendencies, that "men's collective passions are mainly evil; far the

[17]*Icarus*, pp. 5-7, E. P. Dutton & Company.
[18]*Science and Religion*, bulletin of the California Institute of Technology, p. 12.

strongest of them are hatred and rivalry toward other groups. Therefore at present all that gives men power to indulge their collective passions is bad. That is why science threatens to cause the destruction of our civilization."[19] On the contrary, we may firmly believe with Abraham Lincoln and with Jesus of Nazareth that the heart of the common people is sound, that men's collective desire is to do better and to be better. The need is more earnest as well as more ethical and spiritual leadership, on the part not only of religion but of science. The conscious aim of those who are well-wishers of humanity should be a comprehensive development of the nature and virtues of mankind. Narrow and small conceptions of responsibility, opportunity, and achievement will not suffice:

> The world is one, and must not be divided,
>   Nor any part assumed against the whole;
> If aught be lost, experience is one-sided—
>   The sure result a dwarfed and crippled soul.
>
> The all is best; goodness and truth and beauty
>   Each makes its own appeal to every mind:
> To varied claims of knowledge, art and duty—
>   The whole of life—the will should be inclined.

The task of truth-seeking is one which, to be successful, must be co-operative. When art, science, philosophy, and religion shall unite their full ministry in behalf of the accuracy, certainty and influence of truth—becoming the willing channels of the Spirit who is to teach us all things—the Day of Truth will come, and justice, goodness, and peace will reign upon the earth, filling human hearts with supernal joy.

We should be carried further in our appreciation of the service of science to Christianity by the thought

---

[19]P. 63, Dutton. The view of morals exploited by this chemist in some of his writings, if adopted generally, might be expected to disrupt any civilization worthy of the name.

that the search for truth is approach to reality, which may be defined as truth brought to the point of assurance and source of values, or as grounds, qualities, and relationships of existence, which may be depended upon as valid. Relativity does not deny reality. It appears to be the view of Einstein that the actual reality which underlies the various manifestations which come to us as experiences is neither material, spatial, nor temporal, but is a blend of these characters. This unity, man, because of his nature or requirements, has divided arbitrarily. Behind time, space, and matter is the primal reality out of which we have built up such conceptions and their relationships.

Approach to reality may be attempted from different starting-points. A good example is the method of the Orient as distinguished from that of the Occident. The Oriental mind seems to regard the inner world and the Deity as real and knowable, and proceeds from this viewpoint to comprehension of the outward, visible or tangible universe. The Occidental reverses the process. From the outside and physical world he moves inward to make acquaintance with esoteric realities. It is quite a fashion in modern literature to praise the practice of the East, or at least to assert that as much may be said for the one method of seeking reality as for the other. The answer to the question as to which course is wiser and more satisfactory may be in a comparison of the civilizations which have resulted from these opposite plans. The figure and symbol of the Oriental search for the real is India. The example and type of the Occidental adventure is Western Europe and America. Yet this is not to say that the road to success is not found in every portion of the earth, nor can it be shown that the quest of the highest is not being truly prosecuted from these contrary directions. What seems to be assured is that the Western method leads to more valuable practical results than have as yet come to the peoples of the most ancient portions of the earth.

Of the comment which may be and which frequently is made on this conclusion, no one is now permitted to be ignorant. The East, it is affirmed, scoffs at the wealth and culture of the New World. It wants no such civilization as comes from our sciences and material progress. It prefers to be, and is, the home of the spirit, and of spiritual attainments and values. This is the argument, and to many it has a charming sound. The appeal of esoteric literature and of various spiritual involutions is alluring. One almost adopts the philosophy, and comes close to believing that it represents conditions of true and lasting happiness. Many, however, who have studied the life and have pierced to the heart of the thinking of those whom these ideas represent, have discovered well-concealed secrets. The East is now the home of unrest. As an anæsthetic, or as a solace for ungratified longings, expressed contempt for inventions, utilities, physical possessions, comforts, luxuries, and for the practical ideals of the West, may serve the turn. There is ground for thinking that, more profoundly than it realizes, the Orient yearns for the freer and more sensual life of the Occident. Similarly, often but half consciously, the people of the newer world feel that all is not right with their standards and life, and express some desire for an experience having a more spiritual basis.

In various other ways, not few in number, the approach to reality is seen to differ. The reality of mathematics and of the sciences sometimes termed "exact" is said to depend on the process and attainment of demonstration. That of philosophy relies on logical reasoning. That of revelation depends both on its content and on faith in the source from which it is believed to come—in the revealer. The reality of personal experience is conditioned by the nature and states of the individual. All these may be parts or certifications of one reality, namely, the existence of fact, truth, experience in its own right, to which access is open on many sides, and which may be reached, even at times by the most faulty methods.

A very beautiful expression of the universality of the desire for the ideal-real and of the fellowship of its pursuit is found in Cassius J. Keyser's *The Human Worth of Rigorous Thinking*. "Spiritual activities," he asserts, "are one. Mathematics thus belongs to the great family of spiritual enterprises of man. These enterprises, all the members of the great family, however diverse in form, in modes of life, in methods of toil, in their progress along the way that leads toward logical rectitude, are alike children of one great passion. In genesis, in spirit and aspiration, in motive and aim, natural science, theology, philosophy, jurisprudence, religion, and art are one with mathematics: they are all of them sprung from the human spirit's craving for invariant reality in a world of tragic change; they all of them aim at rescuing man from the blind hurry of the universe from vanity to vanity: they seek cosmic stability—a world of abiding worth, where the broken promises of hope shall be healed and infinite aspiration shall cease to be mocked."[20]

The passion for reality is not without its satisfactions. Whenever, by any process, by intuition, by subconscious cerebration, if this occurs, by perception, by syllogistic reasoning, by poetical imagination or revelation, by directed faith, by the use of mathematical formulæ, a point of reality is assured, somewhere in consciousness a bell rings, indicating to the satisfaction of the attentive mind that something vital has happened, and producing some kind of con-

---

[20] P. 48, Columbia University Press.

viction. Nor does it change the situation to assert
that men are often mistaken as to what is or is not
real. Error is itself a form of reality, and one which
has not been wholly escaped by the best minds. It is
easy to note illustrations to this effect. Nevertheless,
there is no ground for supposing that there is no door,
or means of entrance to the real universe—that all
who seek ingress are denied, or that reality is a delusion. It should not be necessary to urge that it is
folly for one who seeks and thinks that he finds this
great end in his own way to deny validity to all other
forms and results of attacks upon the problems of nature and life aside from his own. Not even those
who claim the firm assurance of axiomatic apprehension of truth have ground for arrogance, inasmuch
as all "absolutes," mathematical certainty with the
rest, are being subjected to criticism. This is not
to say, however, that certainty is disappearing. It
is meeting the issues which arise by seeking a wider
and more permanent basis.

Into the metaphysical battle between idealism and
realism in their multiform presentation it is no part
of the plan of this discussion to enter. Modern literature witnesses the same general division of
thought and practice which is found in philosophy.
Idealism and romanticism are opposed by realism
and naturalism. In the one case a writer tends toward an imaginative treatment of his materials. He
invents incidents which are more or less probable,
and clothes his heroic characters with qualities which
reflect strength and beauty. At times it is angels, and
angelic or dream worlds which he represents. His purpose is to improve mankind by moral, æsthetic, and uplifting idealizations. His work is poetical and creative.
The realist, on the contrary, is descriptive and factual.
He insists on representing the things actually found
in experience. He avowedly clings closely to nature,
holding up to her the simple mirror of observation

and faithful reproduction of her forms and phases. He is a reporter, and not a maker of objects, incidents, and characters. At least he will be instructive and, if accurate, profoundly interesting.

The most casual observer must note the influence of experimental science upon literature. Both of its leading schools have been affected by the spirit of the age, and by the revelations which have come with new knowledge. The realistic school claims to be the more scientific in its methods. Unfortunately, in the hands of some of its leading exponents, it has degenerated into vulgarism and bestiality. In its better signification realism is as old as history. It is found in Homer, in the Hebrew Scriptures, in the writings of Egypt, India, and China. Roman, Norse, Saxon chronicles and tales, and English, Spanish, and American literatures reflect its features. Rousseau, with his plan of setting down the minute details of life, concealing nothing, started the type of realistic writing for which Zola found the name "Naturalism." Since that time "Rousseaus of the gutter," and "Zolas of the sewer," of late especially in America, have poured out streams of vice, abnormality, and filth, which, if they represent nature at all, go far to establish almost any theory of human depravity and vanity which could be invented.

It goes without saying that no science worthy of the name would accept responsibility for such exaggerations and perversions as have often masqueraded under the term "naturalistic literature." Nor would scientists accept the observations of most writers of this school as affording a trustworthy basis for knowledge of life.[21] Whatever may be the aberrations frequently associated with the products of the romantic or idealistic mind, they cannot give a more dis-

[21]See R. A. Millikan's comment on the immaturity of the Mencken type of thinking, *Evolution in Science and Religion*, p. 91.

torted and unreal, nor, indeed, a more morbid and false description of racial, national, and personal characters than has defiled the literature of naturalism, particularly in the countries of the Romanic type. It is, however, to be noted that no hard-and-fast cleavage exists between the two literary provinces under discussion. The realist easily passes into idealism, and the reverse as certainly occurs. Among biographers may be found more definitely scientific productions. The diarist and the writer of autobiography are able to supply continuous narrative without the limitations occasioned by fragmentary observations, or the necessary employment of the imagination in order to effect a complete and adequate representation.

If in every other sphere of thought reality has been profoundly affected by modern science, religion can be no exception. What is the effect of this influence? Some have gone so far as to assert that scientific research and the spirit of the age have utterly destroyed Christian reality. The repetition of this claim, and the haste with which it is made, whenever the slightest occasion seems to be given, lead to the suspicion that with these persons "the wish is father to the thought." It is superficiality, however, which is responsible for this absurd view. To begin with, Christian reality is not without other evidences and supports than those which are purely physical or intellectual. Moreover, as long as any certainty is found anywhere, its existence will tend in a manner to give added strength to religious certainty. Reality is one, and whatever aids a part builds up the whole. It is not too much to claim, then, that the progress of science in itself, and especially in the firmer seizure of its own truths which this progress has enabled it to make, constitutes a profound contribution to religion.

To carry this thought a step further, it should be

noted that the establishment of reality on the lowest levels—and we have seen how rapidly and surely this progress is going on—would seem to imply both a higher type and degree of reality in each superior realm of thought and experience. All analogies point in this direction. Wonderful as are the experiences and reactions of the physical world, those which result from the impact of truth upon the mind are still more impressive and enduring. The transcendent reality, however, is not that of percepts, images, or ideas, but that of the feeling-assent by which these are validated and valued. Reality-feeling utilizes every aspect by which knowledge is presented, but comes to its fullness in personal relations, human and divine. This is the highest realm of religion. Here, and supremely in the presence of Christ, is found a reality which is moving the world as no other has ever been able to do. Nor is the basis on which Christian confidence ultimately rests successfully assailable by scientific or anti-scientific methods if one may accept recent expressions of men of broad knowledge of science and philosophy, for example, Pupin, Millikan, Simpson, Coulter, Rice, Hargitt, Foley, Kirkwood, Osborn, Russell, Miller, Frost, Lane, and many others.

One or two illustrations of the foregoing conception may well be presented at this point. Sir George G. Stokes, in his lectures "On Light," says that "man's intellect does not form the sum total of his mental powers. He is endowed with feelings and aspirations, and has a sense of right and wrong too universal to be attributed to the result of education, though, of course, capable of cultivation. This points to a power above him; and it may be doubted whether a nation ever existed so rude and barbarous as to be destitute of a power higher than man."[22] Thus, considerations

---

[22] Page 337, Macmillan & Co., Ltd., London.

derived from totally different sources convey a common conclusion. In one of the most judicious discussions of "Science and Religion" which has come from the pen of a scientist, J. Arthur Thomson gives just recognition to other sources of cognition than "science," in the restricted meaning of this term. "We maintain," he says, "that our appreciation of subtle things requires to be supplemented by doing and feeling as well as by scientific knowing. Obedience may be the pathway to knowledge. On the highest authority we have it that doing the will of God is the way to understanding the doctrine. We attain to some appreciation of a parent, for instance, along a pathway that is not dominantly cognitive. We fail in our appreciation of a countryside if our preoccupying interest in geology has dulled the thrill to beauty; and, similarly, the æsthetic reaction would often be subtler if it had a deeper groundwork of understanding. In any case we plead for a signpost; A RIGHT-OF-WAY TOWARD REALITY ALONG THE FOOTPATH OF FEELING. When the footpath is not only æsthetic, but religious, the reward of vision is greater."[23]

Such an utterance as the foregoing, based as it is upon competent knowledge of the issues involved, and of experience in meeting these problems, may well give assurance and satisfaction to those who have regard for the values of the universe and of existence. Furthermore, as we have seen, Christianity has cause for rejoicing in the realities established by science in its own field. Not only do these not subtract from her glory, but they add thereto, as do various testimonies of science to religious realities, and especially to those of the Christian religion. Elsewhere in this volume appears confirmation from scientific sources of the wisdom and hence of the genuineness of Chris-

---

[23]*The Homiletic Review* for December, 1923, Funk and Wagnalls Company.

tian ethics. In the words and deeds of eminent scientists, as well as of others, is found support for the verities of Christian experience. Scientists of non-Christian faiths also give evidence of the attainment, side by side with their physical achievements, and even by the aid of these studies, of religious characters and convictions. As we have seen, present theories tend toward a conception of nature itself which is being interpreted as fundamentally spiritual. Even physical reality is now regarded by many as being the very opposite of what it should be in the materialistic and mechanistic view of the universe and of life. Insofar as this truth is accepted or even hinted by natural science, its study is an aid to Christian faith.

The chief realities of experience are nature, life, and religion. They are various manifestations of an underlying and all-inclusive Reality out of which they arose and by which they abide. Each makes an appeal to the normal and unprejudiced mind which is irresistible. Each lends a certain weight of confidence and of value to the others. No one of these can ever lose its hold upon the regard of humanity. Nature will not cease to be appreciated, because, among other aspects, many will ever look upon it as "the art of God," and even as "the visible garment of God." Life will not fail to grip the mind, because, as the greatest Teacher has indicated, if a man lose his life, nothing else will profit. Religion will not lose its place in the esteem of the world, since without it nature and life lose significance. Sane scientists do not desire to be known as thinking that religion will pass. Good authorities may be found in every scientific field who approve such an expression of experience as that of Edward B. Mathews: "Geological investigations do not lead to irreligion. Many, if not most, of the leading geologists have been truly religious, for geological phenomena give an insight into the workings of Nature on a scale so large that it sobers the investigator."[24] William E. Ritter, biologist, in "Open Court," January, 1923, in a paper on "The Religion of a Naturalist," exclaimed: "So profound is my conviction of the importance of both biological science and religion, each in its own way and right, for human life, that I cannot run the risk of supposing or being charged with supposing that either may supplant the other without incalculable harm to mankind." In closing his treatise this naturalist assured his readers: "Religion is the common magma of all emotional life, as science is of all rational life. Religion is the individual's one great reservoir of spiritual energy, and as such must be freely available for each and every one of his powers of action, and expands and deepens all his powers of imagination." If the latter judgment be just, as we believe it is, religion must be a reality and the product of a Reality the greatest of which we have any knowledge. Therefore, of course its bow will abide in strength; its force will persist and will continue to exercise a powerful influence.

If there were no other reason for believing in the truth and importance of the Christian religion, two facts would give it impressive evidence. One is that scientists think and write so much on this subject. The greater and more profound minds apply themselves to this theme because of the depth and penetration of their studies, as well as because their highly developed natures respond to notes struck by infinite skill upon the harp of spiritual truth. Certain individuals of less competence write much more voluminously about religious topics, though their statements of detail and their offhand generalizations prove the complete inadequacy of their preparation for adventures in realms of supernal wisdom.

[24]*Contributions of Science to Religion,* Mathews, p. 124, D. Appleton & Company.

Even the effusions of tyros bear tribute to religion, but the splendid utterances of eminent masters of scientific theory and substance give valid and notable testimony to the vitality of religious ideas and concepts. The personal experiences of the most representative characters are in fine accord with these contributions to the literature of the subject, and this situation strengthens the position of Christian scholarship. In view of the facts and typical illustrations presented even within the limitations of this volume, is it possible that the intelligent and thoughtful mind can refer religion to ignorance, priestcraft, obscurantism, or to any other origin except truth as it comes from divine and human sources and is verified in the logic of life? In addition to the witness of scientific participation in religious thinking and knowledge the reality of the spiritual continuum which is thus expressed is further disclosed by its proven persistence in and congeniality with human nature. As Tyndall declared, "Religion lives, not by the force and aid of dogma, but because it is ingrained in the nature of man. To draw a metaphor from metallurgy, the molds have been broken and reconstructed over and over again, but the molten ore abides in the ladle of humanity."[25]

It is felt by many that science has performed an undoubted service to religion by insisting that Christian reality, like all other forms of assured knowledge, is to be looked for, not as a final gift, but as a development. In experience this is certainly the case. However instantaneously one may receive the beginning of divine knowledge and life, Christianity in its fullness comes not *per saltum*, but by slow and sometimes painful educational processes. In this sense it is an evolution, a becoming. Those who have received Christ are represented as "saved" and "being saved."

---

[25]*New Fragments*, John Tyndall, p. 29, D. Appleton & Company.

This is the case alike with the individual and with society, for the state and for the race. In this truth, which modern science has helped to posit and to emphasize, is found one of the best vindications of actual Christianity. For it is not to be judged as a finished but as a progressive work. However justly it may be criticized as to its practices and results, it may claim the right to be viewed as but partially completed. J. M. Coulter, dean of American botanists, places Christianity and science on a parity in this respect, justly observing that both of these fields are to be valued by their ideals even though in performance they may occasionally be open to criticism.[26]

Frank Ballard, in *Christian Reality in Modern Light,* properly admits that Christian reality has not yet arrived. In the larger groups, indeed, it is only in the primordial stage. It has a long journey before it, for it has far to go, and progress is none too rapid. Enough if it can show that it knows the way, that it is on the way, that it proposes to continue in the right path, as it struggles forward. If so, it has a right not only to its own ideals and aspirations, but to the confidence and adherence of others. The Christian's lot and task are glorious, but not easy. He may well take for his own the oft-quoted life saying of Pasteur, and the word which was on his lips as he passed into the beyond, *"Il faut travailler!"*

---

[26]*Science Remaking the World,* Caldwell and Slosson, p. 188, Dodd, Mead and Company.

CHAPTER V

SCIENCE AND CHRISTIAN ETHICS

A RECENT critic, referring to Haeckel's contention that morality in man is produced as a monkey grows a tail,[1] by processes purely physiological, insists that the value of Haeckel's theory is evidenced by his argument for the poisoning of the aged and the incurably sick, by his denunciation of the mother who fights for the frail life of a sickly babe, by his declaration that a mother's duty to society under such circumstances is to tie a string about her child's tiny throat, and stop its breath. If this were a true representation of scientific morality, sane men might well pray, "Good God, let the race perish now, while there still remains on earth some modicum of human pity and affection, to say nothing of Christian idealism."

Jesus Christ taught theology and stressed goodness. Of leaders and teachers he said, "By their fruits ye shall know them." His most learned disciple caught his spirit, and taught his fellows, "Whatsoever things are true, whatsoever things are honest, whatsoever things are just, whatsoever things are pure, whatsoever things are lovely, whatsoever things are of good report; if there be any virtue, and if there be any praise, think on these things." More effectively than by precepts, however, was the highest type of character and of behavior for mankind exemplified in the life of Jesus and in the rectitude of his first followers. As time went on, and as the early Christians fought the battles of their faith, they were not only per-

[1]Reminding one of Cabanis' dictum that the brain secretes thought as the liver secretes bile.

131

secuted but maligned. Most horrible accusations
were made against them. The evidence was sifted
by Edward Gibbon—certainly not a historian of religious bias. He gave the judgment of record, that
the rapid rise and progress of Christianity, achieved
against the greatest odds, was due to the pure and
austere morals of the early Christians.

Those who say that science repudiates the idea of
ethics, or of a moral code based on the deepest sanc-
tions, as being necessary to human welfare, give a
false account of the attitude of its best representatives. Edwin Grant Conklin, biologist, has said:
"The time is ripe for clear utterances upon this subject. On the topic, 'The Old and the New Ethics,' I
took the ground that it is impossible for man to live
a normal life apart from religious hope and aspirations."[2] It would be easy to prepare a long list of
sayings of scientific men in praise of the ethical
teachings of Christianity. Inasmuch as Haeckel has
been quoted, and in justice to his name, it is only fair
to say that in his *Monism as Connecting Religion and
Science—The Confession of Faith of a Man of Science,* though he denied its originality, he admitted
that "the ethics of Christianity appear to us much
more perfect and pure than that of any other
religion."[3] Most critiques on the present stage of
culture which have recently been published seem to
indicate a considerable unfulfilled need of ethical
content which it will probably take Christian ethics
a long time to supply.

Franklin wrote of the founder of Christianity and
of his teaching: "As to Jesus of Nazareth . . . I
think that the system of morals that he taught, and
his religion, as he left them to us, are the best that
this world ever saw, or is likely to see." Erasmus
Darwin referred to the famous sentence of Socrates,

[2]Letter of Doctor Conklin.
[3]Page 63, Black.

"Know thyself," and declared that this utterance "however wise it may be, seems to be rather of a selfish nature. But," he said, "the sacred maxims of the author of Christianity: 'Do as you would be done by,' and 'Love your neighbor as yourself,' include all our duties of benevolence and morality; and if sincerely obeyed by all nations would a thousandfold multiply the present happiness of the world."

What finer statement could be desired than that of Huxley in his reply to Frederic Harrison: "Whoso calls to mind what I might venture to term the bright side of Christianity—that ideal of manhood, with its strength and patience, its justice and its pity for human frailty, its helpfulness to the extremity of self-sacrifice, its ethical purity and nobility, which apostles have pictured, in which armies of martyrs have placed their unshakable faith, and whence obscure men and women like Catherine of Sienna and John Knox have derived the courage to rebuke popes and kings—is not likely to underrate the importance of the Christian faith as a factor in human history."[4]

It is an easy thing to praise the virtues of a good system, or even of individuals. The test comes, however, where Jesus puts it—in personal life. The finest tribute paid by scientific men to the moral excellence of religious teaching is to be found in the conduct of those who have had the benefit of its influence. Here, of course, it is necessary to note that very many fine characters have been achieved without the aid of membership in any religious organization. Superficial judgment not only fails to recognize the true source of the qualities and manifestations of such personalities, but even cites them in contrast with and in condemnation of lower types affiliated with institutional religion. It is with religion as with patriotism—some of the most unpatriotic and

---

[4] *The Nineteenth Century*, article, "Agnosticism," February, 1889, pp. 190-191.

disloyal citizens of any country are found among those whose ancestors enjoyed, as they also have from birth, the benefits of the nation within whose borders and under the protection of whose laws they live. While these, who are among the real "undesirables" of the body politic, bore from within into the vitals of the ship of state, in some instances new arrivals and recently naturalized citizens love the flag, appreciate the privileges granted them, and obey the laws of the land, as they understand them, with a high idealism of which internal traitors and enemies never dream.

Though morality may seem to exist of itself, the law does not so run. William E. Ritter, speaking as a representative of biological thinking, reports that "the deeper insight is being reached that while there is a positive distinctness between morals and religion, and a kind of separateness, yet the two are correlated and interlocked in the most complex fashion. Absolute disjunction of the two provinces is no longer to be thought of. In this the traditional teaching of Christianity is right."[5] While Christianity, like art, science, and philosophy, has been badly represented by some of its professed friends, its consolation and reward has been in its true representatives, and in its influence, admitted or unconscious, on the public mind. The widespread and profound ethical impact which religion exercises upon civilization has not been given its full recognition and meed of praise in all biological, ethical, and historical writings. W. E. H. Lecky discovered that the self-sacrifice of two millenniums is mainly to be attributed to the action of Christianity.[6] The same philosophical historian and publicist also refers to the general acknowledgment of masters of history that Christian-

[5]Essay before Western Society of Naturalists, "Biology's Contribution to a Theory of Morals Requisite for Modern Man," *The Higher Usefulness of Science,* Gorham Press, p. 102.
[6]*Rationalism in Europe,* vol. ii, p. 354.

ity has exerted marvelous influence in arousing the affections of humanity and in the development of pitiful and kindly ideals.[7]

In days when infanticide, human sacrifices, bloody massacres of women and children, licentious orgies and the grosser idolatries of the comparatively recent past have been forgotten the testimony of Charles Darwin to the ethical influence of Christianity upon savage tribes might well be reread. His appreciation of the labors of missionaries of Christ is accompanied by a fitting rebuke to opponents of morality.[8]

Elsewhere in this volume emphasis is placed on the topography of scientific discovery and progress in relation to religion. At this time, without the least thought of claiming that all who exemplify Christian virtues would profess religion of any kind, attention is called, not especially to the large numbers of scientific students who are affiliated with some religious organization, but to the Christian virtues which are expressed and approved by the conduct of so many persons of this class, whether so connected or otherwise. Nor is the thought which at present is in mind primarily that of the effect of religious environment and teachings upon the characters of scientific men, far-reaching as this relationship really is, but of the tribute and contribution—and it is a very important one—of these characters themselves to the integrity, justice, and value of Christian ethics. The reality of this contribution is not disproved by the fact, true for evidence in every general issue, that over against examples of any particular virtue which may be disclosed some illustration of the absence of this quality might also be found and stated. Even as to devotion to truth, Henry Fairfield Osborn has said, "In my fifty years' experience with scientific men I have

[7] *Ibid.*, Vol. i, p. 330.

[8] *A Naturalist's Voyage Around the World,* see especially p. 441.

found them neither more nor less truthful than other
men, because truthfulness does not go on all fours
with genius, with powers of observation and of generalization." The question, then, becomes one of
criticism of individual cases, of examination as to
numbers and proportions, and of ideals and tendencies.

It will not be possible, of course, to cover voluminously the field before our thought. All that can be
done in a brief compass is to give typical instances
of various qualities exemplified by scientists, in the
confidence felt by Thucydides, Dionysius and Boling-
broke that "history is philosophy teaching by example." The reader must be left to supplement these
items from his own knowledge, or from reading which
he may be tempted to undertake. It is most unfortunate that the biographies of scientific leaders are
not better known. Autobiography, one of the best,
as it is one of the most delightful forms of literature, is too exceptional and unsatisfactory in case of
investigators and discoverers. Many scientific biographies are meager in detail, and often they describe
very inadequately the most important object of investigation, namely, the subject of the treatise.
Believing, as most of us do, that man, like God,
is greater than all his works, it may be said that
whatever truth revealed through him or attained
by him may be published in connection with the life
history of a scientist, it is really no proper biography
which leaves one with the impression that he has
been introduced to an abstraction, to a machine or
even to a mere cog in a machine which has turned out
a new and valuable product. Furthermore, it is a
lamentable defect of most public libraries that about
all the biographies of science which they can furnish,
save for a few accounts of individual investigators,
are collections of brief and bloodless sketches, of
little or no human worth or of somewhat adolescent

qualities. At least one recent book, quite generally
circulated, exhibits a pathological tendency in its
extravagant, hysterical attempt to popularize achievements of bacteriologists. Justice can be done scientific
subjects only by reverent minds and careful hands.
"In trying to make science read like a fairy tale," is
the keen criticism of Clarence E. Flynn, "one must
not make a fairy tale of it." A better type of work is
found in D. B. Hammond's *Stories of Scientific Discovery,* Sir R. A. Gregory's *Discovery, Or the Spirit
and Service of Science,* H. F. Osborn's *Impressions
of Great Naturalists,* A. B. Griffiths' *Biographies of
Scientific Men,* C. R. Gibson's *Heroes of the Scientific
World,* J. J. Walsh's *Makers of Modern Medicine,* Sir
Archibald Geikie's *The Founders of Geology. The
Early Naturalists,* by L. C. Miall, interesting from a
scientific standpoint, is not abundant in humanism,
and the same is true of Van Wagenen's *Beacon Lights
of Science.* Some of the older works mentioned in
this volume are more satisfactory from this point of
view.

If it be desirable to attract the right kind of youth
to a scientific career, and to create in the public mind
a friendly attitude with respect to the labors and results of science, the inspiring personalities in this
realm of service should be more fully as well as more
effectively represented. The suggestion of Pupin
should be given favorable consideration. "Why
should not science," he says, "follow the beautiful
example of religion, which has its saints' days? On
these memorial days, say Newton's birthday, an address on Newton and his work should tell the young
student why Newton is the father of the science of
dynamics. Dynamics is not a mere collection of inex-
orable physical laws which to a young student often
sound like dry scientific facts and mute formulæ.
Many textbooks, unfortunately, present it that way.
It is a record of the life-work of men who lived

human lives and became what my mother called
'saints of science,' because they devoted their life-
efforts to the deciphering of divine messages which,
through physical phenomena, God addresses to
man."[9] The inspiring *Popular Research Narratives*,
collected by the Engineering Foundation, would be
improved by more generous recognition of the human qualities of the discoverers and inventors whose
work is described.

It matters little where one begins citing examples
of ethical conduct. There is no set order of virtues.
May we not consider an incident in the career of
Fresnel? The world and even the church contains
so much rivalry and jealousy that it is refreshing, as
well as inspiring, to recall the conduct of this young
Frenchman. In 1815 he presented to the French Institute a memoir on diffraction. According to cus-
tom, the paper was referred to a commission for
examination. The commissionaires in this instance
were Arago and Prony. It happened that Arago
had read in "Philosophical Transactions" a memoir
of Young, the full significance of which he had not
understood. The study of Fresnel's paper caused
the truth to dawn on Arago's mind that his young
countryman's discovery had been anticipated thirteen years before by Thomas Young. Fresnel had
independently determined the principle of interference, and with experimental skill had applied it to
the phenomena of diffraction, clearing away some
difficulties which had not been fully resolved by
Young. Was it a slight thing, after such a trium-
phant effort, to be disappointed by the loss of credit
and praise? Claims might have been made which
patriotism and public sentiment would have supported. It is to the greater honor of Augustin Fresnel
that he unreservedly withdrew all pretensions con-

[9]*From Immigrant to Inventor*, Michael Idvorsky Pupin, p. 196,
Charles Scribner's Sons.

nected with his great achievement. Is it not also
to the credit of the scientific world that his act was
widely approved, just as Lavoisier's attempt to take
from Priestley and Scheele the honor of the discovery
of oxygen has been condemned as unworthy of his
own undoubted claims to respect?

The account of Charles Darwin's behavior toward
Alfred Russel Wallace is of interest in this connection. After the former had been working a score of
years on his fundamental task, the latter mailed him
from the Malay Archipelago a treatise describing the
same theory. Inasmuch as Darwin's work was known
to competent authorities, that of Wallace might have
been suppressed, or at least held back. The great
naturalist forwarded Wallace's work to Sir Charles
Lyell, who, in co-operation with Hooker, sent it to
the Linnean Society, together with some extracts of
Darwin's earlier manuscripts, with which both Lyell
and Hooker had long previously been acquainted.
It should be added that Wallace's reaction toward
Darwin was as creditable as was the generous treatment he had received.

Many beautiful instances of disinterested friendship between men of science have been recorded. In
some cases, when abundant opportunity existed for
envy and contention, co-operation and mutual esteem
took the place of hostile attitudes. The stories of
Jonathan and David, and of Damon and Phintias
(not Pythias) are not more attractive than the account of the relationship between Friedrich Wöhler
and Justus von Liebig, the celebrated chemists. The
circumstances of the beginning of their co-partnership
in labor can be easily understood from the letter
which Wöhler sent Liebig from Sacrow. He wrote:
"It must surely be some wicked demon that again
and again imperceptibly brings us into collision by
means of our work, and tries to make the chemical
public believe that we purposely seek these apples of

discord as opponents. But I think he is not going to succeed. If you are so minded, we might, for the humor of it, undertake some chemical work together, in order that the result might be made known under our joint names." Liebig replied that he would accept joyfully. After that, though in institutions at some distance apart, they labored for nine years on the same problems, getting together when possible. *Annalen der Chemie und Pharmacie* appeared under their joint editorship, as did various memoirs of experiments and their results. When Wöhler's young wife died he found solace in the company of his friend and in mutual undertakings in his laboratory. "The days which I spend with Liebig," he said, "slip by like hours, and I count them among my happiest." These learned men said many beautiful words about each other. They were very different. Baron Liebig was generous and loyal, but impetuous. Wöhler was slower and more conservative. That he sometimes gave his great associate good counsel, creditable to both of them, is illustrated by the letter which he penned Liebig from Göttingen, March 9, 1843, the case being one in which the latter was inclined to engage in controversy with an offender. "To make war against ——," wrote Wöhler, "or, indeed, against anybody else, brings no contentment with it, and is of little use to science. . . . Imagine that it is the year 1900, when we are both dissolved into carbonic acid, water and ammonia, and our ashes, it may be, are part of the bones of some dog that has despoiled our graves. Who cares then whether we have lived in peace or anger; who thinks then of thy polemics, of the sacrifice of thy health and peace of mind for science? Nobody. But thy good ideas, the raw facts which thou hast discovered—these, sifted from all that is immaterial, will be known and remembered to all time. But how comes it that I should advise the lion to eat sugar?" The copartnership in labor of Liebig and Wöhler was broken when the former turned to agricultural and physiological chemistry, the latter devoting himself to studies in inorganic subjects.

Another instance of unenvious and delightful comradeship was that of the two brothers Thomson, James and William. James was two years older than Lord Kelvin. He was an engineer and inventor of eminence, but, though his brother became more distinguished and more highly honored, he was his fast friend. When both were old, Helmholtz saw them together, and gave his friends a picture of their unity in diversity, saying that it was really comical to see how the two brothers talked at each other, and neither listened, and each held forth about quite different matters.

Kindly treatment of an enemy is one of the qualities justly considered Christian. Sir William Crookes' advocacy of Dewar's claims to the Copley medal, despite the bitter enmity which the latter had shown him, was of this nature. Crookes wrote a friend that he did not wish his personal feelings to stand in the way of a reward which he thought Dewar's good scientific work merited.

If it comes to the question of self-denial, which is basic in Christianity as plainly taught and exemplified by Jesus, and which is a test of other forms of religion as well, one may name discoverers who have refused to seek personal profits which they might easily have realized from their labors. Some have patented their inventions, but have devoted the proceeds to the further progress of their undertakings, and thus to the benefit of society. Others have devoted their wealth to charity, to the establishment of scientific foundations or to the development of the institutions of religion. Fabricius said of Linnæus, his instructor, that his early poverty doubtless caused him to care for money. However, to poor pupils he remitted the fees due him, and even from the rich he on many occasions refused to receive any compensation.[10]   The disinterestedness of Cuvier is shown not only by generous gifts of money but by the fact that after having filled high offices of state his family received but a modest sum from the estate which he left them.[11]   Henry Greathead took no steps to secure pecuniary profit from his lifeboat.   The fact that Sir Humphry Davy would not patent his miner's safety lamp has been a kind of stock illustration.   His stated reason was that he had done this work solely for the benefit of humanity.

It would have been easy for Bunsen to have made a large fortune from his battery or his burner, but Roscoe reported him as without monetary ambition and says that he expressed surprise concerning the attitude of a contemporary who had considerable scientific talent but seemed to think of nothing but money-making.[12]   A letter of Joseph Henry to the Rev. S. B. Dod, dated December 4, 1876, and published in the *Smithsonian Report*, 1878, answered a question which his well-known generosity had more than once raised.   "At the time of making my original experiments on electro-magnetism in Albany I was urged by a friend to take out a patent, both for its application to machinery and to the telegraph, but this I declined, on the ground that I did not then consider it compatible with the dignity of science to confine the benefits which might be derived from it to the exclusive use of any individual."[13]   Samuel F. B. Morse was of the type which sometimes prefers to endure wrong rather than resist it.   This characteristic resulted in frequent losses, and caused some

[10]*Lives of Eminent Zoologists,* W. Macgillivray, p. 366.

[11]*Memoirs of Baron Cuvier,* Lee, p. 178.

[12]Bunsen Memorial Lecture, The Chemical Society, London, March 29, 1900.

[13]Page 160.

people who could not understand such a spirit to think him simple and weak.

One of the finest illustrations of unselfishness, modesty and of a mystical devotion to a cause is that of Pierre and Marie Curie, the discoverers of radium. Madame Curie says of her husband that with her agreement he refused to draw any material profit from their discovery. They took no copyright, and published without reserve all the results of their research, as well as the exact processes of the preparation of radium. Both of these earnest students and benefactors of humanity refused Legion of Honor decorations, since Pierre was opposed (though evidently his good wife was less convinced) to all honorary distinctions. Of her husband's attitude, Madame Curie truly thought that practical men are surely needed who do their best for the sake of their own needs without neglecting the general good. But she also felt that dreamers are required to whom it is so imperative to follow purposes unselfishly that they cannot attend closely to their own material needs. On an occasion when Madame Curie was lauded for her achievements, she replied that those who work in science should regard things and not persons. In that, though perhaps not just as she meant it, she was mistaken, for science, and religion, too, must be interested not only in deeds done, but in the nobility of the doers of them. The gift of her own radium to the Paris Institute will seem the more interesting to some who learn that when she visited America, as the train hurried her past the thousands of comfortable homes which are found everywhere in this marvelous country, she exclaimed, with a woman's natural sentiment, that she had always wanted such a little house.[14]

John Tyndall dedicated the proceeds of his notable

---

[14] See *Life of Pierre Curie*, by his wife.

lectures "On Light," delivered in America, to the education of young American philosophers abroad. An oft-repeated reply of Louis Agassiz, when asked to accept a large sum of money for a series of lyceum lectures, indicates his absorption in research problems without thought of returns to himself: "I cannot afford to waste my time in making money." It is worth mentioning that occasional examples of unselfishness cannot be compared with the constant and life-long devotion, not only of the highest scientists and their confreres, but of humble teachers of natural subjects who have given to their pupils and friends their best without stint. It should also be said that the typical quality of the above instances is not changed by such exceptions as that of Cavendish, declared by A. B. Griffiths to have been "a selfish cynic, ignorant of humor and pathos, devoid of all human sympathy: love, joy, sorrow, and pity were absent in his nature. With his vast wealth he did no good, not even to science. Cavendish lived alone, worked alone and died alone."[15]

A very human and touching incident of quite another nature, but no less instructive, is found in a letter of Tancred Robinson to John Ray.[16] It is dated Geneva, April 18, 1684, and relates the destruction of the unpublished works of Marcello Malpighi, Italian physiologist, and founder of modern microscopical anatomy, whose name is still applied to various parts of the human body concerning which he made discoveries. The account says: "Just as I left Bononia, I had a lamentable spectacle of Malpighi's house all in flames, occasioned by the negligence of his old wife. All his pictures, furniture, books and manuscripts were burnt. I saw him in the very heat of the calamity, and methoughts I never beheld so much Christian patience and philosophy in

---

[15]*Biographies of Scientific Men*, p. 40.
[16]*Correspondence of John Ray*, p. 142.

any man before; for he comforted his wife, and condoled nothing but the loss of his papers, which are more lamented than the Alexandrian Library, or Bartholini's *Bibliothec* at Copenhagen." Not even Jeremy Taylor, with his Christian resignation and cheerfulness under similar circumstances, acquitted himself any better.

Patience in toil and duty is a quality of great minds in all professions. It is said that for many hours on one occasion Sir William Herschel's hands never left the mirror he was polishing in order to make a satisfactory telescope. His sister Caroline put food into his mouth and read to him while he worked. He made, or attempted to make, two hundred mirrors before he succeeded in constructing his reflecting telescope of five feet focal length. After five years' labor with this instrument he built a telescope of four times greater dimensions, with which he began a systematic survey of the sidereal universe, leading to his most noted discovery.

It is possible to gain some estimate, both of the personal character of men, and of their influence upon human behavior, by their expressed judgments on ethical subjects. Isaac Barrow utters a splendid sentiment, which he is said to have honored by his own life, in the saying that "He also on whom God hath bestowed wit and parts, if he employ them not so much in contriving to advance his own petty interests, or in procuring vain applause to himself, as in advantageously setting forth God's praise, handsomely recommending goodness, dexterously engaging men in ways of virtue, he doth thereby remarkably honor God."[17] Should there be great wonder that a mathematician and theologian who could write like that had a pupil who developed both in wit and in character as did Sir Isaac Newton? William Pitt and Daniel

---

[17]Vide discourses on Self-Love and Self-Conceit, *The Works of Isaac Barrow,* vol. i, pp. 616-628.

Webster were among the many devoted readers of Barrow's writings.

To such revelations of the virtues of scientists as are contained in records of their labors and sayings, the testimony of reputable contemporaries or of reliable biographers may be added. Accuracy and thoroughness are among the most important characteristics of scientific workers. Valuable as are these qualities, that is still better which Cyrus Adler affirmed of Samuel Pierpont Langley, mathematician and astronomer, who devised the bolometer, extended the invisible solar spectrum, and made early experiments in connection with the problem of mechanical flight, determining what is known as Langley's Law. This is the tribute: "He was a most rigidly truthful man—not truthful in any ordinary sense, but in that extraordinary, Puritan, New England sense which did not permit him to subscribe himself as being 'Very sincerely yours,' if he was not."[18] Who does not think, as he reads this, Would there were more such Puritans! Adler also says of Langley: "A long life filled with many perplexities left his soul white."[19] Laplace was not quite of this mold, as witness his conduct with reference to the election of Biot or Fourier to the French Academy. He professed to write both names on slips, and to draw without seeing it the one he cast. It is said to have been discovered that but one name had been written on the two papers.

A clean life is the highest test of ethical purpose. That was a fine word which Macgillivray could write about Linnæus, "Neither in conversation nor in act has any moral delinquency been laid to his charge."[20] The biographer of Lamarck gives a list of substantial virtues to which the zoologist subscribed, and added

---

[18]Paper, "Samuel Pierpont Langley," Cyrus Adler, read to Philosophical Society, Washington, November 24, 1906, *Smithsonian Report*, 1906, p. 532.

[19]*Ibid.*, p. 533.

[20]*Lives of Eminent Zoologists*, p. 369.

that no one exceeded him in their practice, that, like Cuvier's, his life was blameless. Arago speaks of William Herschel's "infantine candor, inexhaustible benevolence, and sweetness of character."[21] John Tyndall says of Faraday, his predecessor: "Surely no memory could be more beautiful. He was equally rich in mind and heart. The fairest traits of character sketched by Paul found in him perfect illustration. For he was 'blameless, vigilant, sober, of good behavior, apt to teach, not given to filthy lucre.' " Like some others who have been mentioned, Faraday showed throughout his career that he "loved the labor better than the gold." Of Muhlenberg, the botanist, W. J. Youmans states that "freedom from self-glorification and from solicitude for the recognition of his work are patent in all his writings and transactions."[22] Helmholtz names as qualities of Heinrich Gustav Magnus, chemist and physician, thoughtfulness, purity of intentions, moral and intellectual tact, modesty, and true humanity. One of the tributes paid to Helmholtz himself was that he was a most quiet and humble man, whom no one could meet without realizing the charm of his personality. While not all scientists have been modest and humble, it is remarkable how very often this characterization is found in encomiums on living leaders and in scientific memoirs. Shenstone comments impressively on the simple bearing and absence of self-confidence of the fast friends, Faraday and Liebig.[23] It is said that Davy, affected by success and by association with wealth and fame, was sometimes arrogant and overbearing. On the other hand the *London Journal of Science* once said of Sir John F. W. Herschel, astron-

---

[21]*Biographies of Scientific Men,* François Arago, p. 171.

[22]*Pioneers of Science in America,* p. 63, Appleton.

[23]Vide, *Justus von Liebig, His Life and Work,* W. A. Shenstone, p. 202. A. W. Hofmann, in his Faraday Lecture, *The Life-Work of Liebig,* p. 132, speaks of Liebig's absence of anything like personal vanity.

omer and acute mathematician, "It is not to many
men that intellectual powers of so high order have
been given; it is not in many men that we find such
perfect balancing of those powers; it is in few men
that we discover such profound humility and such a
deep sense of reverence for the Creator of those works
the study of which has been a life-labor of love."

John James Audubon, the famous ornithologist,
honored by Cuvier and Humboldt, whose *Birds of
America* originally sold for a thousand dollars a copy
and is now valued at several times this sum, was a
man whose perilous adventures and sacrifices made
him unassuming. A visitor to his home observed that
"his self-forgetfulness was very impressive. I felt
that I had found a man who asked homage for God
and nature and not for himself."[24] John Wilson, of
Edinburgh, known in literature as Christopher North,
said of him in the *Noctes Ambrosianæ* that in private
life his virtues endeared him to a large circle of devoted admirers; his sprightly conversation, with a
slight French accent; his soft and gentle voice; his
frank and fine face, "aye gat him friends in ilka
place."

A striking contrast may be seen in the writings of
Darwin and Huxley. Darwin was given to courtesy
and caution, due to a more generous temperament and
to a more scientific sense of responsibility. He has
been criticized for using in his works eight hundred
times the phrase, "We may well suppose," or its
equivalent. Pity that anyone should have taken time
to count these expressions, and still more that they
should be severely rebuked. Should not such a habit
of mind with reference to judgments not positively
demonstrated be highly praised?

Lord Kelvin was very far from conceit and pride
in his own accomplishments. At the time of his

---

[24] *Life and Adventures of John James Audubon*, Robert Buchanan,
p. 364.

"jubilee" he reported to his associates that his life-work had been a failure. "I know no more of electricity and magnetic force," he declared, "than I knew and tried to teach my students in my first session." "Yet who of us," commented Silvanus P. Thompson, "has not learned much of these things because of his work? We shall not look upon his like again."[25]

The admirable traits of Baron von Humboldt noted by Guyot are "that ardent, devoted, disinterested love of nature which seemed, like a breath of life, to pervade all his acts; that deep feeling of reverence for truth so manifest in him, which leaves no room for selfish motives."[26] On the other hand, Karl Bruhn approves his concealment of personal faith and noted in him no perceptible development in moral culture.[27]

Of Gerard Troost, mineralogist and chemist, first president of the Academy of Natural Sciences of Philadelphia, a minute of the trustees of the University of Nashville, where he labored for more than twenty-two years, records that "He was without reproach, and above suspicion. Beloved, trusted, honored, venerated, he could not make an enemy—he had none."[28] The careful critic, W. J. Youmans, physician and chemist, pays the following tribute to Agassiz: "In his methods of investigation he was perfectly honest. His intercourse with his fellow men was pervaded by his goodness of heart and childlike simplicity. With inexperience he was most patient and painstaking, never wearying in his efforts to aid. His students will all bear witness to the unvarying cheerfulness and ready sympathy in him they had learned to look up to as their master." Arnold Henry Guyot, physical geographer, was represented by his

[25]*Smithsonian Report*, 1908.

[26]*Smithsonian Report*, 1887, p. 720.

[27]*Life of Alexander von Humboldt*, pp. 412 and 416.

[28]*Pioneers of Science*, p. 489, D. Appleton & Company.

colleague, James D. Dana, as having a virtue in excess, an unobtrusiveness that would not permit him to assert himself. His home life was exceptionally happy, and his gentleness, consideration, and warmth of heart enabled him to contribute his share to that happiness. Cantley testifies that he had never seen Romanes out of temper, even under great provocation. He was gentle, always kind, never overbearing, thoughtful of his friends. William Alford regarded Simon Newcomb, the American astronomer and mathematician, as an example of intellectual and moral honesty carried to the highest degree. He loved truth and hated shams. He had a veritable passion for justice, both in personal and civil matters. Seligman pays high tribute to the qualities of Mayo-Smith, the scientific statistician. He was characterized by intellectual honesty and by unfailing courtesy and kindliness. His balance of mind and his rare good judgment gave him an influence equaled by few.

One of the greatest of recent chemists was Sir William Ramsay, who with Rayleigh isolated argon in 1894, and who prepared helium in 1895. Tributes paid this original investigator describe his cheerfulness and good humor, his helpfulness on all occasions, his private charity and benevolence, and the simplicity and purity of his life.[29]

Those who are disposed to scoff at virtue may dismiss the characterization recorded in this chapter by flippantly quoting, *"De mortuis, nihil nisi bonum."* On the contrary, Sir William Mather takes such items with great seriousness and gives a very probable account of the personal qualities of scientists of the highest order when he suggests that patient investigations and accurate methods required to obtain results in experimental and technical science cannot

---

[29]See *Sir William Ramsay,* Sir W. A. Tilden, especially pp. 292-295.

fail to impress, refine, and ennoble the characters
of those who work in this field. Speaking of the idea
of inflexible honesty and of unfaltering loyalty to
truth which is the scientific standard, Charles W.
Hargitt, zoologist, exclaims, "Just here we have one
of the many points of common contact between science and faith—the ethical element which inheres
in such method."[30]   Pupin records an address of
Andrew D. White, which gathers up into a paragraph
a characterization, not certainly of all, but of great
numbers of students of the phenomena and laws of
nature. Let these words stand for many other personal illustrations which might be given: "I will
confine myself to the value in our political progress
of the spirit and example of some of the scientific
workers of our day and generation. What is the
example which reveals that spirit? It is an example
of zeal—of thoroughness, of bravery, of devotion to
duty, without which no scientific work can be accomplished—of faith that truth and goodness are in-
separable."[31]

Whoever is familiar with the nature of the processes to which the scientific mind is devoted, and of
the motives and standards by which its work is usually directed, will find himself in general agreement
with such a representation as that of Ira Remsen:
"I believe," says this chemist and educator, "that
the constant use of the scientific method must in
the end leave its impress on him who uses it. The
results will not be satisfactory in all cases, but the
tendency will be in the right direction. A life spent
in accordance with scientific teachings would be of a
high order. It would practically conform to the
teachings of the highest types of religion. The motives would be different, but so far as conduct is

---

[30]"Problems of Science and Faith," *Methodist Review,* November-
December, 1924, p. 843.

[31]*From Immigrant to Inventor,* p. 274, Charles Scribner's Sons.

concerned the results would be practically identical. Unfortunately, abstract truth and knowledge of facts and of the conclusions to be drawn from them do not at present furnish a sufficient basis for right living in the case of the majority of mankind, and science cannot now, and I do not believe it ever can, take the place of religion in some form. When the feeling that the two are antagonistic wears away, as it is wearing away, it will no doubt be seen that the one supplements the other, insofar as they have to do with the conduct of man."[32]

Names of scientists are to be found in the history of various reformatory movements. It is an interesting fact that Erasmus Darwin, grandfather of Charles Darwin, wrote against slavery and supported Howard's efforts to redeem prison life. Though not in all respects an ethical model, he was one of the early advocates of temperance. This physician, naturalist and poet strongly opposed, by voice and example, the use of alcohol as a beverage, declaring that no practice has led to so much suffering and inherited ill health.[33] Thomas Young, discoverer of interference of light, as a Quaker, denounced slavery and in early life denied himself the use of products of West Indian planters as a protest against this iniquity. Benjamin Rush, the distinguished physician, philanthropist and American surgeon-general, in 1804 wrote an important paper on temperance. He was also president of a society for the abolition of slavery and was vice-president of a Bible society. "He was distinguished for his industry, benevolence, and piety." Elwood Haynes, chemist and automobile inventor, an active Presbyterian layman, was an ardent opponent of the use and sale of alcohol and made large expenditures in the interest of reform and philanthropy. David Starr Jordan adopts as his own

---

[32]"Science," January 1, 1904.
[33]See the passage in *Loves of the Plants*, cantos ii and iii.

the saying of another, "I hope I may be remembered as one who has done something to save humanity from its two worst scourges—war and rum."[34]

Edward Livingston Youmans, chemist, scientific writer, and founder of *The Popular Science Monthly*, wrote in 1854 a work on *Alcohol and the Constitution of Man*.

Without question science is able to give most valuable aid in the teaching and practical application of Christian ethics. Dayton C. Miller very properly urges that "the scientific method is greatly needed in the solution of social and moral problems. We need," he also says, "the scientific method in municipal affairs." He emphasizes the use of this principle in national and international issues as being requisite to better world conditions.[35] All of this is strictly true, and it should be one of the chief efforts of Christian leaders, as, indeed, it frequently is, to create favorable sentiment in behalf of scientific investigation and handling of vexed questions of moral conduct and discipline. It is a thousand pities that in the task of human improvement there should be division of forces. Christianity and science, at least, should be united in spirit and purpose in this important sphere of activity.

Even a brief study of the personal virtues of scientists has been sufficient to show that they are in harmony with and, in this sense, illustrative of Christian ethics. They are characteristics which are taught and best displayed by Jesus of Nazareth, and which are illustrated in the lives of many of his followers, and, in part, by the founders and disciples of other religions. Manifestly, the outstanding ethical principles of Christianity are congenial to the scientific mind at its highest level. While no proof is discoverable here or elsewhere that science can safely be made

---

[34]Letter to author.
[35]Commencement Address, 1927, "The Spirit and Service of Science."

the sole guide of life, or the only arbiter of ethics, these facts, and the great and valuable service rendered by scientists generally to the cause of human morality must not only be applauded by the friends of religion, but should be regarded as a magnificent contribution and support to the cause which religion seeks to serve—the glory of God in the development and happiness of mankind.

With full appreciation of the modesty, humility, unselfishness, and rectitude displayed by scientists, two questions must nevertheless be asked. The first one, which has already been answered in part, is, Are the virtues which these men approve and exemplify the product of nature and of natural philosophy? Kepler is said to have declared that two things filled him with wonder—the starry heavens above, and the moral law within the soul. A similar saying is ascribed to Kant. Whence came the starry heavens, and whence came the observer of nature, and the moral law in the human soul? Soddy declares that "the self-contained organism is not comprehensible, but the combination of an inanimate mechanism and an external will is more intelligible. But there is in men a conscience as well as a consciousness, an ineradicable aspiration toward virtue which is no less difficult to understand."[36] Sir William Thistleton-Dyer thinks that the religious sentiment represents in part the desire for a supernatural sanction to principles of conduct. Its varied but virtually universal appearance must be accounted for by evolution as truly as the possession of a vertebral column. It is of no avail to dismiss it as being irrational.

Undoubtedly, it is true that religion, with all its content, must be accounted for. But can mechanistic evolution of itself do this? And are rules of conduct, for which divine sanction is sought, the mere result

[36]*Science and Life,* Frederick Soddy, p. 166, E. P. Dutton & Company.

of biological processes? Affirmation of the rationality of religion is, of course, acceptable to many who
do not believe, as, indeed, Thistleton-Dyer does not
here assert, that the moral nature of man is a resultant
of purely physical laws and forces. It is not apparent
that such powers are able to develop the conception
of morality or even to sustain such an idea when it is
apprehended. Ethically speaking, nature has two
aspects. It cannot be the whole truth to think with
Ferdinand Brunetière that nature is thoroughly immoral to such an extent that whatever is moral is in
a sense, and especially in its origin, in its first principle, but a reaction against the teachings and ad-
vices of nature. No vice is without natural example.
We are dissuaded from every virtue, and behold all
species in arms against each other *in mutua funera*.
Many observers see hints of righteousness, kindness,
and self-sacrifice in the lives of animals. Darwin believed that a little beast which fought for its young
was a better ancestor and prototype of humanity than
a bloodthirsty savage. When all is said, however, it
seems that by natural forces alone no living species
or race of men has ever risen to anything nearly
approaching virtue, and that the Christian ethics
as a plan of life are so far above any known natural
development as to have been accused of being unnat-
ural and impossible in practice. As to this last, the
answer of science seems to be that no adequate trial
has been made. At least certain writers on natural
philosophy use a good deal of ink in exposing failures
of professors of religion to live up to the teachings
of Jesus.

Now, it is just here that the utter failure of natural
morality, in the common meaning of this term, is
forced upon the mind. Lecky, who certainly is an
independent thinker, says that "the great characteristic of Christianity, and the great moral proof of its
divinity, is that it has been the main source of the

moral development of Europe, and that it has discharged this office not so much by the inculcation of a system of ethics, however pure, as by the assimilating and attractive influence of a perfect ideal." Describing this ideal as being due to "the character of the Christian Founder," he says that "there is nothing more wonderful in the history of the human race than the way in which that ideal has traversed the lapse of ages, acquiring a new strength and beauty with each advance of civilization, and infusing its beneficent influence into every sphere of thought and action." Of the way in which this ideal has survived and has stood out from all dogmatic conceptions, Lecky affirms: "This is a phenomenon altogether unique in history; and to those who recognize in the highest type of excellence the highest revelation of Deity, its importance is too manifest to be overlooked."[37]

It is far too much to ask of any dogma of science, reason, or religion that it should explain everything in earth and heaven. Hamlet's sage observation to Horatio applies here. Therefore it should not be considered remarkable that mechanistic theories of evolution are unable to solve the problem of moral excellence and development. Many years ago, the writer was greatly indebted to Joseph LeConte for the closing chapters of his book, *Evolution,* the usefulness of which to minds at a certain stage of thought is still considerable. This book, said to have been written at Henry Ward Beecher's suggestion, represents, as the author himself intimates, reaction of an evolutionist against materialistic and irreligious interpretation of the doctrine of evolution. The memory and influence of this great teacher are a permanent contribution to the realms in which he lived and wrought, giving weight to such conceptions as that of

[37]*History of the Rise and Influence of the Spirit of Rationalism in Europe,* vol. i, pp. 111, 112, D. Appleton & Company.

C. A. Dinsmore that man is the virtual and effectual reconciliation of science and religion. It has been asserted of LeConte, however, as of Darwin, Huxley, Tyndall, and other leading evolutionists, that he was not widely read nor greatly interested in philosophy, and was not strong in his grasp of its principles. Wherefore George H. Howison, of the same institution as that which LeConte so honored, contends in his *Limits of Evolution* that the attempt of the latter to explain human life and conduct upon the basis of natural laws, even with the corollaries of divine immanence and transcendence, is not adequate to all the facts and problems involved.

In truth, human personality and God, while they are approachable through the door of the senses, and while they are conformable to the assured revelations of science, when properly understood, and are contradictory to none of them, are facts to which mechano-mental evolution does so much less than justice, that, as John Wright Buckham indicates, it submerges the one and extinguishes the other. The latter thinks that "by a fine act of his Christian faith, won long before he became an evolutionist, LeConte transcended the bounds of evolution, and by positing a God at the very beginning of the evolutionary process, found him again throughout."[38] To this, objection is not made by Buckham, but the interpretation of God, "Whom the soul comes to know first in its own consciousness, enlightened by Christianity," as coming to the soul through nature, and confined therein, leads to a pantheism against which LeConte contended, even though it was the implication of his doctrine. God must be conceived as both immanent and transcendent, to escape deism and pantheism. As for man, he must be considered as a spiritual as well as a natural being. He is not merely pushed upward

---

[38]Inaugural address, "Christianity and Evolution," in *Religion As Experience*, p. 93, The Abingdon Press.

by physical forces, but, as LeConte himself says, is
drawn upward by the attractive force of ideals. He
is also empowered in his efforts to attain character
by superior personal forces. "Blessed inconsistency
of the true seer!"[39] Buckham comments on LeConte's
view. But, it must be asked, is it the work of "resident forces" to draw upward by ideals, and can ideals
of themselves produce the fruits of righteousness?

John Locke, the moral philosopher, whom many
class with the scientists, thought that the Christian
ethics, rightly considered, were capable of being
demonstrated as incontestably as the conclusions of
mathematics, but he complained of the slowness of
the processes of natural morality. Others observe the
incompleteness and lack of system of the latter, though
of course these defects are probably to be attributed to our imperfect comprehension. Sir Richard A.
Gregory notes one clear lesson: "Science may not be
able to provide a complete code of ethics, but it does
teach that every action carries with it a consequence."[40] Fournier d'Albe thinks that nature represents the outcome of our simplest act as thundering
down the ages. This is but an elementary principle,
however, and sad experience shows not only that it
has to be learned over and over by each generation
and by individuals, but that it does not carry us
far. James Y. Simpson, in *The Spiritual Interpretation of Nature,* described the limited power of
physical processes in the development of character.
"The fact that it is possible to trace the development
of morality," he says, "does not necessarily imply that
that development has throughout followed the method
of development of physical characters. In the case
of the latter, natural selection has played a very important part. But in the case of the former, just in

[39]Inaugural address, "Christianity and Evolution," in *Religion As
Experience,* p. 96, The Abingdon Press.
[40]*Discovery,* p. 46.

proportion as the character becomes distinctly moral does natural selection cease to have to do with its development. The moral character is like the student that has passed beyond the capacities of his early instructor: the latter ceases to have any hold on him."[41] The point of this pithy comment is far more than apparent when it comes to the Christian ethic, and particularly as to the ideal character and power by which it has been produced and continues.

Mechanistic evolution of itself alone can no more account for Jesus Christ than it can discount him. Many who are grateful to theistic evolution for its emphasis on the truth of divine immanence, find it impossible to conceive that this principle, as it is usually formulated, is a sufficient explanation of the personality of Jesus, of his arrival ages in advance of the readiness of the world as a whole to follow him, or of his impact both on individual minds and on civilization. There is more pull in a great character than is furnished by any discoverable law or principle, but this is not all. The need of humanity is not merely knowledge of science, with its enormous values and contributions to human welfare and even to religion. Mankind requires redemption from sin in and through the life communicated by the Divine Spirit to the soul of man, which is further not only drawn forward and upward, as Lecky says, by the sublime ideal seen in Jesus Christ, but is furnished by the reception of his Spirit and life with motivity and power to achieve the goal of dependable and useful virtue. It is notable that many eminent men mentioned in this volume as being religious characters believed in the necessary relationship of Christ to the problems of personal and universal morality. They held, as do millions of intelligent people to-day, that "The Great Teacher," as John Harris called him, the "Only Teacher" of Renan's tribute, is the Redeemer

---

[41]Hodder & Stoughton, Ltd., London, pp. 273-274.

of broken lives and the Saviour of all souls, and that
he will forever hold his place in the realm of ethical
force and values.   He can never pass away, for he
can never be surpassed.   With the lapse of centuries
the personality and power of Jesus increase their
strength, and his precepts shine with an effulgence
of light and beauty which the achievements of all
truth-seekers have reflected more or less consciously
and clearly before the eyes of their fellows, making
themselves great as they have helped to enhance his
greatness. Well-considered and thoroughly tested judgment is therefore assured that long after the name of
Newton sounds as far off as that of Archimedes, when
Kepler's fame has grown hoary with age, and
Herschel's stars have faded out of our skies, when
Darwin's researches are reduced to musty records,
and the glory of Faraday, Helmholtz and Kelvin has
been eclipsed by the labors of thousands of successors,
the inspiring Source and Norm of all goodness will
forever tower above human seers and sages, vivifying
as well as drawing upward and empowering the
spirits of those who know and trust him—Son of
man and Son of God, the universal Lord of Truth!

CHAPTER VI

SCIENCE AND FAITH

INASMUCH as eminent representatives of religious thought have expressed faith in science, it may be profitable to ask what place the general principle of faith occupies in the operations of science; what, if anything, science is able to do for religious faith, and whether the latter is to be regarded as an organ of knowledge.

It must be understood in this inquiry, as elsewhere, that universal agreement as to these or any other important questions is not to be expected. As to everything in the realm of thought and of experience the opinions of men are divided and often exactly opposing. Take the case of imagination, for example. An able naturalist discourses learnedly concerning "The Scientific Use of the Imagination."[1] He also publishes the saying of Sir Benjamin Brodie: "Physical investigation, more than anything besides, helps to teach us the actual value and right use of the imagination—of that wondrous faculty, which, left to ramble uncontrolled, leads us astray into a wilderness of perplexities and errors, a land of mists and shadows; but which, properly controlled by experience and reflection, becomes the noblest attribute of man; the source of poetic genius, the instrument of discovery in science, without the aid of which Newton would never have invented fluxions, nor Davy have decomposed the earth and alkalies, nor would Columbus have found another continent."[2] Now,

---

[1] *New Fragments of Science*, John Tyndall, vol. ii, p. 101 *et seq.*

[2] Presidential address to Royal Society, November 30, 1859, *The Works of Sir Benjamin Collins Brodie*, vol. i, p. 578.

though a statement like this elicits almost universal and instant assent, it has been declared by more than one individual reputed to be an authority that the progress of science is attained by the destruction of imagination, which is chiefly the mother of errors and follies.

Two of the greatest difficulties with which the human mind has to deal are those connected with varieties of language—confusion of tongues; and with diversities of definition—confusion of ideas. By the word "faith" anything may be implied, from intellectual to fiducial confidence, and from credulity to the most well-founded conviction. In different undertakings of the mind the term is used with connotations peculiar to particular situations to be met It should not be claimed that the scientist and theologian attach identical meanings to the faith which each employs. Nevertheless, it is not possible for the scientist to assert that he makes no use of any form or degree of assumption, and has no need of dependence upon authority or testimony, nor upon instinct and intuition. Science cannot get far without generalization and deduction, both of which are in good part credent processes.

Faith is indispensable, alike to scholar and critic, skeptic and believer. Every science begins with assuming something which, however axiomatic it may seem, is really postulatory, and is based also on the scientist's confidence in his own existence, in his possession of reliable senses, in the accuracy of his observations and of his reasonings from them, in some actualities of nature, of experience and of relationships, in the rationality and systematism of the universe, in the consistency, continuity and uniformity of natural laws and associations. Poincaré very appropriately speaks of a point of departure in seeking truth by scientific methods, which has something arbitrary about it often, in order to establish

confidence in continuity. This he considers a belief
hard to justify by apodeictic reasoning, but without
which any science is impossible. The scientist believes in method, and has confidence in the particular
methods which he employs. His procedure, therefore, based, as is that of religion, on authority, experience and hope, is an act of faith. Indeed, even
the skeptic reaches his ends by the same assistance.
Doubter or denier that he is, he places faith somewhere, even if it be put in the notion that a man
can be lifted only as he uses for the purpose his own
bootstraps.

The scientist is not able to get on by traveling on
sensational ground alone. He needs some form of
aviation. Even Haeckel, who affirms that religious
faith contradicts natural law, admits that science,
like religion, cannot do without faith. He is not willing that gaps in the orderly chain of nature be filled
by religious faith; but he desires that scientific faith
be permitted to fill the gaps in our knowledge of
natural law, for the time being, by hypotheses. Very
well, says common sense, provided there are no
known better hypotheses, and with the understanding
that others have the right, at least temporarily and
pending verification of Haeckel's hypotheses, to fill
existing gaps and deficiencies in nature, if there be
such, and in present-day science, with such conceptions as seem to them to be of highest probability
The radical has a good deal to say about freedom—
for himself. True freedom of thought and belief is a
circle of large enough diameter to take in everyone
who seeks reality.

Any who doubt that faith, at least in the sense of
accepting what many do not regard as proven, enters
into the life and operations of science should read
the literature of the various schools of evolutionists.
Masses of people, including some persons of considerable education, think of but one name in connec-

tion with the subject of evolution—that of Charles
Darwin. This, of course, is a great mistake. Ideas of
development occurred far earlier than the nineteenth
century. At length the theory of environment, proposed by Erasmus Darwin, Saint-Hilaire, and Goethe
to account for development and evolution in nature,
was made more specific by Lamarck, "founder of
organic evolution," with his idea of successive modi-
fications by the use or disuse of physical organs because of changed environment. New species were held
to be the result of gradual accumulation of such
changes in the organism. Charles Darwin, grandson of
Erasmus, fixed upon natural selection of the organisms
fittest to survive in the struggle for existence as being
the true story of nature. The strongest beings and
those best adapted to their environment, he thought,
are chosen to live and reproduce their kind, thus
originating succeeding types. Hugo De Vries added
experimentation to observation and inference as a
method of explaining evolution. He found that new
types of individuals occasionally appear in a pedi-
gree of some species. Such qualitative rather than
merely quantitative varieties are the "mutations"
from which De Vries taught that new species are derived by natural selection and development. Neo-
Lamarckians, Neo-Darwinians and mutationists
have created a voluminous literature. Weismann
and his disciples attained an impressive adherence to
their theory of "germinal selection." In addition to
the classical explanations are the partial theories of
"isolation," "hybridization," and "orthogenesis." Attempts have been made to combine part or all interpretations of the facts of the universe, and especially
of its living forms, into a comprehensive synthesis
which utilizes acceptable points of various schools.
The most superficial study of this work reveals the
faith quality which in varying degrees enters into it.
Students and authors of evolutionary science are

great believers, not always, it is true, in natural selection, often miscalled "Darwinism," nor in the transmission of acquired characters, nor in mutations, but in one or several hypotheses. Who will claim that any one of these views is a complete account and demonstration of the processes of nature? Strong varieties of opinion still appear after three quarters of a century of discussion on the part of men of high scholastic attainments. Scientists as a class are evolutionists, but their views, either of details or of fundamentals, are by no means identical, and it is to be noted that individuals are found who assert that in the main the very idea of evolution rests on faith rather than on knowledge.

It may be that Einstein would assert that he has proved relativity beyond the shadow of a doubt. Other observers and mathematicians, like Eddington and Minkowski, may claim that they have fully confirmed this view of the universe. Who thinks for a moment that all scientists who hold to this and to various scientific doctrines do so on a firmer basis than that of confidence in authority, and in evidence, which, so far as their own knowledge is concerned, stops far short of demonstration?[3] What far-reaching scientific theory has not had its doubters and its opponents? In many cases, it was faith which first supported these conceptions, and in certain instances they were sustained by the same principle for long periods before any convincing verification was obtained. Nor are these instances to be cited in disparagement. Whatever mistakes have been made—and we have seen that scientific history has not been free from them—it is perfectly evident that the progress of civilization and enlightenment would have been seriously retarded, and that many of the most valuable discoveries which have enriched the mind

[3] See comments on relativity near the close of Chapter I.

and ministered to the necessities and comfort of man would still await revelation, had not the scientist been a man of faith.

That was a rather witty, but not very profound remark of Huxley in *Lay Sermons:* "The man of science has learned to believe in justification, not by faith, but by verification."[4] If he meant to suggest that Saint Paul and Martin Luther did not believe in verification of the faith which justifies the repentant and forgiven sinner who opens his heart to the incoming of the new life in Jesus Christ, he was simply ignorant of their teaching. But if he was saying that science waits for verification before it exercises faith, his own writings cry aloud against his affirmation. He seems to have been a person of implicit confidence in one authority—Darwin—of far higher scientific ability than his own, and not only in established truths but in various theories which neither he nor any other man ever verified.

What has been said on this topic thus far may be readily supported by testimony. For example, Edwin B. Frost, astronomer, assures the readers of *The Heavens Are Telling* that "the principle of faith is not at all foreign to science and to its workers, and this faith is quite akin to that of religion."[5] It is a clear lesson of history that the times of its most adventurous scientific faith have been those of the greatest progress in science. One has an irresistible temptation to add that it would be better for the government and for the church, as well as for many social institutions, if their leaders as a whole exercised as firm and absorbing a faith in their ideals, methods and ascertainable facts as has been displayed by many observers and philosophers of nature.

When we come to the question of religious faith, one could easily multiply sayings to the effect that

---

[4]Page 18, D. Appleton & Company.
[5]Publication, American Institute of Sacred Literature, pp. 23-24.

science has nothing whatever to do with it. This is an attitude which it is hardly needful to say is rather more consoling to believers in religious reality than that which simply sweeps aside the whole spiritual conception and system as unfounded and unthinkable. The latter process, however, has proved to be at least difficult. Therefore it is more common to find such expressions as that of E. Ray Lankester, "It appears to me that science proceeds on its path without any contact with religion, and that religion has not, in its essential qualities, anything to hope for, or to fear from, science."[6] Over against this view may be put the opinion of Dean Inge, concerning one form of religious verity, that the natural history of the religious consciousness, as it manifests itself in individual life, has now taken its place among the sciences.

Of course, the issue here may seem to turn upon definition of the term "science." What is science? Joseph Henry's broad statement was: "Science is the knowledge of the laws of phenomena, whether they relate to mind or matter."[7] Another answer is, it is simply knowledge. What is or may be known, is a fact, law, or system of science. It is possible to narrow the connotation. If one says, Science is knowledge of the inorganic, then life is ruled out. If he affirms that science relates to physical objects, consciousness and intellectual experience disappear. If one eliminates feeling, will, and the entity which we call personality, with its reactions to other personalities and relations with them, then indeed religion has nothing to hope or fear from science. Nor, indeed, has it much to hope or fear from anything else— for the subject is dead! But if, on the contrary, man is a being possessed of powers beyond those of physi-

---

[6] *Kingdom of Man,* p. 63, Constable, Henry Holt and Company.
[7] "Biographical Memoirs of Joseph Henry," Asa Gray, *Smithsonian Report,* 1876, p. 156.

cal existence and intellection, and which are capable
of being known, utilized, and reduced to laws, then
whatever is contained within his own nature, whatever he does as a behaving being, and whatever actually affects him, determining his states, conduct or
relations, is a proper object of study and must be
comprehended within the circumference of the sciences. W. K. Clifford rightly contended that the subject of science is the whole human universe; which
is to say, all that is, has been, or may be related
to man.

If not merely the physical order, but the human
being, and not simply man's lower but also his higher
nature and its experiences, are within their range,
those who are interested in religious beliefs and systems have much both to hope and to fear from the
processes of science. Not that there is anything to
fear from appropriate and competent investigations
and from thorough and ultimate judgments. The
danger is from investigators who insist upon apply-
ing one canon of criticism to all classes of inquiry,
going with special technique into regions which will
not bear such measurements; from those who lack
well developed logical faculty, and from those who
approach their task with preconceived opinions or
with ineradicable prejudices. Of course the results
attained by such persons are often not science at all,
but they are published abroad in the great name of scientific teaching, and they do much harm, because ordinary people are not able to discern that they are mere
instances of bad logic. Poor philosophers ought not
to speak in behalf of those whose studies make them
too exact as well as too proficient to utter irresponsible
negations. When one of these men, for instance, asserted, "Miracles do not happen," a saying, of course,
literally true enough, he sounded all-wise. Too many
did not know that he was not a scientist, nor were
they aware that the a priori possibility of the miracu-

lous, in the reasonable Christian meaning of the term, and also the fact of the exercise of spiritual forces in the course of history, have been affirmed by men of distinguished ability, achievement and repute in the scientific world. Tyndall said, "If you ask me who is to limit the outgoings of Almighty power, my answer is, 'Not I!'" Again he avers, "You never hear the really philosophical defenders of the doctrine of uniformity speaking of impossibilities in nature. They never say, what they are constantly charged with saying, that it is impossible for the Builder of the universe to alter his work."[8]

As we have seen, scientists speak and write about "miracles," even including creation under this term. They discuss "the miracles of science," and "religious miracles," and one writes about "the commonplace of miracle." Some of them plainly teach that biological phenomena are miracles in the realm of the inorganic and that the same may be said of each superior sphere of nature's existence and thought in its relation to lower realities. Very probably most careful scientists of religious character incline toward the idea phrased by J. E. Kirkwood, botanist, "To my mind the miraculous is but the expression of natural law not understood."[9] This is quite dissimilar to a crude denial that what are called miracles ever did or do occur. It would seem that no fault should be found with a point of view which acknowledges the occurrence of certain phenomena, often referred to supernatural origin, as Kirkwood does, but which continues seeking for natural explanations. Wherever possible such causes should be sought and discovered, and, of course, this practice cannot be denounced as irreligious, nor as denial of final causes. Surely, God

[8]*Fragments of Science,* vol. ii, pp. 37 and 134, Appleton.
[9]Letter to author. In a paper on "Finding God Through Nature," Kirkwood also says, "There seems to be something noble in the faith that believes where it cannot prove. Our religion would lose some element of value if we could prove everything about it."

is in nature, as well as over it, and it is little better to deny him the wisdom of operating as a rule by what are called "natural" laws than to imprison him in his own creation.

Edwin B. Frost, astronomer and one of the editors of *The Astrophysical Journal,* sententiously remarks: "When mysteries are solved after patient research, it will, of course, be found that they are operations of natural law in God's world. For Omniscience and Omnipotence, there are no miracles."[10] It should be recalled that in a letter to Locke, Sir Isaac Newton affirmed concerning early Christian history that "miracles of good credit continued in the church for about two or three hundred years."[11] The chapter on "Science and Miracle," in James Y. Simpson's *The Spiritual Interpretation of Nature,* is a statement which in many points confirms the age-old conception of a Deity who on extraordinary occasions breaks through the trammels of the commonplace by the exercise of superior principles.[12] Henry Norris Russell, astronomer, in *Fate and Freedom,* expresses the judgment that Christian miracle is of secondary importance to religious experience. He thinks chief emphasis in the discussion of the Gospels should be placed on the teaching and character of Christ. It seems to him, however, that if Jesus Christ belonged to a spiritual order above that of our ordinary life, unusual—miraculous—phenomena might be expected to occur in connection with his career. In these cases the important thing is not the exceptional event, but the religious principles illustrated.[13]

Scientists are compelled frequently to face the question, What about the relation between science

[10]*The Heavens Are Telling,* American Institute of Sacred Literature, p. 31.
[11]*The Life of Sir Isaac Newton,* Sir David Brewster, p. 275. Also *Life and Letters of Locke,* Lord King, p. 222.
[12]Hodder & Stoughton.
[13]Pages 113-115, Yale University Press.

and religion? An interview with Thomas Martin
Lowry, physical chemist, Cambridge, England, represented him as feeling a bit wearied over this ancient
discussion. He nevertheless proceeded to make sen-
tentious remarks which relate to the subject under
consideration. "All scientific work," he said, "is
based on the conviction of the faithfulness of God.
One felt quite certain if one repeated one's experiments correctly they must always give the same results, since the laws of nature were enacted by a God
in whom was no variableness, neither shadow that
was cast by turning. Natural science does not deny
the existence of miracles. It cannot. It is full of
miracles—things to be wondered at. The difficulty
of accepting unnecessary miracles is a religious one.
The difficulty scarcely arises in the New Testament,
since Christ himself is so much greater than his
own miracles. Moreover, so many of these seem to
proceed along natural lines, although we cannot tell
by what knowledge he was able to work them—any
more than a native of Uganda can understand how a
European doctor had been able to cure him of a
sleeping sickness. In an honest religion there is no
use for two departments of knowledge. Religion
must cover the whole range of human life and experience. It is a far greater loss to teach our young
people to believe in a God who does not even keep
his own laws than to allow them to doubt the literal
truth of some incidents, say in the history of
Israel."[14]

The contents and tenor of this book are intended
to convey the impression that religion has not only
much to hope for ultimately from science, but that
the latter has made and is constantly supplying valuable contributions to Christian knowledge. Nevertheless, no one should expect, nor would it be immedi-

---

[14] *Methodist Magazine,* London, January, 1924.

ately desirable, that knowledge should come to such completeness as to make faith no longer necessary. Indeed, this is unthinkable in a universe in which the vasts of truth and wisdom lie in the domain of the transfinite. A collection of *Cambridge Readings in the Literature of Science* closes its account of modern progress with a sentence which indicates how difficult the wise and frank biologist considers his task to be, and how unlikely he thinks his method is finally to solve the chief problem presented to the human mind: "It is now widely accepted that higher species arose by descent from lower species. We are endeavoring to understand the path which the evolutionary movement took, the forces which guided and controlled it. Our ultimate success may well be doubted."[15]

Faith is not only a necessity; it is one which will always be requisite to man. It is not only that he does not know, and must therefore often venture, but that moral values and spiritual strength are acquired, as the bird learns to fly, by the testing of untried wings. Science aids Christian faith by its own examples of faith. The experiments of Langley are not without spiritual suggestiveness, even if analogy be denied. Each physical discovery seems to imply that new regions may be sought and found by the use of any human faculty. Science teaches that success comes, not to the closed but to the open mind, not to the doubting and faithless but to the hopeful and daring spirit. The courage of those who toiled on and died before the confidence in scientific facts and theories which they held was vindicated, tempts the believer in spiritual powers and ends to "carry on," to be strong and tireless, to "see it through."

It is shown elsewhere that science aids Christian faith to keep in bounds, to hold itself to its own province, and within reasonable limits. Other forms

---

[15]University Press, Cambridge, England.

of religious belief, aside from Judaism and Christianity, share but slightly in this influence, and this for the reason that it is in the countries where Christianity is most powerful, and where Judaism is free, that science is encouraged and is most generally and effectively cultivated. Moreover, at its best estate, science tends to the exaltation of faith to higher levels and to wider vision. Emerson truly exclaims, "Science necessitates a faith commensurate with the grander orbits and universal laws which it discloses!" For these reasons, among others, it is in the lands of greatest intelligence and of scientific activity that religion is purest and most useful.

Science often helps theology to clarify its statements. Does it also give religion firmer ground and added facts on which to rear the structure of its doctrine and confidence? Some will answer, "No!" I will say, "Yes!" Life-long reading of scientific literature has tended to furnish what seemed to me to be increasing cause for assurance of spiritual reality rather than in any wise to shake the foundation of the temple of divine truth. That this has not been the experience of every one is too painfully evident. If the reaction of one who finds the study of nature not only not inimical to Christian faith, but conformable thereto, is regarded as being due to failure to comprehend what has been discovered by the scientist, he may freely confess that he has not believed all he has heard and read of scientific doctrine. He has taken the meat of fact, and has cast aside what he thought but bones of dogma. He obtains much encouragement from the suggestion and experience of John Fiske, as stated in his letter to Rev. John Langdon Dudley, dedicating the *Excursions of an Evolutionist:* "If we would fain learn something of the Infinite, we must gird up our loins anew and diligently explore on every side that finite realm through which still shines the glory of an ever-present God for those who have eyes to see and ears to hear."[16] It will be recalled that in his essay, *Through Nature to God,* Fiske, speaking as an evolutionist, affirmed that of all the implications of the doctrine of evolution with respect to man the one which is deepest and strongest is that which declares the everlasting reality of religion. For myself, I go further and not only hold with Bishop William T. Manning, in his significant York Celebration sermon of 1927, that science has proved nothing that makes it impossible for the humble and sincere to kneel before Jesus Christ, but I am convinced, as Bishop Manning states in a recent publication, that "the appeal and claims of Jesus in their influence upon the intelligence, as well as on the heart, in no way conflict with any discovery of science or of modern knowledge." I believe in science and in the Saviour and Teacher of men.

There are doubtless instances in which faith is entirely distinct and separate in its origin and development from other forms of knowledge and experience. George Jackson in *The Fact of Conversion*[17] gives an account of a Swiss teacher, Gaston Frommel. He was asked by his students, "How do you succeed in maintaining the affirmation of your religious consciousness over against the frequently contrary affirmations of science?" His reply was: "My religious consciousness, in its sources and its contents, is independent of my scientific consciousness. And I add that, in my own case, it was a long way anterior."

We are reminded of Drummond's experience, as stated in the preface of his most popular book, *Natural Law in the Spiritual World,* and as explained by George Adam Smith. This much-admired

[16]Houghton, Mifflin Company.
[17]The Cole Lectures, Vanderbilt, 1908, p. 41, Fleming H. Revell Company.

teacher for a time kept religion and science shut away from one another in two different compartments of his mind, in the sense that at first he felt that the laws of each were without the least likeness or relevance to the other. This position, as is well known, he abandoned for an extreme in which he made natural and spiritual laws practically identical, thus erring to some extent, it seems, in the contrary direction. But neither his life nor the influence of his religious teachings was in serious error. As a dynamic Christian he became a creator of human values.

That it should not be considered necessary to keep scientific and religious ideas and concepts entirely separate from each other is a view of the matter which in the end must prevail, if truth is really one. That each of these kinds of knowledge has its proper limits, and that they should aid each other to observe these limits, seems perfectly evident, but so does the fact that each may make appropriate seizure of the information which is furnished by the other party. Therefore the great word of J. Arthur Thomson: "What we are pleading for is not the hopeless notion of trying to have idea-tight compartments in the mind, but the very opposite—intellectual consistency and fair play. Scientific formulæ may be supplemented by religious interpretation, provided it be clearly understood that the scientific conclusions cannot by any possibility be tampered with to suit religious considerations. It is the duty of the religious mind to ask whether the *form* in which it expresses its feelings and convictions is consistent with what we know to be the facts. Thus the doctrine of the resurrection of the body, *as often stated,* is insulting to the scientific intelligence. But the concessions cannot be all on one side. If science promulgates as one of its conclusions an apsychical view of man, that is insulting to the religious intelligence. Far from suggesting idea-tight compartments, we are pleading for a more strenuous endeavor to harmonize the contributions which science and religion and other activities make to the TRUTH. If a scientific conclusion does violence to other aspects of experience, the inquiry should include the question whether the scientific conclusion is being rightly stated. The two sets of ideas may clash in form, but in essence they are incommensurable."[18]

Many intelligent and thoughtful people believe that faith exists in its own right, and is under the operation of its own forces and laws, both in case of those who possess and of those who are without competent scientific knowledge. It is no violation of the principle laid down by Thomson to say that it is fortunate that in the flux of human thinking the spirit of man is able to attain and to retain confidence in the essentials of the religious life without servile deference to current tendencies, and even at times against unassimilated facts.

As to wise and justifiable *statements* of religious and scientific doctrines it may well be asked, Why be too precise and, above all, why be grossly materialistic in such expressions? With reference to "the resurrection of the body," for instance, might not the difficulty of some scientists concerning this belief be lessened, if more were left to spiritual insight? Is it inconsistent, even for a devout Christian, to believe that the "body" referred to in our creeds is to be understood as representing, not the flesh and blood of our physical tabernacle, whether immature, developed, or senile, whether well constituted or full of imperfections, but whatever of form or substance, finely material or wholly spiritual, may be necessary to individuality, identity, self-consciousness and adaptation to the needs and activities of eternal life? Similarly, has not scientific doctrine been sometimes

---

[18]*Homiletic Review,* December, 1923, Funk & Wagnalls Company.

so stated as to constitute a *reductio ad absurdum* to
those who think in terms of reason and of divine
truth? "Death ends all" is a materialistic dogma
which seems to many trained and logical minds to
be as offensive and impossible to sane judgment as is
a carnal conception of resurrection. In this connection, attention may be called to the Moffatt translation of Philippians 3. 20-21. "But we are a colony
of heaven, and we wait for the Saviour who comes from
heaven, the Lord Jesus Christ, who will transform
the body that belongs to our low estate till it re-
sembles the body of his Glory."[19] It is probable that
this phraseology better represents the view of intelligent believers than do the usual statements of bodily
resurrection. A unique treatment of this theme from
the standpoint of the physicist, Fournier d'Albe,
appears elsewhere in this book.

The wise man fears nothing from truth. Youmans pictured John Torrey, botanist and chemist,
as having been possessed of justifiable courage and
poise: "Knowing that all truths are compatible, he
was never disturbed by the results of scientific research, being confident that they would be found in
final agreement with all that is best and truest in
man's religious needs." Experience has shown that
religion, however constrained, thwarted, or ruled out
of the court of reason for the time being, always
comes back with credentials in response to the firm
patience of faith. On the other hand, science yields
to penetration and interpretation deep-lying principles which are unrealized by superficial observers.
This was recognized by William Lowe Bryan, psychologist and educator: "If science has any excuse for
being, it is because every fact is a sacred bearer of
everlasting truth. And this that science has realized
as the highest truth, the poets do realize as joy, and

---

[19]Reprinted from The Holy Bible: A New Translation, by James
Moffatt, copyright, 1926, by George H. Doran Company.

the saints do realize as worship."[20] Herein is probably the explanation of Shaler's recovery from a period of spiritual uncertainty through, he said, "further insight into the truths of nature." It was when the toiling Romanes, after a tiresome journey through the wilderness of naturalistic negations, at last found himself upon the highlands of spiritual perception and refreshing atmosphere, that he coined the inspiring phrase, "the hallowed glory of the Christian faith."

What autobiography is more charming and instructive than Michael Idvorsky Pupin's *From Immigrant to Inventor?* As a specimen of beautiful English, as a study in Americanization, as a review of a half century of scientific progress, it is of compelling interest and of permanent value. The book excels as a human document, however, containing many clean-cut character etchings, of which the most attractive is that of the scientist's mother. Olympiada Pupin—the name tempts one to comment—never left her tiny peasant Serbian village, Idvor, but she made her world a large one nevertheless. To her son's aspirations she gave the greatest encouragement. She resolutely sent the boy away to be educated. She followed him on the adventurous journey to a new continent with her confident love. She insisted that he was wise in seeking the most complete preparation for his life-work in post-graduate studies at Cambridge and Berlin. When he came back to her with a head full of new learning, she listened with pleasure to his revelations. Then he reminded her of her oft-repeated saying during his boyhood, "Knowledge is the golden ladder over which we climb to heaven," and asked her whether she included in this the knowledge which he was describing. Her reply, that of instinctive if not of inspired judgment, one might comment,

---

[20]"The Mortal Immortal," in *The Spirit of Indiana,* p. 129, University of Indiana Press.

was, "I include every knowledge which brings me nearer to God; and this new knowledge certainly does." Wherefore Pupin closes this chapter of his life record and of a still more wonderful biography, that of Olympiada Pupin, with the expression of a profound conviction: "Her religion taught her how to catch the spirit of science, and I was always certain that science can teach us how to catch the spirit of her religion."[21]

Attractive as a continuation of this portion of the discussion is to the writer, we must pass to the query as to whether science may so enter into the life and practice of religious faith that the latter may become useful to him as a seeker after truth. It is said that "faith is the organ by which we apprehend the unseen." If this is at all true, may it not be so for the scientist as certainly as for others? We shall see that by the employment of this faculty notable men of scientific history have come to such assurance of unseen realities that they regarded its products in their minds as being of the nature of true knowledge. But has this faith been to any an organ of scientific knowledge? Undoubtedly it is chiefly the habit of religion to establish useful contacts with the invisible Ultimate which is the absolute heart of the flowing universe of phenomena. Yet, if there be a Spirit which visits and in any wise informs the human spirit, what is to prevent the influence and assistance of that Spirit within the mind of one who is devoted to the attainment of physical truth, and who seeks to realize his ideals? Upon the premise stated, is not this to be expected, and is there any inherent impossibility involved in the suggestion? Anciently it was believed that "He giveth wisdom unto the wise, and knowledge to them that know understanding; he revealeth the deep and secret things; he knoweth what is in the darkness, and the light dwelleth with him."

---

[21] *Op. cit.*, pp. 245 and 246, Charles Scribner's Sons.

In considering the problems involved in the discovery of truth formerly unknown to the world it would be well if more attention were paid to the difficulties which attend the process of generalization, and which are increasing rather than diminishing in complexity. A group of scientific investigators were recently considering a situation which is becoming evident, namely, that "while science is advancing by leaps and bounds it is true that facts and phenomena are being discovered at a rate far in excess of their assimilation. We were discussing," says the account, "whether or not it would be possible for the world to produce a twentieth-century Newton—in other words, whether or not the vast array of facts and figures that a man would need to know before he could make any great generalizations such as Newton made would not be so great that no man could, in a lifetime, become familiar with them. The point was made that occasionally a man arises who seems to see things intuitively, and who does not need to know the million and one things that the average man needs to know before he can draw conclusions. Such a man seems to see directly through to the heart of things. Such a man has more than what we are wont to speak of as intellect."[22] In this account of an interesting incident, Arthur L. Foley does not indicate what in a man may be "more than what we are wont to speak of as intellect." If genius be suggested, it may be asked, What is genius? And what is intuition or insight? Why is it, also, that some stumble where others less able and less widely informed see clearly and make swift progress? Answers to these questions should be approached in the light of further observations in this chapter.

It is frankly admitted that any hint of divine inspiration of students of nature is uncongenial to certain scientists. Such a conception seems to them

[22]Contributed.

disloyalty to the scientific method, and one cannot refrain from saying that in some cases the idea seems to annoy as being a personal affront. This can hardly be the consistent attitude, however, of those who believe that humility and teachability are the first requisites—*sine qua non*—of the scientific spirit. That reluctance to admit the possibility of divine guidance by no means expresses the view of all scientists may be indicated by such utterances as that of Richard Arman Gregory, "It is the Divine afflatus which inspires and enables the highest work in science."[23] This reminds one of Disraeli's aphorism, "Science, like spiritual truth, has ever from the beginning been descending from heaven to man."

What did Kepler mean when he talked about thinking God's thoughts after him? It is related of Joseph Henry that when he had prepared the materials for a great experiment he told his pupils that he had asked God a question and that they must await the answer. Did he have in mind the same thought which Sir John Herschel put into the words, "He who has seen obscurities which appeared impenetrable in physical and mathematical science suddenly dispelled, and the most barren and unpromising fields of inquiry converted, as if by inspiration, into rich and inexhaustible springs of knowledge and power, . . . will surely be the very last to acquiesce in any dispiriting prospects of either the present or future destinies of mankind"? "As if by inspiration!" What was it that stirred the mind of Sir Joseph Prestwich so that he seemed to have intuitive consciousness of something for him to do—that he himself might aspire to demonstrate some truth in God's nature?

A very interesting experience is that of Colonel Sir Ronald Ross, who determined the facts by which the causes of malaria are certainly known, and by which many dangerous regions of the earth are being

---

[23] *Discovery*, p. 50, The Macmillan Company.

transformed into places of healthfulness and beauty. In despair, as he viewed the sufferings of the people of India, Doctor Ross wrote down the plea:

"The painful faces ask, 'Can we not cure?'
  We answer, 'No, not yet; we seek the laws.'
O God, reveal through all this thing obscure
  The unseen, small but million-murdering cause."

When at last the knowledge came to him, he paid this tribute:

"This day relenting God
  Hath placed within my hand
A wondrous thing; and God
  Be praised. At his command,
Seeking his secret deeds,
  With tears and toiling breath,
I find thy cunning seeds,
  O million-murdering death.
I know this little thing
  A myriad men will save.
O Death, where is thy sting?
Thy victory, O grave?"[24]

Emerson says, "It was a conviction of Plato, of van Helmont, of Pascal, of Swedenborg, that piety is an essential condition of science, that great thoughts come from the heart."[25]

A biographer of Carl von Linné says that "He honored the Lord, who permitted him to visit his secret council-chambers." None knew better than he that what we do of ourselves is not the best we can do; we must, for the best, seek for divine strength and light. Linnæus concluded the record of the occurrences of his life with these words: "The Lord was with thee wherever thou didst go." Would it not be more just, if divine assistance in the achievements

---

[24] By permission from Ross, Major Ronald: *Memoirs, With a Full Account of the Great Malaria Problem and Its Solution.* London, John Murray: New York, E. P. Dutton & Company.
[25] Vol. iii, Riverside edition, Houghton Mifflin Company.

of life were frankly acknowledged? The English chemist Sir W. H. Perkin, discoverer of mauve, replied to high tributes paid him by admirers and friends by saying, "When I look back on my life and consider all the way I have been led, above all I thank God, to whom I owe everything, for all his goodness to me, and ascribe to him all the praise and honor. What have I that I have not received?"[26]

In an address, "How Genius Works," delivered to the graduating class of the American University, Edwin Emery Slosson said: "Science is built up by patient and persistent labor, most of it drudgery of the hardest kind. But it is not altogether done by work of the bricklayer sort, the slow fitting together of fact upon fact and cementing them in place with the mortar of logic. There must come to somebody some time a vision of the edifice as a whole, the fundamental theory of the thing complete and perfect. This vision may come in a flash quite like the inspiration of the author or artist, and often, when the mind is not consciously working on the problem, but is, so to speak, off guard, it seems almost as though the answer were being whispered to him from without by someone who had watched with sympathy his fruitless efforts to solve it. We find in the biographies of men of science frequent references to this so curious sensation of inspiration."[27] Doctor Slosson illustrated this principle by the experience of Kekulé, the German chemist, when he conceived the idea of atomic linkages; of Poincaré, the mathematician, when striving to work out the Fuchsian functions of the hypergeometric series; of another great mathematician, Sir William Rowan Hamilton, when he discovered the form of calculus called quaternions; and of Kropotkin, the geographer, when he found the true prin-

[26]From address at "Jubilee of the Discovery of Mauve and of the Foundation of the Coal-Tar Industry."

[27]*American University Courier,* December, 1924.

ciples in the disposition of the mountains of Asia. In *Sermons of a Chemist* Slosson has also discussed "The Faith of a Chemist" in an interesting way.

History discloses the fact that peril attaches itself to the conception and practice of any type of illuminism. It is not difficult to deceive oneself as to sources of spiritual impressions. The purpose and end of efforts to attain knowledge, and the uses and results of applications which follow its acquirement, are criteria by which the sources may be judged from which remarkable revelations of truth have come. Goethe, who thought himself a profound scientist and who was a master poet, was very clear as to the source of the so-called great achievements of genius. No productivity of the highest type, he insists, no notable discovery, no great thought which is fruitful and brings forth results, is within the power of anyone; such matters are exalted above earthly control. Man must regard them as unlooked for gifts from above, as pure children of God, to be received and venerated with joyous thanksgiving. George A. Coe, in the *Religion of a Mature Mind,* goes even further than the statements quoted when he suggests that "down in its deepest heart, we may assume that the scientific spirit is an inspiration."[28] William North Rice, geologist, in *The Return to Faith,* penned some profound sentences: "To those who believe that the material universe is but the vesture of immanent Deity, every scientific discovery is in the truest sense a revelation of God." He also says: "A half century ago it was widely believed that the new scientific doctrines were destructive of religious faith and even of the foundations of ethics. To-day we are able to see that God's great revelation in science came not to destroy, but to fulfill."[29] So then, nature, as Rice views it, is

---

[28]Chapter on "The Scientific Point in Religion," p. 55, Fleming H. Revell Company.

[29]*Op. cit.,* p. 124.

both a means of knowing God and a vehicle by which divine wisdom is apprehended in increasing measures.

It may not be necessary, in order that one's spirit become the vehicle of the influence of a higher personality, that he be wholly or even at the moment at all conscious of the source of the truth which he has received and transmits to others. The chief evidence of the revelation of knowledge to and through the intelligence of scientists is not to be found in the indisputable fact that some have felt and confessed that they believed themselves to have been in this way privileged and honored. Rather the proof lies in two more general conditions. The first is that so great a number of outstanding discoverers, not the followers and distributors, but the originators of knowledge of fundamental laws—eternal truths— have been men of admitted religious faith and character. The argument becomes more far-reaching and compelling still when the topography of scientific progress is taken into consideration. It has been the men who, whatever their personal relation to religion, were the product of a religious civilization and environment, and it has been the individuals and peoples who have been affected by the most elevated and spiritual types of religion who have penetrated furthest into the arcana of nature and who have most fully realized the enjoyments and benefits of scientific advancement.

In *The Progress of Science,* by J. V. Marmery, are tables representing those countries whose achievements illustrate the theme of the book. Under the various national headings appear names of scientific men of distinction whose labors have reflected honor upon the countries mentioned. The record is divided into two parts. The first one reflects the scientific study of England, France, Germany, and Italy. The second table refers to America, Poland, Portugal, Denmark, Sweden, Holland, Switzerland, and Russia, the last named country being credited only with Baer and Mendeléeff. Marmery's book is more than a third of a century old. It is hardly necessary to point out that to-day the United States of America would be on the first list and that England would be replaced by Great Britain unless Scotland and Canada, at least, were to receive separate attention. Is it not a striking tribute to Christianity that the countries named as being the centers and mediums of scientific advancement are precisely those in which Christianity is most completely domiciled, and where its influence is at its maximum? It is possible to go further and to maintain the thesis that the degree of scientific progress made by each particular nation compares almost exactly with the type and grade of its religious development. If any confutation of these facts can be adduced, it has not yet appeared. It is perfectly evident that such a parallelism exists, and its explanation seems equally obvious. That such a phenomenon has not been more generally and clearly recognized and published seems passing strange. Here is a reconciliation of science and religion which simply exists, without need of argument, and which is most suggestive. Does it not also indicate a method which when properly regarded and related to other methods may be made most fruitful? By fuller recognition and use of this principle—that of religious faith as an aid to intellectual endeavors—might it not be that knowledge and civilization would make still more wonderful advances than those of the past, fulfilling the ancient testimony, "In thy light we see light"?

CHAPTER VII

HEROES AND MARTYRS OF SCIENCE

THIS book opened with the Acts of the Apostles of Science; it should go on and conclude with added knowledge of these men, and particularly of the heroes, martyrs, saints, and prophets whose lives have brightened the pages of scientific history. We do not hesitate to claim a parallelism between the ideals and deeds of these eminent characters and those of Christianity. Christian recognition goes further, and includes those who devote their lives to any cause of human value, who render service to that cause or suffer for it, as being thereby—in deed, if not in deliberate intent, and often in both—followers and helpers of Jesus Christ in his ministry to men. They are shown as "God's fellow workers" by the results of their labors in the fulfillment of the prophecy that we "shall know the Truth," and in the advancement of Christian civilization, which, as we have seen, has reciprocal relations with scientific progress.

Science, as well as religion, has its Book of Martyrs. The sufferings and sacrifices made have not always been intended or deliberate. Nor were those of Christianity. Neither Huss, Savonarola, nor Cranmer planned or expected to lose his life for his fidelity to the light revealed to him. No historian, Foxe or any other, has listed all the Christian martyrs. The stout spirits who went to the arena or the stake were few in number compared with the many who gave, and sometimes lost, their possessions, strength, or lives for Christ and the gospel. Lecky acclaims the martyrs of literature, who pressed their way through dire penury to ends of the highest value to mankind. Many never reached those ends. They sac-

187

rificed, suffered, or died in their struggles to achieve, but are unknown to history. It is the apparent successes of life which are recorded, and not often the seeming failures. In considering martyrs of science also, it should be remembered that a large part of the record is buried in oblivion, or in the books of God's remembrance.

Most successful men were developed by early limitations, privations, and embarrassments. Many instances of this truth may be gleaned from scientific history. Lamarck's life was saddened by afflictions, as well as by the rigid economy he had to practice and the unending poverty of his whole experience. The author of *Philosophie Zoologique,* which has been called the first biological classic, did not receive a permanent burial place. His bones are probably mingled with those of the unknown in the catacombs of Paris. Darwin was born to plenty, but Kepler suffered much from penury, while Scheele died prematurely, not only from exposure to poisonous gases but from long-continued want of warmth and comfort. More scientists have suffered severely from extreme strain in their tasks than from early difficulties. Malpighi was a victim of overwork, neglect of food, and eyestrain. Many have ruined their sight, as did Thierry, in studying historic sources, Weismann, who announced the theory of the physical basis for heredity now so much in vogue, suffered similarly from constant use of the microscope. Alexander Wilson prepared an elaborate treatise on ornithology. After the seventh volume had appeared he realized that he was far from being in good health. Intense application to study had hurt him much. His eighth volume was in press and would soon be published. One volume more would complete the whole. But he never saw even the book which was about to be issued, for his unremitting toil cut him down at the age of forty-seven.

It is said that Lalande, the astronomer, by devotion to his profession contracted an illness from which he suffered during his entire life. The protracted and severe toil of Laënnec, discoverer of auscultation and inventor of the stethoscope, brought on consumption from which he died at the age of forty-five. The case of Francis T. Buckland, with outdoor exposure added, is similar to that of Laënnec. Sir Robert Ball, by continuous astronomical observations, not only affected his eyes, losing the sight of one altogether, but was forced to write part of his *Story of the Heavens* while lying on his back on the floor, suffering from lumbago. An earlier astronomer, and one of the greatest, Sir William Herschel, took many risks in the prosecution of his work. His sister Caroline said: "I could give a pretty long list of accidents which were near proving fatal to my brother as well as myself. To make observations with such large machinery where all around is darkness is not unattended with danger, especially when personal safety is the last thing with which the mind is occupied." Observations were not the only duty, for Herschel was obliged to give exhibitions to persons of prominence. He so taxed his strength by acting as a "showman of the heavens" to members of the court that for a whole month he had not a free evening. One night with crowds of these visitors, whom the requirements of his office compelled him to please, he was on a grass-plot without nourishment or time to put on sufficient clothing from dark until past midnight. He suffered a nervous shock, followed by an illness from which he never recovered.[1] One of sixteen members of a family of Gregorys, who have been distinguished holders of scientific chairs in Great Britain, was stricken with blindness at the age of thirty-six, while showing his students the satellites of Jupiter. This

[1] *Stories of Scientific Discovery*, D. B. Hammond, p. 67, Cambridge University Press.

James Gregory was the first exclusively mathematical professor in the University of Edinburgh. It was probably due in good part to his devotion to duty that Edwin Brant Frost of Yerkes Observatory suffered serious loss of vision.

Laboratory work in certain of the sciences is often very hazardous and results in injury to the experimenter. Davy and Faraday received many bruises and cuts from explosions of chloride of nitrogen, which cost Dulong the loss of an eye.[2] Ascanio Sobrero endangered his life frequently in experimenting with his discovery of nitroglycerin. Once a tube containing the explosive burst in his hands, cutting his face and injuring others. Sobrero fed nitroglycerin to a dog, which died. He tasted it himself, and suffered from violent headaches and weakness of limbs. Robert Bunsen, inventor of the "Bunsen burner," of a battery, calorimeter, photometer, and of a standard method of gas analysis, lost the sight of one eye, and suffered a long illness from an explosion of a cyanide derivative of a compound of arsenic which he was studying. The youngest brother of Alfred Nobel, inventor of dynamite and founder of the Nobel peace prizes, lost his life in an explosion which blew up the Nobel nitroglycerin factory at Heleneborg. Alfred Nobel risked his own safety often when perfecting his process for commercial production of nitroglycerin.

In co-operation with Wöhler, Liebig began the study of fulminic acid, but on November 18, 1830, he wrote his associate: "The fulminic acid we will allow to remain undisturbed. Like you, I have vowed to have nothing to do with this stuff. Some time back, I wanted, in connection with our work, to decompose some fulminating silver by means of ammonium sulphide. At the moment the first drop fell into the

---

[2] Tyndall's essay on "Life and Letters of Faraday," *Fragments of Science,* vol. i, p. 399, *et seq.*

dish the mass exploded under my nose. I was thrown backward, and was deaf for a fortnight, and became almost blind." Charles Mansfield, assistant of A. W. von Hofmann, was burned to death in 1856 while distilling benzine.

During the World War many took great risks in scientific researches. Colonel E. F. Harrison was affected by poisons taken in studying gases used on the battlefields and succumbed to influenza. Workmen developing the deadly tetranitroline lost the red corpuscles from their blood. Four chemists risked their lives in tests which proved that only dark-pigmented races could be safely employed in manufacturing this gas.

The pioneer experiments in the discovery of radium were not only difficult but dangerous. Before safe methods of keeping and handling radium had been devised much harm was done to the workers. Pierre Curie's hands were badly crippled. Broca states that Becquerel, by carrying in his arm-pit for several hours a preparation of radium, contracted an ulceration in his side which was long in healing. These two great men, Becquerel and Curie, he regarded as victims of the discovery which led them both to glory, and he thought that perhaps the weakness caused by their injuries was partly to blame for their premature ends.[3] To refer again to Scheele, it is remarkable that he did not met with death by reason of his dealing with such poisonous gases and vapors as those of prussic acid and other cyanogen compounds. In 1924 occurred the death from inhaling carbon monoxide of William E. Hyslip, laboratory instructor in automotive engineering at the University of Pittsburgh. Hyslip was instructing a class in automobile mechanics, and was zealously demonstrating the working of an eight-cylinder motor in

[3]Vide "The Work of Henri Becquerel," André Broca, in *Revue Générale des Sciences*, Paris, October 30, 1908.

motion. In going from one part of the motor to another he inhaled the deadly fumes of the exhaust. This incident recalls the fact that Sir Humphry Davy once was made so ill by carbon monoxide that he nearly lost his life.

Service in behalf of the theory and practice of medicine has furnished many illustrations of heroic conduct. One of the early naturalists, Conrad Gesner, was also a medical practitioner. He was public physician in Zürich at a time of visitation of a "plague." He combated the scourge successfully, but at cost of injury to his health. The next year, when the disease reappeared, Gesner again stuck manfully to his post. He was not less effective than before, but this time he did not escape the general epidemic, and, because his system had been weakened by over-exertion, he was carried off before he had quite reached the age of fifty.

Investigators in the field of bacteriology and similar subjects have often taken very great risks, and whatever the result they deserve the credit of possible consequences. Pasteur, in his eagerness to discover a cure for rabies, actually sucked saliva from the mouth of a mad dog. Von Siebold and others became convinced that certain bladder-worms found in oxen and pigs were really the same as a kind of tape-worms found in man. In order to test this theory they took the chance of swallowing the bladder-worms. As they were soon after found infected with the tape-worms, the experiment proved a success.

Visitors to the London, England, Hospital may see there a tablet which says: "On 10th October, 1890, when this ward was a male medical ward, the first case of Sleeping Sickness seen in England was admitted into this bed . . . The House Physician, Arthur St. L. Fagan, examined the blood of the patient every four hours for two months and discovered three filaria, one of which, now called trypanosome,

has since been proved to be the cause of the disease.
Fagan was enabled to carry on these researches by
the permission and help of the patient himself, a
Christianized African Chief named Mandombi, who
voluntarily submitted to the experiments for the good
of his people in Nigeria." Of the event here described
The Medical Review of Reviews said, "When a man
offers himself to save a million lives, as Chief Mandombi did, he deserves a place in the memory of men."
This journal also recorded the statement of
Fagan, made at the time when the tablet was assured.
Among other items the discoverer said: "Mandombi
was a fine type of African Negro, who in the Congo
had come under the influence of Doctor Grattan
Guinness, and embraced Christianity. Like so many
of his unfortunate fellow countrymen, he had become
a victim of the dreadful disease of sleeping sickness,
and suggested to Guinness that he should, for
the good of his race, allow himself to be experimented upon, with the result that he was sent to
England and came under my charge in October,
1890, at the London Hospital, where I was then house
surgeon. Thenceforward for nearly three months I
took specimens of his blood day and night every four
hours, a task which nearly killed me, but, unfortunately we could not save Mandombi's life. Nevertheless, the experiments he allowed us to make enabled
me to make the test, which had never before been
applied, of examining the blood of the patient, with
the result that I found the little ribbon-like trypano-
somes, or worms, which were the cause of the disease." Whole regions of Africa which had become
uninhabitable because of sleeping sickness have now
been redeemed. Very high estimates have been made
of the number of white as well as colored men saved
from inevitable infections and death from this
dreaded malady.

One of the most instructive incidents in this department of scientific activity is connected with the conquest of yellow fever, a disease which had ninety times invaded the United States, entailing widespread death and losses of multiplied millions of dollars. During the Spanish-American War the camps of the voluntary troops were devastated by typhoid, and Major Walter Reed, U. S. A., a medical officer, was put at the head of a board to study the cause and spread of the disease, valuable reports being made. In June, 1900, Major Reed was sent to Cuba as president of a board to study the infectious diseases of the island, particularly yellow fever. With him were associated acting surgeons James Carroll, Jesse W. Lazear and Aristide Agramonte, a Cuban. Every previous effort to ascertain the cause of yellow fever and to prevent it had failed. Reed became convinced that its cause was the bite of an insect. General Leonard Wood, military governor, was appealed to for aid in money and for permission to experiment on non-immune persons. Doctor Carroll allowed himself to be bitten by a mosquito that twelve days previously had filled itself with the blood of a yellow fever patient. He suffered a very severe attack of the disease. Doctor Lazear also experimented on himself, but was not infected. Later, while in the fever ward, Lazear was bitten by a mosquito, and observed the fact carefully, giving his notes to Doctor Carroll. He acquired the disease in its most terrible form and died as a hero and martyr to science. While no other fatalities occurred, other experimental cases were arranged and carefully observed, with the result that the cause in the bite of the *aëdes calopus,* formerly called *stegomyia fasciata* mosquito, was determined, and the successful treatment and prevention of the disease were made possible.[4] More than thirty years later a pension was granted one of the persons used in these experiments, whose health had suffered.

[4] See *Walter Reed, a Memoir,* Walter D. McCaw.

About the same time as the above events the Liverpool School of Tropical Medicine sent Doctor Walter Myers and Doctor H. E. Durham to Para to study yellow fever. Both of these men contracted the malady and Myers died on January 20, 1901. By such sacrifices are human health and welfare assured.

The account of the discovery of the use of chloroform as an anæsthetic by Sir James Young Simpson furnishes another instance of risks taken for the sake, not alone of science, but of humanity. With his associates, Doctors Duncan and Keith, Simpson employed in his experiments the hazardous method of inhaling various substances, but there was no valuable result. Finally it occurred to him to try the contents of a small bottle of chloroform which he had set aside as of no likely value. The tumblers were newly charged, and inhalations were resumed. Soon those making the tests were seized with an unwonted hilarity; they became happy and loquacious, praising the delicious aroma of the new fluid. Suddenly sounds seemed to be heard similar to those of a cotton mill. Next came quiet, and then—a crash. When Doctor Simpson awakened his first thought was that he had found an anæsthetic far stronger and better than ether. He discovered that he was prone on the floor, and that his comrades were much alarmed.

Among modern perils of students in various fields it may be mentioned in passing that X-ray operators have in certain instances been attacked by invisible radiations which brought on slow and lingering death. Nevertheless, observations, experiments, and efforts to apply occult forces to the cure of human ills go steadily forward, as does the practice of callings which science has evoked, telegraph and wireless operation, engineering and others, which are attended often by the gravest perils.

Among early X-ray students and investigators two

Frenchmen made extreme sacrifices. In the hope of curing cancer, Professor Emile Bergonie conducted researches which caused severe burns, and induced in him the disease he was fighting. Racked with pain and partly numbed by opiates, he directed medical workers for three years after the loss of his right arm and part of his left hand. Charles Vaillant, of Paris, continued his investigations until both arms were infected and amputated. These men were awarded Legion of Honor decorations. The former received the Grand Cross of the Legion on his death-bed, and the latter was given the Gold Medal of Paris and the Carnegie Medal for Heroism. Frederick Henry Baetjer, of Johns Hopkins, belongs in the class of these distinguished men. His researches cost him an eye and the loss by X-ray ulcers of eight fingers. More than three-score operations occasioned by his labors were performed on this determined and dauntless benefactor of humanity. "I'll die with my boots on," Doctor Baetjer declared after one of his last operations. It is said that experiments with the use of radium in the cure of cancer have cost the lives of nearly eight-score scientists.

The study of Rocky Mountain spotted fever claimed four victims in 1924. Doctors T. B. McClintock, Arthur McCray, W. E. Gettinger, and Henry Cowan, working on the belief of Howard Taylor Ricketts that the cause of this dangerous disease is the bite of a tick from an infected animal, contracted the malady and died. Doctor Ricketts shortly after gave his own life in Mexico where he and a colleague established the fact that typhus is communicated by the body louse. Thousands of lives were saved by these sacrifices. Maurice C. Hall, of the United States Department of Agriculture, risked his all on a theory concerning the cure for hookworm. Carbon tetra-chloride was found to overcome the evil in the case of animals. What effect would the chemical have upon human beings? In order to find out, Doctor Hall took the remedy himself with no bad effects, and it was said that success attended use of the specific indicated.

Miss Alice C. Evans was elected president of The American Bacteriologist Society, December 30, 1927. At the time she was in the Marine Hospital, Norfolk, Virginia, suffering from the latest of several attacks of Malta fever, contracted five years previously when studying the disease. Her election was a recognition of the importance of her discoveries in this investigation, and also of her work concerning infantile paralysis and sleeping sickness.

New revelations of truth in natural as well as in other spheres of investigation have often met with misunderstanding and opposition. Among those who suffered from disparagement of other scientists or from public disapproval one may mention Vesalius, Harvey, Steno, Laënnec, Jenner, Young, Ohm, and Pasteur.

Many were the discouragements which in earlier times attended the work of inventors. They often encountered opposition and even persecution, sometimes based on mere prejudice, and sometimes on threatened personal and corporate interests. Many instances might be recalled. James Watt was badly treated and grievously annoyed by the Cornish miners despite the fact that his condensing-engine and other remarkable mechanical devices were of the utmost value to their industry. Lukin, and especially Greathead, saved thousands of people by the invention of lifeboats. The former went to his grave "a neglected and disappointed man." The very date of Greathead's death is not certainly known, and "it is beyond a doubt that he was carried to his last resting-place 'unwept, unhonored and unsung.'" James Hargreaves, inventor of the spinning-jenney, was an object of jealousy because he could produce more yarn than his neighbors. The latter broke into his dwelling and destroyed his machine. He felt obliged to remove to Nottingham. After refusing 3,000 pounds for his patent, it was declared invalid, because he had sold a few machines before taking it out. The only public recognition his work received was a small bounty granted nearly seventy years after his death to his last surviving daughter. Sir Richard Arkwright, whose spinning-machine greatly extended the cotton manufacture of the British Empire, suffered from envy and passion on the part of competitors, but his unusual genius enabled him to surmount all difficulties. He made a fortune and was knighted for public service. Edmund Cartwright invented the power loom. Other manufacturers and their weavers were angered by his success, and the latter destroyed five hundred of his machines. However, he patented other inventions, and Parliament gave him a grant of considerable size. John Kay, who created the fly-shuttle and a power loom for the weaving of narrow goods, was not so fortunate as were those who have been mentioned. His devices so embittered the working classes that they stole his machines, wrecked his house and made it necessary for him to flee to France, where he died in poverty, a martyr of applied science.

The experience in Georgia of Eli Whitney, inventor of the cotton gin, is widely regarded as a lasting blot on the record of the State. His machine was stolen and it was impossible to secure any redress. The hostility of the mob drove him from the State only to find that the influence of those who had profited by these outrages, or who hoped to do so, still followed him. Several States promised Whitney royalties for the wealth received from his labors, but did nothing; the Carolinas, to their credit be it said, proving to be the exceptions. North Carolina gave him a royalty, and South Carolina, a payment of fifty thousand dollars. These sums were wholly used up, however, by expenses of lawsuits and of the steps necessary to protect the patents from infringement. To complete these indignities, the Southern delegation in Congress succeeded in preventing his patent renewals, thus robbing Mr. Whitney of any compensation whatever for the invention, which has proved to be of vast commercial value to the South. Everywhere his machine was in successful use, its merits were universally acknowledged, but the genius who produced it was allowed to beg at the doors for justice which never came. The experiences of Charles Goodyear were similar to those of Whitney. In 1858 the United States commissioner of patents said, "No inventor probably has ever been so harassed, so trampled upon, so plundered by that sordid and licentious class of infringers known in the parlance of the world as pirates!" Goodyear was worn out with work and disappointment, died insolvent, and left his family heavily in debt.

It is interesting to note the change of attitude toward invention which has taken place almost universally. Those who create new products of genius and skill are now honored, and are usually well rewarded. Nevertheless, as a rule, men of ability to achieve something original have to toil unremittingly and overcome multiplied difficulties. When they succeed, they often become the victims of those who seek to rob them of the productivity of their labors. Machines are sometimes stolen and patented by the thieves. Expensive litigation consumes earned profits. Inasmuch as scientists, like other professional men, are by no means always good financiers, and are often too trustful, such advantage is sometimes taken of their confidence as that which robbed Lesueur in his advanced years of his entire fortune, to enrich an unscrupulous attorney and supposed friend of the family. In various instances clever impostors have taken the very laurels from the brows of those whom posterity would delight to praise. Despite all, men to whom, as it was said of Watt, invention is martyrdom go forward with undertakings which engross their thoughts, rob them of rest and drain their very life-blood. An inner urge impels them to a fidelity which in its results upon their lives and happiness allies them with all loyal and martyrly spirits.

Not only inventors, but those who have made valuable physical discoveries have often suffered from prejudice and from professional jealousy. William Harvey, who completed and demonstrated the work of Fabricius and Servetus as to the circulation of the blood, said that his labors had resulted in additions to knowledge so new and unheard of that he feared only evil from the ill will which they aroused. "I am afraid," he exclaimed, "of having all men for my enemies," and, indeed, not a physician of maturer years and influence took his part, while he was violently attacked by Pliolanus, Primerosius, and Parisanus. He was also a sufferer from the bitter political partisanship of the times in which he lived. His house was burned, and the unpublished works destroyed of which Cowley mourned:

"O cursed war! Who can forgive thee this?
  Houses and towns may rise again
    And ten times easier 'tis
To rebuild Paul's than any work of his."

Joseph Priestley, one of the discoverers of oxygen, who obtained hydrochloric acid gas and sulphur dioxide, and who synthesized salammoniac, had many trials and enemies. He was a nonconformist preacher, whose chapel in Birmingham was burned by a mob. His house at Fairhill was sacked, and, while the family escaped, his material possessions and the labor of years were destroyed. Most painful of all, when he fled to London, even the fellows of the Royal Society shunned him. This seems, however, to have been a case of persecution of a scientist, but not of his science. His alleged "unorthodox" opinion, which cost him an appointment as astronomer to Captain Cook's second expedition to the South Seas, and his reputed sympathy with the democratic movement in France, were the probable causes of his misfortunes. Finally he followed his sons who had emigrated to America, and after ten years of useful activity passed away in Northumberland, Pennsylvania.

An interesting illustration of persecution based on purely personal grounds is that directed by Lord Brougham toward Thomas Young, physicist and archæologist. When Young was making known his views on the undulatory theory of light, Henry Brougham was a contributor to the *Edinburgh Review*. In some way the discoverer of "interference" had given offense to the younger man, who had scientific pretensions and some ability of his own. He used his opportunity as a writer to attack Young without scruple or remorse. He scoffed at his position in the Royal Institution and tried to have his papers excluded from "Philosophical Transactions." When Young cautiously revised any of his opinions, he held him up to ridicule as a changeling. "It is difficult," he said, "to deal with an author filled with a medium of so fickle and vibratory a nature." He said that "his productions have scarcely stamina to subsist until the fruitful parent has furnished us with a new litter." He charged him with falsely claiming inheritance to Newton, "pompously parading that Newton left as hints in a series of propositions with all the affectation of system." Young replied to Brougham's coarse assault in a masterly and exhaustive treatise, but no one at the time was able to comprehend the issue. The poison so filled the public mind that for a dozen years, until Fresnel's confirmation, the splendid work of Young was left to oblivion.

That the troubles of those who teach strange doctrines are by no means always to be attributed to the
ignorant classes or to religious prejudice is further
evidenced by the experience of A. Desmoulins.   In
1825 he announced to the French Academy that old
age atrophies and makes lighter the human brain.
Was it because this principle had already taken effect on the members that the eminent body, in wrath,
forbade Desmoulins any further appearances?   Not
only have scientists suffered in this manner, but their
friends and supporters also, as Buckland was denounced and distressed in 1827 because he sustained
the geological testimony of the rocks, as this was
revealed by scientific observers.

The case of Lavoisier, the French chemist, who
gave the final blow to the old "phlogiston" theory,
differs from that of Priestley in that the jealousy of
rivals took the place of alleged heresy.   This influence
abetted the enemies aroused by Lavoisier's political
activities.   He was a member of various bodies, such
as the Farmers-general, which fell under the disapproval of the Republic.   The Academy, of which he
was a prominent member, was held to be tainted with
incivism.   Lavoisier was driven from his house and
laboratory and, two years later, with twenty-seven
other accused persons, he was condemned to death.   It
is said that a petition asking for clemency was met
with the reply, *"La République n'a pas besoin de
savants."*   He was guillotined in the Place de la
Révolution.

Sir Marc Isambard Brunel, as he came later to be
called, was driven from his native country by reason
of having taken part in the proceedings of a political
club.   He dared to denounce some of the ferocious
doctrines then taught, and escaped proscription only
by making his way to America.   In the United States
he aided in surveying the Champlain Canal, but
after six years of this and of various architectural

undertakings, he made his home in England, where he constructed the Thames Tunnel. The political troubles of Priestley, Lavoisier, and Brunel recall the experience of the foremost mathematician of antiquity, Archimedes. He was much honored in Syracuse, Sicily, but when his native city and home were besieged by the Romans, he invented new weapons for its defense. When the Romans, after three years' effort, finally took the city, Archimedes was slain in the massacre which followed. The tradition is that the soldiery who burst into his house were particularly incensed because they found the owner absorbed in contemplation of mathematical figures which he had drawn on sand. When interrupted, he only exclaimed, "Don't disturb my circles."[5]

The history of scientific exploration has claimed many victims. We do not have in mind travelers and adventurers. Sight-seeing and hunting are not the business of science, and when men suffer from exposure or accidents incurred in the pursuit of pleasure or profit, their pains and loss are not to be given the credit which is attached to the pursuit of knowledge. Human life is so precious a possession that it is not easy to be satisfied with the reply of Tyndall to Mr. Seiler when the latter asked him whether, in view of future ascents of the Matterhorn, it would not be wise to place ropes or chains at the dangerous points. He replied that by doing so he would save life, but would spoil the mountain. Their friends have not ceased to regret the unnecessary loss of President W. E. Stone, of Purdue University, and of Doctor Frank B. Wynn, physician, naturalist and royal spirit, who perished in mountain climbing.

It was in the interest of scientific fact that Elisha Mitchell, chemist, mineralogist and geologist at the University of North Carolina, made various ascents

---

[5] In the introduction to *The Works of Archimedes,* T. L. Heath, xvii and xviii, various forms of this tradition are recounted.

and measurements in the Black Mountains of that State. He had just determined the highest point, and that it was the greatest elevation east of the Rocky Mountains, when he was killed by a fall from a precipice. On this height, now known as Mount Mitchell, the body of the discoverer, who perished in 1857, is buried.

Australia became known to the world by the explorations of the nineteenth century, which cost a number of lives. Ludwig Leickhart was either killed or died of starvation on one of his journeys there in 1848. June 24, 1925, William Curtis Farabee, anthropologist, died in Washington, Pennsylvania. Three years before he was stricken with a mysterious malady while heading an exploring expedition into the wilds of South America, and fought courageously but unsuccessfully to overcome the disease. More than twenty-five blood transfusions failed to save the life of this intrepid adventurer after knowledge. The scientist does not need to go to some remote part of the world in order to meet death by reason of his absorption in observations afield. Abut a month before the passage of Doctor Farabee a telegraphic dispatch from London, England, announced that Thomas Waddington, of the Kettering Naturalists' Museum, had been killed by a train while studying the habits of a snail which was making its way along a railroad track.

The most thrilling acts of scientific adventure have been in the work of polar exploration. The voyages and heroism of Sir John Franklin have become part of the moral inheritance of the race. Into the spirit of this intrepid leader's high purpose entered, however, another mind as bold and selfless as his own. When Franklin's arctic expedition of 1825 was ready to begin its journey, Mrs. Franklin lay upon what proved to be the bed of death. Knowing how much depended upon the venture, this remarkable woman entreated her husband, as he valued her peace and his own glory, not to delay a moment on her account, but to leave England on the appointed day. As a parting gift, she gave him a silk flag which she had prepared, and which he was to use only when the polar sea was reached. This memorial was placed on Garry Island, but long before that date the hands which had fashioned it had been numbed by a coldness which is dreaded by many as being more penetrating than that of the arctics.

In the month of May, 1845, Franklin sailed on his last voyage with two ships, Erebus and Terror. The fearful sufferings of his second expedition, when in desperate straits the company were glad to eat hides and lichens, and to consume soup from putrid flesh or bones left by the wolves, and when several of the party perished of starvation and frost, were destined to be exceeded by this adventure. Two years elapsed, and as no news of the expedition was received the British government fitted out searching parties, some of whom toiled northward by the seas between America and Greenland, some by Behring Strait. The ships for which they searched seemed to have vanished without a trace. Rae finally found Esquimaux who had relics of the Franklin party, and who reported that the ships had been abandoned. Some of the explorers were dead and others had gone on into the wilderness. Two American searching parties were sent out. Haven's expediton found nothing, nor did E. K. Kane, who sailed in 1853. The world's admiration was elicited by the frightful experiences of Kane's party and by its heroic sacrifices of labor and life. Lady Franklin, in 1857, sent out the Fox, under command of McClintock. The grave of Franklin was found on the northwest shore of King William's Island, and records showed that after his death those who yet remained sought to reach the American continent. None of them ever

arrived. The documentary evidences found showed
that Sir John had succeeded in his quest. A Northwest Passage had been discovered—too ice-bound to
be of much avail to man. Is it possible that in a universe so saving of physical substances and forces
such spirits as these have utterly perished? Who
can wonder that some unknown writer, penning a
poetical tribute to Crozier, Fitzjames, and Sir John,
would not have it so, but declared, in the faith which
outlasts the losses of time:

> "Let the wild waves roar on the frozen shore
>   That circles the icy Pole:
> For there is no sleep, no grave so deep
>   That can hold a human soul!"

A privately equipped expedition under Captain
George W. DeLong was sent northward from San
Francisco through Behring Strait in the Jeannette
in 1879. The ship was crushed and sunk. The company retreated toward the Siberian coast in three
boats, one of which, commanded by Lieutenant
Charles W. Chipp, became separated from the others
and was never seen again. One boat reached land
safely and with no losses. Captain DeLong reached
the Lena Delta, where he perished from starvation.
Only two of his party survived.

The expedition toward the north pole under A. W.
Greely, sent out by the United States government in
1881, in the steamer Proteus, was instructed to co-
operate with the work of representatives of other
nations in the establishment of circumpolar weather
stations and to secure scientific data. In this task
success was realized by the accumulation of important facts, and by the attainment of a higher latitude
(83° 24′ 5″) than had previously been reached—an
honor which England had held for three centuries.
Much scientific material was obtained, but unfortunately expected relief ships failed to arrive on time,

and nineteen of the twenty-five men under Greely's command, including Lieutenant James B. Lockwood, who had led the successful advance party, perished before help reached them at Camp Sabine.

The polar work of Nansen and Peary was attended with success, and the leaders were rewarded. The Danish expedition of Erichsen was undertaken for scientific research, but was unfortunate. Food and clothing gave out. Erichsen and his two fearless comrades struggled forward bare-footed and hungry, striving to reach a supply depot and to leave their records where they might be found. The last survivor was Brönland, who reached the depot, ate a little food, made out his report, and died. His last statement was that he had reached this place under the waning moon, but could not go on because of frozen feet and darkness, and that the bodies of the others were in the middle of the fiord. Hagen died on November 15, 1907, and Mylius Erichsen some ten days later.

Undoubtedly, the record of exploration which has most impressed the mind of the world is that of the British Antarctic Expedition, the members of which perished when attempting to return home from the south pole. The company was in command of Captain Robert Falcon Scott. This officer, with Captain Oates, Doctor E. A. Wilson, Lieutenant H. R. Bowers, and Petty Officer Edgar Evans, reached the pole on January 18, 1912. They had pulled their sledges nearly one hundred and fifty miles, and when they began the return trip the season was too far advanced for safety. The sickness and death of Officer Evans caused delay, but they pushed on, carrying heavy collections of specimens which they had acquired. All suffered severely, but Captain Oates more than the others. Of him, Captain Scott wrote: "He was a brave soul. He slept through the night, hoping not to wake, but he woke in the morning. Oates said, 'I am just going outside and I may be some time.' He went into the blizzard, and we have not seen him since." On a post near the place where Oates walked out into the wild and met the end alone is written the tribute, "Hereabouts lies a very gallant gentleman, Captain L. E. G. Oates, of the Inniskilling Dragoons." He had felt that he was about to die, and rather than delay his friends and further endanger them, he had taken himself out of the situation. Captain Scott and the remaining members of his party pushed forward as well as they were able. Finally, March 21, 1912, they were forced to encamp eleven miles from a depot where there was an abundant store of supplies. The storm was so furious that they could not leave their tent, and therefore they could only await the certain event. In two days their food was exhausted. Later Captain Scott wrote words which will long be an assurance of the courage and royalty which are resident in man at his highest elevation of spirit. "We are weak, writing is difficult, but for my own sake I do not regret this journey, which has shown that Englishmen can endure hardships, help one another, and meet death with as great a fortitude as ever in the past. We took risks—we know we took them. Things have come out against us, and therefore we have no cause for complaint, but bow to the will of Providence, determined still to do our best to the last." This message was found the following November where it had been placed, together with his diary, between the explorer's head and the tent-pole against which he leaned. It does not seem possible that the information gathered by such expeditions is worth the cost in lives like those of Franklin, DeLong, Scott, and the others who have perished in the frozen north and south. Who does not believe, however, that from the graves of such daring friends of truth there flows a stream of influence which will never cease to inspire the hearts of men to high endeavor and which will always enrich the current of human history?

The martyrology of science would not be complete without some reference to religious persecution. Before entering upon the discussion of the comparatively few names which can be mentioned in this connection, it is worth while to remark that nearly all of them represent Christian believers of life-long faith. This fact has been too generally ignored. First to be mentioned is Roger Bacon, 1214–1292. This Franciscan monk was scientist, philosopher, linguist, and theologian. So great was his learning and his mechanical skill that he was suspected of magic. In 1278 a council of his own order condemned his writings and committed him to confinement in a monastery in France for ten years, until his release by Pope Nicholas IV. His trouble was in part due to his censures of important personages, especially the noted Franciscan theologian, Alexander of Hales. He wrote various theological works, as well as books on science and philosophy. He insisted on the reading of the Bible in the original, by the laity even, if possible. He probably died at Oxford.

It is hardly likely that historians of science would care to lay claim to the student of astrology and demonology, Cecco d'Ascoli. He taught astrology at Bologna, but went to Florence in 1325. He was author of "Acerba" (Bitternesses), a poem which treated of natural science, philosophy, astrology, and other subjects. There is little reason to regard him as a man of science, properly speaking. For expression and defense of heretical views he was condemned by the Inquisition and was burned at the stake in 1327.

The one inexcusable blot on the record of John Calvin was his treatment of Michael Servetus. Servetus was a Spanish theologian and physician. Aside from his theological works, he published a *Universal*

Theory of Syrups. He is one of the anatomists who made an early approach to the discovery of the circulation of the blood. As Servetus was opposed to certain Catholic doctrines, he was arrested by the Inquisition in France but escaped to Geneva. There he was apprehended, and Calvin and other Protestant preachers aided in his prosecution, and joined with those who demanded his death. He was burned in Geneva in 1553, not because of his science, but as a religious heretic.

If Giordano Bruno, born 1548, is not to be classed as a philosopher rather than a scientist, he belongs in this list. In youth he was a Dominican, but became restive under the strict rule, fled to Rome, and became a wanderer in various parts of Europe. He was the first philosopher to espouse the Copernican theory, which he gave metaphysical interpretations. These views opposed the philosophy and science of the time, and subverted the most cherished teachings of the church. Against Aristotle he posited the absolute boundlessness of the universe. He taught that God and the world are not the same, but that God is identified with the universe or that he may be designated as matter conceived in extended substance, essentially immaterial, the immanent cause or soul of the world. Later philosophers borrowed much from him. He was condemned and burned at Rome in 1600. Three centuries later, on the spot where he died, a monument was erected to his memory. A physicist makes the comment: "The burning of Giordano Bruno is often cited as an example of the prevailing attitude of the church toward science. While it was a futile attempt to crush heresy, science was not in the least involved, as Bruno was in no sense a man of science." It may be added that Bruno's last words express his confidence that his spirit would mount up to heaven in his chariot of smoke.

Sir David Brewster's *Martyrs of Science* relates

the experiences of Galileo, Tycho Brahe, and Kepler. W. C. Curtis, zoologist, in *Science and Human Affairs* lists the names of Copernicus, Galileo, Buffon, and Darwin as sufferers for their fidelity to science. It will be well to consider what happened to these men. Copernicus was adopted and educated by his uncle, the Bishop of Ermeland. He was nominated canon of the Cathedral of Frauenburg, and while residing in the episcopal palace at Heilsberg vigorously attended to capitular duties, though he never took orders. His chief scientific teaching was approved by Clement VII. It is said that though he realized that he had solved the greatest astronomical problem he delayed to publish his book, *De Orbium Celestium Revolutionibus,* "probably from a presentiment of the persecution which is assured for great reformers and innovators." While he was afraid that ignorance would hold his discovery to be hostile to the Bible, it is also said that he had a profound reverence for the Holy Scriptures, and that none of his natural studies and conclusions shook his faith in the revelation of the gospel. He died in prosperity and honor, with the first printed copy of his book under his hand, "seeing it only as a dim object through the deepening dusk."

We are come to Tycho Brahe, descendant of a noble Swedish family, who, when his law tutor at Leipsic was asleep, read astronomy, observed the heavens, and with a mere pair of compasses detected a large error in the Alphonsine Tables. He offended his aristocratic relatives by marrying a peasant girl, and to replenish his purse he cultivated alchemy. Frederick II gave him a grant for life of an island near Copenhagen and built for him a magnificent observatory called Uraniberg or Oranienberg, "City of the Heavens." This was the finest plant of the kind which had ever been erected in Europe. There Tycho labored for twenty years, cataloguing seven hundred and seventy-seven stars and forming his theory of comets. He opposed the Copernican theory and preferred the view of our universe which seemed to him to be more consistent with the language of the Scriptures. He aroused considerable jealousy on the part of the medical profession by treating many diseased persons who, despite his lack of complete training for the practice, flocked to him for help. After his royal patron died in 1588, courtiers who envied his possessions and honors succeeded in getting his pensions withdrawn and, being unable to keep up his establishment, he migrated to Germany, where, under the patronage of the Emperor Rudolph, he settled at Prague. Kepler became his assistant for a short time only, as Tycho Brahe passed away in 1601. One can extract very little martyrdom from this account. It is affirmed that he was "a devout man, a great student of the Holy Scriptures."

The affair of Galileo, as it has been critically studied, has been found to require some amendment. It is true that his writings were condemned by the Roman Catholic Church as being revolutionary. There is no doubt that he was required by the Inquisition to recant, nor is there question that he said the words he was commanded to say. The exclamation, *"E pur se muove,"* "But nevertheless it [the earth] does move," is pronounced by some historians as fiction. He was sentenced to imprisonment, but opinion is divided as to the carrying out of the sentence, and if he was confined at all, he was permitted to carry on his studies and investigations. What was the real cause of the trouble? Certainly it is impossible to defend the Inquisition, whose infamies, however, were far greater in the case of thousands of simple Christian folk than with regard to a few scientists. Justice requires attention to both sides of every event. It seems that Galileo offended the Aristotelian philosophers, especially Scipione Chiaramonte, teacher of philosophy at Pisa, who exerted himself

to the utmost to inflame against him the populace
and the church authorities.   It is no excuse for the
latter that Galileo lacked tact and was addicted to
biting sarcasm, but his chair at Pisa where students
and faculty hissed him and accused him of magic
seems to have been lost by reason of his ridicule of
the mechanical pretensions of an illegitimate son of
Cosimo I, and by philosophical and scientific controversy.   Then came the wounding of the vanity of Pope
Urban VIII.   This prelate was angered by representations to the effect that in a dialogue written concerning his world system Galileo had satirized him
as "Simplicio," a character careless of scientific truth
and an adherent of the outworn maxims of antiquity.
In early life Galileo would have taken orders had not
his father prevented him from this course.   All his
life he is said to have been a devoted Catholic.   He
probably suffered little actual injury, except that of
the insolent prohibition of Paul V, through Bellar-
min, the moral injustice and turpitude of his com-
pulsory recantation, possibly some brief and not
severe confinement, and his enforced transfer from
the University of Pisa to the University of Padua.
There, however, he was appreciated and was twice
elected to six-year terms.   His studies finally became
difficult by reason of failing eyesight, but he seems
to have lacked no comfort or ministration.   Dying
in the year of the birth of Newton, he was buried in
the church of Santa Croce, Florence, where his splendid monument is near to that of Michael Angelo.

The celebrated astronomer Johann Kepler was unfortunate in his parentage, and was educated at the
expense of the Duke of Würtemberg.   At Tübingen
he paid particular attention to theology, and intended,
it is said, to enter the ministry.   The controversy
over the "Formula of Concord" annoyed him, and as
he opposed the doctrine of ubiquity, then an article
of the state religion, he turned from the ministry to

mathematics. An offer of the astronomical lecture-ship at Grätz, in Styria, was accepted, though he knew little about the subject, and was forced to qualify himself as he went forward. The necessary studies led him to recognize the mathematical conven-ience of the Copernican system, which he espoused. When he wrote his *Mysterium Cosmographicum* he sought to avoid persecution by consulting eminent theologians of both churches, Protestant and Catho-lic, but the faculty at Tübingen to whom he submitted his manuscript condemned it. The Duke of Würtem-berg, however, both commended the work and financed its publication. About 1600, with other Protestant professors, Kepler was driven from Grätz by persecu-tion, at which time he became assistant to Tycho Brahe, whom he later succeeded as mathematician to Emperor Rudolph at Prague. The Jesuits, anxious to employ the learning of Kepler, secured permission for his return to Grätz. His refusal to join the Cath-olic party or to eat their bread increased the opposi-tion against him. He went on, however, to the discovery of the famous laws which Sir John Herschel characterized as the most important and beautiful system of geometrical relations which have ever been discovered by a mere inductive process. The third law, which Playfair thought had a value beyond what Kepler could possibly conceive, was formulated in 1618. *The Rudolphine Tables,* published in 1627, were highly prized. He invented the astronomical telescope with two convex lenses. He was so devoted to science that he was accustomed to say that he would rather be author of his books than to possess the duchy of Saxony. He died at Ratisbon, leaving four sons and three daughters.

John Locke's persecution at Oxford University seems to have been due in the main to his devotion to the principle of civil and religious liberty, and to political enmity toward his patron, the Earl of

Shaftesbury. His *Treatises on Government* opposed
the Oxford theories. At a later time he might have
been readmitted to Oxford, but would not accept. He
was one of the fathers of mental science, a theologian
as well, and, as we shall see, a devoted Christian.
John Ray was a martyr to conscience, not to
science, since both Cambridge and the church
were closed to him because he would not declare the Solemn League and Covenant, reprobated
by the Act of Uniformity, not binding on those who
had taken it. After this refusal Ray's valuable life
was mainly one of poverty and seclusion.

Georges Louis Leclerc, Comte de Buffon, was the
son of a wealthy family, and lived in affluence. He
was educated by the Jesuits, and became a naturalist,
but was not himself an investigator nor even an
observer in the scientific sense. He wrote voluminously and picturesquely, with an eccentricity of
method which extended even to his attire when at
work. He was inaccurate and erroneous in his literary methods and results, but was very interesting
and deserves credit for the popularization of nature study and for producing in comprehensive style
the first general compilation of the achievements of
scientific work, the imposing *Histoire Naturelle,* in
which he was aided by a number of assistants. His
helper in the first fifteen volumes, Daubenton, was a
competent anatomist.[6] He expounded many weird
and fantastic hypotheses, and made wild guesses as
to the future, some of which were partially predictive
of what has since been logically established. He hastened to publish and defend, as we note elsewhere,
such pseudo-science as that so well exploded by Spallanzani, concerning spontaneous generation. It is
little wonder that he was attacked both by scientists

---

[6]For contrast between this portion of the work and that which
followed see *A Popular History of Science,* Robert Routledge, p.
406.

and by theologians of the Sorbonne. The latter, connected with the University of Paris, were required by the crown to exercise theological censorship, as the papal Index was not recognized in France. The critics of the Sorbonne marked fourteen passages of the extensive *Histoire* as being reprehensible. On hearing of this, Buffon hastened to state that no evil was intended, that his hypotheses were not meant to contradict Scripture, and to declare submission. In 1779 Buffon referred to the foolish explanation he had been forced to sign thirty years before. It seems that when criticized, he did not wish, as himself an officer of the Crown, to have trouble with another department of government. Inasmuch as both Voltaire and Marmontel acted independently in such affairs, it seems that Buffon might have done the same had he possessed the courage to risk inconvenience or possibly dismissal from his office at the Jardin du Roy. As a matter of fact, no paragraph of Buffon's work was canceled, he suffered no dismissal, and he lived and died in luxury. The honor came to him of the erection of his statue during his lifetime. It was placed at the entry of the Royal Cabinet of Natural Curiosities, and bore the inscription, *"Majestati naturae par ingenium."* He had one son, an army officer, who was executed during the reign of terror as an aristocrat.

To include in a martyrology of science, as some have done, the name of Charles Darwin, born to wealth and living to old age in comfort and in honor given only to the greatest, is simply beside the mark. Of course his theories have had to run the gantlet of opinion and prejudice, as all innovations must do. Equally of course, he has had defenders and exponents far more zealous, and a fame much more widespread than could have been secured by any other process. Curtis is wise when he finally dismisses the Darwin "martyrdom" with the observation that no

real inconvenience came to Darwin at the hands of
his critics.   A. F. Shull, in *Principles of Animal
Biology,* justly testifies that in the main churchmen
watched the early progress of evolutionary teaching
goodnaturedly.   The fact that Darwin's particular
contribution to evolutionary science never met with
universal scientific approval is evidenced not only by
the failure of certain individuals, as mentioned elsewhere, to accept his conclusions, but by the delay of
the French Academy to give him recognition.   It was
on the basis of his botanical and not his biological
achievements that he was finally honored by that
body.

In recent times Loisy was excommunicated by his
church for disloyalty to its doctrines.   There may
be two sides to such issues as this, for all the public knows, and at all events an organization must be
thought to have some right to its own judgments and
policies.   In case of Protestant preachers who sow
disaffection and division in the denominations which
they are under obligation to serve, an ethical question is involved which is not necessarily related to
scientific doctrines which they teach.   Science has
had its suffering sons, but such as these hardly rank
among them.   Nor has religious persecution very
seriously affected the progress of science, except,
sometimes very unwisely and in at least a few instances fortunately, to delay general acceptance of
new teachings. Therefore, is it not unreasonable, if
it be true, that "men of science are still under the
delusion that they are hounded by a host of enemies,"
especially the representatives of religion?   One who
has spent his whole life in scientific pursuits says of
the centuries preceding the Renaissance that "there
is little or no evidence of definite and organized opposition to science by the church."

Even if the statement too often appearing that the
church has always been the persecutor of science were

sustained by far more evidence than the above or any other known facts indicate, it would still be true that science has had no monopoly on suffering from persecution.   Military and naval leaders have been cruelly mistreated for the wrongdoing of others, as was Admiral Byng, who was shot, in 1756, for the failure of the British expedition against Minorca. Political leaders have been outrageously treated and even hounded to death, not only for errors of judgment but for their sanity, honesty, and vision. George Washington was lied about and was in peril from enemies in his own ranks.   All the world knows what fate befell Lincoln, who had previously endured much abuse and treachery at the seat of government. William E. Gladstone's career was marked by malicious misrepresentations, continued, and legally rebuked, long after his death.   Whole races, notably the Jews, have suffered persecutions of many types. Christianity has a roll of martyrs in the cause of truth, goodness, and love which can be duplicated in no other history.   Persecution is by no means to be palliated or to be excused, but neither is it to be held before the mind as if confined to one party.[7]   "It is quite certain to me," says L. T. More, "that men of science have greatly exaggerated repressive measures by the church."[8]   If this judgment be not accepted, let the comfortable truth be noted that opposition is the lot of creators, and a badge of honor.   Fortunately it has become less common and cruel, but it is well to remember, as it disappears before the light of advancing knowledge, that it has not been in vain.

---

[7]David Starr Jordan's sensible view of this matter may be found in *Footnotes to Evolution*.   This naturalist-educator holds that in the real sense of it conservation lies not in theology.   He compares with the spirit which burned Servetus and Bruno the attitude of the Parisian "liberals" who sent Lavoisier to the scaffold.   Gladstone's rejection of natural selection is paralleled with Haeckel's condemnation of the views of Weismann.

[8]*Dogma of Evolution*, Princeton University Press, p. 84, nota.

Every cause which had enough life in it so that some would toil and die therefor has been prospered, just as "the blood of the martyrs was the seed of the church." It may also be remarked that while religious leaders are learning that there is no Christian value in *odium theologicum,* equally fair-minded scientists have been discovering the parallel truth that *odium anti-theologicum* is by no means a fruitful scientific method.

It must not be forgotten that the greater glory of science has not been in the labors, sacrifices and trials of a few exalted persons, but in the toil, self-denial, and devotion of many to scientific observation, experimentation, invention, discovery. By the investment of time, strength, resources, and the values of life, obscure, unknown, and poorly requited men, as well as others more fortunate, have made possible the vast enrichment of this wonderful age, and have placed humanity forever in their debt. Moreover, the teachers of the world, not a few of whom have regarded the impartation of scientific truth as being quite as important as invention or discovery, and who have given to human needs their best of knowledge and spiritual character, have often wrought at such cost in consecration and self-abandonment as not only deserves the highest praise but entitles them to rank among the Heroes and Martyrs of Science.

Perhaps no greater praise can be paid to scientific heroes of every type than to say of them that few even of those who labored most arduously or suffered most severely from the effects of their efforts ever thought of themselves as martyrs. We view them in this way, but it has been justly said that "they regarded themselves as adventurers rather than as martyrs." It is, after all, the love of adventure, of investigation and of discovery that is one of the strongest elements in scientific achievement. That it is not the love of fame in most instances is shown by the fact that "after the discovery is made it is mere drudgery to prepare it for presentation to the world."

When any good work in scientific exploration and progress has been accomplished, and its value proved, the church has taken a prominent part in giving praise to those responsible for the results. The space in Westminster Abbey granted the remains and memorials of Sir Isaac Newton had often been refused to the greatest nobility,[9] and let it not be forgotten by those who discuss the attitude of the church to science that Charles Darwin was also given a place of honor in that sacred temple, not alone of national pride but of Christian faith.

[9]*The Life of Sir Isaac Newton*, Sir David Brewster, p. 323.

CHAPTER VIII

CHRISTIAN MEN OF SCIENCE

In an admirable address on "Religion and Education," delivered in October, 1924, Ernest De Witt Burton, President of the University of Chicago, not only acclaimed Jesus as "the world's greatest thinker in the field of religion," but represented him as the author of the much applauded scientific approach to truth. "The method," he said, "by which Jesus dealt with religion in his day is essentially one with that which the world has now in modern times discovered to be the best and only method of dealing with all problems that have relation to human life. In short, Jesus was the first great exemplar of the scientific spirit as the most enlightened men of science understand and practice it to-day. He faced facts squarely, made them, rather than opinions, however ancient and honorable, the guide of his thinking and the basis of his action, set facts in relation to one another, penetrated beneath their surface to find their meaning, brought imagination into service, and to all that mere induction or deduction could prove added an estimate of values and a strong element of faith. Slowly the world is learning that this is the best way to think." Who can feel any sense of surprise, if this be a true estimate, that President Burton should declare that no college can afford not to give Jesus and the religion of Jesus a central place in its life and plans? He clinched his argument by pointing out that Jesus not only had the right way of thinking, but that "he reached right conclusions, and realized an ideal of character than which we can think of no better." He said that because of what he was, as well as thought, and because "the prime business of the

221

college is to develop personalities, Jesus ought to be an ever present force in the life of the college."[1]

It is evident that throughout the long period of the history of modern science many of its exponents and most of its greatest representatives have looked upon Christ and Christianity in much the same way as did the educator whose views were stated in this striking manner. It will not be claimed that any considerable number of scientists have been members of the Two Seed in the Spirit Predestinarians. We have not determined how many were or are connected with the New Dunkers, the Pillar of Fire or the *Kleine Gemeinde*. There is one church, and all who in their hearts acknowledge its Head and share in its life, whether Anglicans or Non-Conformists, Lutherans or Methodists, Protestants or Catholics, are fellow members. Are we able to go further and say, There is one church; but more folds than one: Jesus said, "And other sheep I have, which are not of this fold: them also I must bring, and they shall hear my voice; and they shall become one flock, one shepherd."

Who are the Christian men? the confessors? Undoubtedly, if they are also possessors of the life in Christ. But what in cases where we know of no profession? Certainly, we cannot forget that training and circumstances make great differences in such items as public confession, membership in organizations and outward demonstrations, important as these are to our thinking and to the various systems of faith. Without denying the obligation of open discipleship when the privilege and duty are clearly seen, may not the previously quoted saying of the Master himself have some bearing upon our judgment, "By their fruits ye shall know them"? At all events, against one thing we protest, namely, the

[1]"Religion and Education," pp. 22 and 23, The University of Chicago Press.

attempt to divide classes of people arbitrarily, and
to say, These groups only are Christians, for their
views conform to our own standards of religious
thought and practice.

It would be just as erroneous, though not as harmful, to suppose that the representative Christian men
named in this chapter arrived at their religious conceptions or maintained them in the same manner.
They differed as have others in beliefs, in experiences,
and in expressions of faith. What is here maintained
is simply that there is justification for the claim that
science has afforded illustrious examples of men who
acknowledged allegiance to Jesus Christ, and that the
names which are cited are among the number of those
who by the testimony of observers displayed qualities
which are properly attributed to Christian character.
If criticism as to teaching or life may be directed
against any of them, it is surely fair to remember
that the same might occur were the illustrations
chosen from the ranks of poets, statesmen, literati,
or even of theologians. Whatever may be thought of
perfectibility in man, perfection is to be attributed
to One only.

It is but right that the greatest intellects should
acknowledge their belief in God, and that they should
accept Jesus Christ as their Teacher, Saviour, and
Lord. Nevertheless Christianity—the human organization—has much cause to rejoice in the personalities
which adorn her history. Moreover, no branch of
knowledge or form of lay activity has furnished to
Christian records a greater proportion of its most
distinguished names than has science. As they were
returning from Westminster Abbey after the funeral
of Lord Kelvin, Joseph Larmor remarked to Sir
Archibald Geikie, "Conceive a perfectly level line
drawn from the summit of Newton's genius across all
the intervening generations, probably the only man
who has reached it in these two centuries has been

Kelvin." An interesting statement and estimate of greatness! And not the least significant feature is that both of these towering peaks in the range of human knowledge and achievement are illustrations of humility in the presence of God and of close affiliation with the Christian religion.

Whose are the figures which stand out as colossi on the headlands of scientific history? Are they those of enemies of Christian faith, of atheists and scoffers, or is there sufficient ground for the claim that our most godlike knowledge comes from the most godlike minds? What a roll it is which, together with most talented artists, most inspiring poets, most illustrious rulers, most generous philanthropists, most eloquent preachers, bears inscribed upon it in letters of gold: Roger Bacon, Nicolaus Copernicus, Galileo Galilei, Johann Kepler, William Hunter, Robert Boyle, Blaise Pascal, Isaac Barrow, Isaac Newton, Gottfried Wilhelm Leibnitz, Carl von Linné, Joseph Priestley, John Dalton, Georges Cuvier, Humphry Davy, André Marie Ampère, Michael Faraday, Joseph Henry, James Clerk Maxwell, David Brewster, John F. W. Herschel, Claude Bernard, James Young Simpson, Joseph Lister, Louis Pasteur, Lord Kelvin, and a host of others! Men now living, only a few of whom are mentioned in this book, belong to the same illustrious company. In view of the nature of their labors, and of their necessary absorption in them, it is remarkable how many profound students of all times have thought and acted as Christian men.

While we may not reveal too freely the intimate secrets of contemporary character, after a time men feel perfectly free to disclose what they have known concerning personal friends. Historians also gather information from original sources of many kinds. Diaries, letters, legal papers, memoirs, treasured relics, conversations with relatives, business associates and chance acquaintances, as well as newspapers and books, furnish facts whose reliability may be tested by comparison with each other, by historical and personal verifications, and by various well-known laws of evidence. It is sometimes said that history is a blunder and biography a lie, but this is cheap and unworthy pessimism. It is as certain as anything can be that we have, in the main, very trustworthy knowledge concerning the eminent characters who have been among God's best gifts to the world.

"When it has all come out," we know that Lord Bacon was a rather weak kind of Christian. In theory he was profoundly religious, and he was by no means as dissolute as ordinary men of the world in his day. Frail is the word! He deserves much pity for his faults and considerable credit for his periods of virtue, characterized by noble thoughts and acts. He must not, however, be quoted as a typical example of what we now regard as being Christian character.

Far earlier than the times of the Earl of Verulam, another Bacon—Roger—was a man of profound reverence for the Scriptures, of full acceptance of Christ, of true humility and strong faith, of toleration and charity, and of deep conviction of the close connection between religion and science. He was a Franciscan monk, who gathered up into his *"Opus Majus"* such knowledge as the sciences then possessed. He did some advanced work in optics, made remarkable scientific prophecies, and may have given Sir Francis Bacon the germinal thoughts of *"Novum Organum."* "A man before his age!" As we have seen, judges of his own order condemned his theories and caused his imprisonment. He is said to have discovered gunpowder, and he wrote a *Compendium of Theology*— two somewhat dynamic achievements.

A unique character, partly chemist and partly alchemist, Nicolas Flamel, scrivener of the University of Paris during the latter part of the thirteenth century, is said to have acquired great wealth. He spent a good part of his resources in the erection of churches and in works of charity. Half of his estate was left to the church in Paris in which his body was laid to rest.

Nicolas Copernik, better known by the Latin name Copernicus, is described as a man who was devoutly religious, full of faith and prayer. Stoughton says, "He had lived a life of ·Christian virtue—imitating his Master, who went about doing good, healing the sick and preaching the gospel to the poor—yet so far from having anything whereof to boast before God, he said himself that he felt his need of infinite mercy; and in seeking the pardon of his sins he would not place himself on a level with Paul or Peter, but, rather, chose a point in self-humiliation by the side of the penitent thief."[2] The latter statement is evidently based on the record that shortly before he expired Copernicus repeated this saying:

> "Non parem Paulo gratiam requiro,
> Veniam· Petri neque posco; sed quam
> In crucis ligno dederat latroni
> Sedulus oro."

In modern times, much is made of the disturbance to Christian belief which came from the Copernican Theory. Let it again be recorded, however, that it was said of Copernicus himself that neither his profound reverence for the Scriptures nor his Christian faith was shaken by his scientific discoveries. He was a regular attendant at Frauenburg Cathedral, and was much engaged in charitable tasks.

In the preceding chapter it was stated that Tycho Brahe, Galileo, and John Kepler were men of undoubted piety. Despite life-long bad health and family troubles, Kepler is said to have maintained courage, cheerfulness, and a truly religious spirit.

---

[2]*Worthies of Science,* John Stoughton, pp. 42, 43.

When Blaise Pascal was a boy of twelve he diagramed with charcoal a proposition corresponding to the thirty-second problem of the first book of Euclid. At sixteen he wrote a small treatise on conic sections, and at eighteen produced a calculating machine. By the time he was twenty-six he was not only famous for his mathematical ability but for his experiments in hydrostatics and pneumatics. Soon after this he gave up his scientific labors and devoted himself wholly to religion, except when he prepared a remarkable solution of the problem of the Cycloid. Hallam declared that Pascal was able to annihilate the arguments of Voltaire and Macaulay affirmed that the intellectual powers he possessed were such as have been rarely bestowed on any of the children of men. Henry Rogers, in the *Edinburgh Review,* said: "Upon all the great features of his moral character one dwells with the serenest delight. Greatly as he is to be admired he is yet more to be loved. His humility and simplicity, conspicuous as his genius and acquisitions, were those of a very child." Pascal's theory of belief was that it is an affair of the heart. He had a strong personal reliance on Jesus Christ. "What he professed, he believed, and what he believed, he practiced." He was a Jansenist, and another Saint Bernard. When he spoke all Europe read and admired, laughed and wept. Though a devout Catholic he did not like the Jesuits. They tried to answer his exposures of their policies, but only to their injury. A work, the *Pensées,* which he was preparing, on the fundamental principles of religion and the evidence of Christianity, was never completed, and now exists only in fragmentary but profound and momentous notes. G. L. Strachey ranks Pascal as in sheer genius one of the very greatest writers who ever lived upon the earth.

Robert Boyle was discoverer of the law (Boyle's law) which Mariotte independently stated several years later, that the volume of a gas varies inversely as the pressure. With Robert Hooke he constructed a "Pneumatical Engine" and experimented on the properties of air, discovering the part taken by air in the propagation of sound. Both applied and theoretical chemistry owed much to his labors. Boyle is said to have possessed devoutness of spirit in connection with the investigation of divine works. He is also reported to have been a man whose "piety sanctified all his doings; it was not a theory, but a practice." Of this chemist and experimental philosopher, it was Hallam's opinion that no Englishman of the seventeenth century after Lord Bacon raised to himself so lofty a reputation in experimental philosophy. He was one of the founders of the Royal Society, but declined election as president. He repeatedly refused peerages offered him. He wrote *Reconcilableness of Reason and Religion, The Studies of Natural Philosophy Favorable to Religion,* and other works related to Christian themes. He printed and circulated an Irish Bible at his own expense. He was greatly interested in missionary work among the American Indians, contributing to this cause three hundred pounds a year during his life and leaving a legacy for the same purpose. Another of Boyle's legacies was fifty pounds a year for a lectureship on the evidences of Christianity, and in opposition to infidelity. He had the Gospels and Acts translated for the Malays, and assumed the expense of a Turkish New Testament.

John Locke, author of the *Essay Concerning the Human Understanding,* whose place in the history of mental science seems secure, is not only commended for his extensive knowledge of philosophy, medicine, and the whole range of the sciences of his age, but for his genius, penetration, and judgment. It is further asserted that he was no less distinguished for his virtues and piety than for his extraordinary intellectual endowments. All his writings (would that this might be said of many another) had for their object the improvement of mankind in knowledge, liberty and virtue. Locke extolled the goodness of God, the provision made for salvation through faith in Jesus Christ, and the value, as he had experienced it personally, of the knowledge of our Saviour. He lived in full communion with the Church of England, but was strongly opposed to its exclusive doctrines. These facts are enhanced by the tributes paid him by Sydenham, LeClerc, and others. Aside from his better-known books, he wrote on *The Reasonableness of Christianity,* 1695, a discourse on miracles, and *Commentaries on the Epistles of St. Paul.* He drew up in ten paragraphs his idea of a pure Christian community, under the title "Pacific Christians." It is said that Locke's last word was, "Oh, the depth of the riches of the goodness and knowledge of God!"

The many writings and the memorials of John Ray, "ablest botanist and zoologist of his day," who first divided herbs into monocotyledons and dicotyledons, and whose researches traversed the whole domain of natural history, give convincing evidence of his attachment to the teachings and life of the Christian religion. Perhaps his most celebrated work is called *The Wisdom of God Manifested in the Works of Creation.* The date was 1690, and in 1700 he wrote a book devoid of cant on *A Persuasive to a Holy Life.* In his *History of Plants* he states his motive in studying nature: First (*primo*), for the illustration of divine glory, since the indescribable variety of plants, their surpassing beauty, their wonderful order, and their great usefulness are among the most striking evidences (*luculentissima indicia*) and arguments of the infinite power, wisdom, and goodness of the Supreme Artificer."[3] Ray had a deep reverence for

---

[3]Vol. i, Prefatio, 3rd paragraph, London, 1686.

divine revelation, and accepted fully the gospel as given in the New Testament. A memorandum on the death of his mother, which is found in the *Memorials*, closes by saying, "Yet have I good hope that her soul is received to the mercy of God, and her sins pardoned, through the merits and mediation of Jesus Christ, in whom she trusted, and whose servant she hath been from her youth up."[4] A prayer of John Ray on the death of a friend contains these supplications: "Give us a sanctified use of these heavy afflictions, and when our hearts are moved and affected with a sense of our loss, give us to consider our sins, and to spend some part of our tears in lamenting them. Give us to consider the vanity and uncertainty of our lives, and the emptiness of all things here below to satisfy the vast desires of our immortal souls."[5] Ray was a loyal and consistent member of the Church of England.

Nicholas Steno, Danish anatomist, found and described the duct of the parotid gland. He explained the nature of fossil animals and the stratification of rocks. He wrote a *Treatise on the Muscles and Glands* and a book on brain anatomy. At length he decided to give his life to the church, and was made a Catholic bishop and vicar apostolic in northern Germany.[6] Sir Archibald Geikie assigns Steno a high place among founders of modern geology.[7]

Gottfried Wilhelm Leibnitz was a historian, a jurist, a mathematician, a geologist and a philosopher. In his *Theodicée* he expressed the thought that "it becomes us to judge of the works of God not less wisely than Socrates judged of those of Heraclitus, when he said, 'What I understand pleases me well; and I believe that the rest would please me, if I under-

---

[4] *Memorials of John Ray*, Life by William Derham, p. 37, nota.
[5] *Ibid.*, "Prayers," p. 57.
[6] Various references in *What Civilization Owes to Italy*, James J. Walsh.
[7] *The Founders of Geology*, p. 60.

stood it.' " Leibnitz declined election to the Academy
of Science of Paris rather than abjure his Protestant
religion.   Another martyr?   Leibnitz inclined toward a moderate Calvinism.   He tried to form a plan
to reunite Catholicism and Protestantism.

A great thing is affirmed of Barrow, Newton's
predecessor and teacher at Cambridge, namely, that
he practiced what he preached and was a "beautiful
example of Christian virtue."   Both scientist and
profound pulpiteer, he combined the love of nature
and the love of God in a personality which imparted
its strength to his matchless pupil, and which flowered
in the glory of his devoted life.   Montucla spoke en-
thusiastically *de ce savant géomètre,* and praised the
fertility of Barrow's ideas as a man.   Archbishop
Tillotson regarded him of all whom he knew "freest
from offending in word; coming as near as is possible
for human frailty to do to the perfect idea of St.
James." Would that in every generation such divine
preceptors might orb their wisdom in like peerless
pupils!

The "great glory of the Royal Society" and the
chief of all Cambridge dons was Sir Isaac Newton.
Newton was the posthumous son of a farmer. Between
the years of twelve and eighteen, when he entered
college, he had shown much mechanical ability, having constructed a sundial, a waterclock, and a wind-
mill.   He also wrote verses.   His preparation for
Cambridge was slight, but Euclid seemed to him
elementary, and within three years he had gone
through Kepler's *Optics,* Descartes' *Geometry,* and
Wallis' *Arithmetica Infinitorum.*   Immediately after
his graduation, and during his absence from Cambridge on account of the plague, he discovered the
binomial theorem, and the direct and inverse method
of fluxions, and had computed the area of the hyper-
bola.   This is by no means the place to attempt a
description of Newtonian physics, of the work of

this genius in the field of optics or of his contributions to mathematical knowledge. His chief hypothesis, the theory of gravitation, while it has not been absolutely demonstrated beyond the limits of actual observation and experiment, is to this day described as the key which resolved primeval chaos into harmonious cosmos. It is not surprising that the lapse of centuries has required revision of some of his theories, and has reversed some conclusions which he seemed fully to demonstrate. When these reductions have been made, the fame of Newton still shines resplendent, and is one of the permanent achievements of the race.

It is doubtful whether any character of history, save one, has ever received such tributes of praise and admiration as have been lavished upon Sir Isaac Newton. In his own day, he suffered considerable annoyance from envy, prejudice, and opposition, but also received many honors. He served as a member of Parliament from Cambridge, and for twenty-four years, until his death, was annually re-elected president of the Royal Society. During most of this time his surpassing services were but meagerly rewarded in terms of money. It is said that the reason Newton never married was because during the whole of his youth he was too poor to ask another to share his fortunes. At length he was knighted by Queen Anne, and toward the end of his life he became prosperous. With it all—despite his intense labors, his preoccupations, his successes—he was human and kindly in his relations with others, and looked upon his own attainments with modesty. Bishop Christopher Wordsworth, who wrote *The Newtonian System; Its Analogy to Christianity,* pays deep respect to Newton's work and worth: "No one since the creation has ever so clearly unfolded as Newton has done the laws by which the material world is regulated, or has done the work with more of that reverential and devout spirit of faith and love which is the fairest ornament of the Christian philosopher."[8]

Spencer believed that devotion to science is a tacit worship. Newton, however, was not content with a religion of nature.

> "For his was not the cold philosophy
> Which, finding Law throughout the Universe,
> Believes the world drives on beneath the curse
> Of soulless Force and blind Necessity;
> But, reading still above the unfolded Law,
> Love's revelation touched his soul with awe."

On one occasion Newton declared, "I find more sure marks of the authenticity of the Bible than of any profane history whatever." John Locke, in one of his letters, refers to Newton's "great knowledge in the Scriptures, wherein I know few his equals."[9] A higher tribute, however, was that of his own life. "That the greatest philosopher of which any age can boast," says Brewster, his biographer, "was a sincere and humble believer in the leading doctrines of our religion, and lived conformably to its precepts, has been justly regarded as a proud triumph of the Christian faith."[10] The great philosopher wrote books on the prophets and arguments in proof of Deity. The latter were in a series of four letters to Doctor Bentley. *Observations on the Prophecies of Daniel and the Apocalypse of John* was printed in 1733.

The accounts which describe Newton as becoming so absorbed in abstruse calculations and researches that his physical appetites were inhibited are circumstantial and must be accepted. As he never married, he was free to put his whole heart into the chief

---

[8]Vide *Miscellanies Literary and Religious*, vol. iii, "Religion in Science," p. 2.

[9]*Life and Letters of Locke*, Lord King, p. 263.

[10]*The Life of Sir Isaac Newton*, Sir David Brewster, p. 269. Brewster disproves a statement that Newton was an Anti-Trinitarian. Biot also states that nothing in Newton's writings can be so construed.

passions of his career, science and religion. That his exceptional powers were retained into old age is shown by such incidents as that of the test problem which Leibnitz sent to England "for the purpose of feeling the pulse of English analysts." It was proposed as a severe test of expert mathematics. Newton was then seventy-five years of age. After a busy day at the Mint on the subject of the coinage of the country, at 5 P. M. this problem was handed him. He solved it that evening, proving, it has been justly asserted, that, whatever the case may be with self-assured youngsters who interpret Q. E. D. to mean "quite easily done," there are minds to which the most abstruse questions are relatively simple.

Some of the legends which have gathered around the name of Newton have been disproved, but the testimony of contemporaries and of Sir David Brewster, who had full access to the papers and relics of this lofty genius, remains as a permanent memorial of the devotion to the truths of the physical universe and of Christianity of one who has been called "pure intelligence," "Columbus of the skies," and "Priest of Nature."

One of the greatest mathematicians of the eighteenth century was the Swiss, Leonhard Euler. He wrote half of the forty-six volumes published by the Saint Petersburg Academy during more than fifty years. He is described as an inventive genius of high order, and as a profoundly religious man who conducted regular family worship in his household. He was afflicted with blindness during the last sixteen years of his life, but the mathematician Condorcet testifies that he preserved a calm and serene spirit.

Carl von Linné, better known as Linnæus, the eminent Swedish botanist, whose work is called the starting point of modern nomenclatorial rulings, began and ended his most important works with Scripture verses. As we have seen, he believed that he was attended in his scientific labors by the divine presence. Macgillivray says that in all his writings appears a deep feeling of reverence and gratitude to the Supreme Being.[11] Over the door of his room was the motto: *"Innocui vivite, Numen adest"*—"Live innocently, for God is present." On his excursions and in his lectures he delighted to speak of the greatness and glory of the Creator and Preserver of all things. *Through the Fields with Linnæus*[12] informs us that in 1773 he was selected as a member of a committee to superintend the better translation of the Bible. The task of ascertaining and describing the plant and vegetable productions to which reference is made in Holy Scripture was intrusted to his care.

On the testimony of Benjamin Rush, David Rittenhouse, astronomer and statesman, was a believer in the Christian revelation, to which he gave many proofs, not alone "in the conformity of his life to the precepts of the gospel but in his letters and conversation."[13] Rittenhouse succeeded Franklin as president of the Philosophical Society, Philadelphia. As Fontana also did independently, he brought spider lines into use in astronomical instruments, and anticipated modern discoveries about the Milky Way.

John Michell, a pioneer of the modern science of seismology, gained attention by a remarkable essay on earthquakes, and became a geologist at Cambridge. He invented the torsion balance and wrote a *Treatise of Artificial Magnets*. Gradually his strong religious interest led him into ministerial work, and he became rector at Saint Botolph's, Cambridge, and for the last twenty-six years of his life at Thornhill, Yorkshire.[14] At about the same period the Abbé Geraud-Soulavie

---

[11]*Lives of Eminent Zoologists*, p. 369.

[12]Florence Caddy.

[13]*Memoirs of the Life of David Rittenhouse*, William Barton, p. 501.

[14]Vide *The Founders of Geology*, Geikie, p. 222.

planted the earliest seeds of stratigraphical geology in France. Abraham Gottlob Werner, geologist and mineralogist, who gave scientific standing to the theory of the formation of the earth, classifying the rock layers of its crust, was a devoted churchman.

The discoverer of vaccination, Edward Jenner, first also to hint at a possible relation between heart disease and rheumatism, a generous humanitarian spirit, was thoroughly religious, and was not reluctant to make known his attitude on this subject. He believed in nature study as an approach to knowledge of the Creator, and he felt that religious training was essential to sound education. He expressed consciousness of the omnipresence of Deity.[15] His repartee when introduced by the celebrated preacher, Rowland Hill, as one who had saved more lives than any other man is oft quoted. He said, "Ah, would I like you, could say souls."[16]

Pierre Simon Laplace, mathematical and physical astronomer, who has been called "the Newton of France," and whose name is associated with the "nebular hypothesis," was born and died a Catholic. This is perhaps the place to record the fact that among the names of "good Catholics" in the field of science are listed the physiologists Vesalius, Fabricius, Redi, and Morgagni; the physicists, Biot and Foucault; the chemist, Chevreul, very devoted to religious worship; and the mineralogist Haüy.[17] Baron Georges Cuvier, of high repute as founder of comparative anatomy, was a French Protestant, a Lutheran, who was "warmly attached to that system of Christian faith and order which had been bequeathed to their country by the heroic Huguenots." All accounts of Cuvier affirm his appropriate Chris-

---

[15] *Makers of Modern Medicine*, J. J. Walsh, pp. 105-111.
[16] *The Life of Edward Jenner*, John Baron, vol. ii, p. 100, nota.
[17] *What Catholics Have Done for Science*, M. S. Brennan.

tian character and his activity in good works. Because of his eminent ability and of his church affiliations Cuvier was made superintendent of Faculties of Protestant Theology and was intrusted by the French government with the management of affairs related to the ecclesiastical interests of Protestants. This office he is said to have discharged with his accustomed zeal and effectiveness. Fifty new cures were established by reason of his activity. When he came to the end of his career he was at work on some fresh regulations for the discipline of the churches. He was vice-president of a Bible society, and was a promoter of the circulation of the Scriptures.[18]

Olinthus Gilbert Gregory, one of the twelve founders of the Royal Astronomical Society of England, wrote a work on *Evidences of Christianity*. It is reported that he was highly regarded and admired not only for his goodness of heart but also for eminent Christian virtues.

The chemist John Dalton, discoverer of the atomic theory, which made possible precise chemical analysis and synthesis, was, like Thomas Young, a Friend. Dalton was regular in attendance at meeting, exceedingly loyal to the Scriptures and to Quaker principles, to which he was attached from youth to age. While reserved in conversation as to religious experience, he gave every manifestation of devoutness in worship and of faith in God. A lifelong associate declared of Dalton that his reverence for the great Author of all things was deep and sincere. Sir John F. W. Herschel, astronomer and mathematician, was a Christian philosopher who lived a long, honorable life. He called light his first love, and he lived under stars of both physical and spiritual firmaments.

One of the most remarkable groups of Christian men of science is that of investigators in the field of

---

[18]*Memoirs of Baron Cuvier*, Lee, p. 139.

electricity. The outstanding names, from Galvani
of the eighteenth century to Pupin and Millikan of
the twentieth century, are names of religious believers. Galvani is described by James J. Walsh as almost quixotic in his devotion to Catholic principles
and in obedience to the dictates of conscience, even at
material loss to himself. He was a member of the
Third Order of Saint Francis. Alibert, in his historical address of 1801, recalled the fact that, contrary to the fashion of his day, Galvani in all his
lectures showed in some way how the things of nature recall the Creator, and how Providence is concerned in the maintenance of the natural order.
Count Alessandro Volta was a pious church member
and attendant, greatly given to good works among
the poor, and beloved by them. Hans Christian
Oersted· wrote works pervaded with his predominat-
ing thought, which was that of the unity of sciences
and of their position as the servants of religion. At the
tenth centenary of the introduction. of Christianity
into Denmark he gave an address, on "The Influence
of Christianity on Science." Of André Marie Ampère, Sainte-Beuve expressed wonder and admiration
at the way in which, without effort, he united religion
and science; confidence in man's intellectual possibilities with adoring adherence to the revealed word
of God. He was one of many who have much profited by à Kempis. The *Imitation of Christ* was a constant companion. Ampère wrote on the divineness
of Christianity, and is said to have done what he could
to bring home to the men of his generation the
truths of the Christian religion. The appendix of
Claude A. Valson's *La Vie et les Travaux d'André
Marie Ampère* contains the *"Memoire inédit d'Ampère sur les preuves historiques de la divinité du
Christianisme,"* the date being cir. 1804. There are
three parts, containing proofs drawn from the Old
Testament, from the writings of enemies of Christian-

ity, and from the Christian writings. Ampère's son, Jean Jacques Antoine, wrote an introduction to the philosophy of his father, which was printed in *Philosophie des deux Ampère,* Paris, 1866, Jules Barthélemy Sainte-Hilaire. In the chapter "Theodicée," the younger Ampère reviews his father's religious philosophy, showing his belief in the reasonableness of Christianity. Many of Ampère's religious opinions may be found in his correspondence and especially in the letters to Bredin. Ampère suffered at times from doubts which made him unhappy and which he declared the greatest torment that a man suffers on earth. The Bible and the writings of the church Fathers were his refuge when oppressed in this way.

The coulomb, as is the case with the volt and the ampere, preserves the name of a disciple of Christ. Charles Augustin Coulomb was not carried away by rationalism, which followed the French Revolution, just as godlessness is seeking to gain foothold since the last Great War. Biot reports that Coulomb maintained always the justice, the calmness, the firmness, and the dignity that became a great man of science. Ohm also! A deeply religious man, as Lamont testifies, was George Simon Ohm, noted for unselfishness, lovableness, and belief in God. In the preface of *Molecular Physics* he expresses hope that God will prolong his life to complete other volumes —perhaps even to the fourth.

Michael Faraday must certainly be named among those worthy of the title of this chapter. He was the child of parents so poor that during at least one period of general distress they had to receive public aid. His father was a blacksmith and died too early to witness his son's successes, which his mother was permitted to enjoy. His early education was meager, and he was employed from the age of seventeen by a bookbinder and stationer. During this period he found time to read the works on science which were near him, and he began making electrical and chemical experiments. Attending a series of lectures on natural philosophy by Tatum, he gained both information and scientific friends. Benjamin Abbott encouraged and aided his inquiries and experiments. About the time he was attaining his majority he fell under the influence of Sir Humphry Davy. After hearing some of the lectures of this inspiring experimenter and teacher, he wrote him, inclosing some notes of his lectures. The result was employment as a laboratory assistant at the Royal Institution.

Visiting Europe in company with Davy, Faraday met and heard Ampère, Clement, Desormes, Gay-Lussac, and Volta—splendid preparation for his own life-work. He saw Galileo's first telescope and a primitive voltaic battery, and was associated with his master in studies at Paris of iodine, discovered two years before by Courtois. At Florence he made use of the "great burning-glass" of the Duke of Tuscany. In 1815 Faraday returned to England and to the Royal Institution, which was the scene of his life-work. He was already becoming famous and shortly thereafter began to lecture, a task for which few have ever been better fitted. It is, however, as a scientific discoverer and not merely as a popular speaker and teacher that his fame is secure. He was in the Royal Institution for fifty-four years out of the seventy-six of his life. As a chemist, among other items, he determined two new chlorides of carbon, he liquified several gases, and produced new kinds of glass for optical purposes. His electrical discoveries, however, far surpassed his other achievements. These are of the highest importance, and have led to those marvelous developments in electrical knowledge and arts which make the present an electrical age. The results of his labors have by no means yet been exhausted.

Eminent scientist as Faraday was, he was even

greater in his human qualities and reactions, and in his response to the spiritual impulses which came to him. It was no less an authority than James Clerk Maxwell who, after speaking of Faraday's energy, accuracy, persistence and completeness in the labors of his profession, added the comment that there was another side of his character, to the cultivation of which he paid at least as much attention as that which he gave to science, and which was reserved for his friends, his family, and his church. Faraday was not only given to close application in his researches, but was a many-sided, fully developed personality. He was by no means narrowed to the magnitudes of the units of force with which he labored, but was immeasurably more than an observer, discoverer and professor. Tyndall names him "Just and Faithful Knight of God,"[19] and both as scientist and as a Christian leader this is his best description.

Michael Faraday was a member and lay preacher of that Protestant branch of the church which is called "Sandemanians," or "Glassites." This society was founded in Scotland and extended to England and America. It opposed all national religious establishments and interference of the state in religious affairs. It insisted that the Church of Christ should be modeled on the churches of the New Testament. Members were almost communistic, in that all were required to hold their possessions at the service of the poor and of the church. Faraday made his confession of sin and profession of faith necessary for reception into full membership with the Sandemanians without telling anyone of his intention, "so sacred was the step in his estimation." When questioned about his reticence concerning this act, he

[19]Closing words of *Faraday as a Discoverer*, John Tyndall, p. 171, D. Appleton & Company.

replied, "That is between me and my God."[20] It is affirmed that the Christian qualities of love, of truth, of kindness, and of energy were made stronger by his religion, which also produced in him unusual humility. In science he was ever eager to be corrected, and he was so far from arrogance that he had no false pride in any of his works. His broad knowledge of nature and the sharpness of his powers of criticism gave him no reason for losing faith in the revelations of Christian truth as found in the Scriptures. "He could have no sympathy whatever," says Stoughton, "with those who contend that if modern science be true much of what is commonly called Christianity, and of what was included in his faith, must be false."[21] As for Faraday's sermons and writings touching Christianity, it is declared that his religious ideas are as clear-cut, as straightforward, as penetrating, and smacked as little of self-deception as the logical notions that enabled him to make his great experiments. The oft-quoted remark of Sir Humphry Davy, "My best discovery was Michael Faraday," seems to have been fully justified. Tyndall preserved details of his visits with his distinguished predecessor, one of which pictures the beautiful simplicity of Faraday's daily piety. There is an account of a dinner in the Faraday home. Tyndall says: "He said grace. I am almost ashamed to call his prayer a 'saying of grace.' In the language of Scripture it might be described as the petition of a son into whose heart God had sent the Spirit of his Son, and who with absolute trust asked a blessing from his Father."[22] The tribute to this eminent Protestant scientist printed by James J. Walsh for the

[20]*Stories of Scientific Discovery*, D. B. Hammond, p. 107, Cambridge University Press.

[21]*Worthies of Science*, John Stoughton, p. 276.

[22]*Fragments of Science*, John Tyndall, vol. i, p. 420, D. Appleton & Company.

Catholic World is evidence of the essential oneness of Christian believers and is prophetic of future rapprochements: "Michael Faraday, the great English physicist, to whose discoveries in the department of electricity we owe so much, though not a Catholic, was an eminently good Christian, and a faithful believer in the care of Providence for the world."[23] Cuvier criticized Faraday because at various periods of life his theological views were amended, but he found no fault with his Christian character. Dumas, the French chemist, before the *Académie des Sciences,* passed striking judgment: "The simplicity of his heart, his candor, his ardent love of truth, his noble soul, independent and bold—all these combined to give an incomparable charm to the features of the illustrious physicist. I have never known a man more worthy of being loved, of being admired, or of being mourned. Fidelity to his religious faith, the constant observance of the moral law, constitute the ruling characteristics of his life."[24]

The names of two Americans should be mentioned here. Samuel F. B. Morse, the inventor, believed in a Power greater than that of electricity, and thought of the Bible as the guidebook of the country to which he was going. On the dreadful night when he believed that Congress had refused him the money for his great experiment, he left the session at a very late hour. He did not go to rest, however, until after earnest prayer. In the morning Annie Ellsworth, daughter of his friend the commissioner of patents, gave him word of his victory, and she was permitted to send the first telegraphic message over the Baltimore-Washington line—"What hath God wrought!" The second name of this group is one of the greatest in the history of American science. Joseph Henry,

[23]Confirmed by letter from Doctor Walsh.
[24]Faraday lectures, J. B. Dumas, London Chemical Society, 1869.

sometimes called the Franklin of the nineteenth century, in later life secretary of the Smithsonian Institution, was the philosopher whose experiments at Albany, New York, paved the way for the practical development of Morse. Henry was an independent discoverer of magneto-electricity, deserving to share the honors of Faraday as to this achievement. He constructed and operated in 1832 the first electromagnetic telegraph. He was a member of a Presbyterian church, and is described in a memoir of Asa Gray as "the model of a Christian gentleman."[25] The same reliable witness speaks of Henry's "entire freedom from doubts" concerning matters of religion.[26]

Werner von Siemens, German leader in electrical technology, did not hesitate, even in scientific assemblies, to talk of Providence, the work of creation, the wisdom of the Creator, and the humility of mind induced by scientific studies.

Joseph George Cumming, geologist and archæologist, was both scientist and preacher. After some time passed in scientific studies and writings, especially connected with the Isle of Man, he spent the final years of a comparatively short life as rector of churches in Suffolk and London, his metropolitan parish being that of Bethnal Green.

The oldest of the famous trio of natural philosophers who gave distinction to the school of mathematical physics at Cambridge University in the central years of the nineteenth century was Sir George Gabriel Stokes. He was Lucasian professor, secretary and president of the Royal Society and member of Parliament for Cambridge. He wrote over

---

[25]"Biographical Memoirs of Joseph Henry," Asa Gray, Smithsonian Report, 1878.

[26]*Idem.* Henry's views as to God and nature may be found in *History of the First Half Century of the Smithsonian Institution,* pp. 154-156.

a hundred memoirs on scientific themes. Many English scientists believe that he anticipated by several years the work of Kirchhoff on spectrum analysis, which view, despite the modest and generous disclaimer of Stokes himself, seems to have been true in part. This profound student of sound, reorganizer of the science of hydro-dynamics and discoverer in the field of optics was an outspoken Christian and, as Gifford lecturer, was the author of a work on *Natural Theology.*

James Clerk Maxwell is one of the greatest names of nineteenth-century science. His connection with the electro-magnetic theory of light and with many abstruse scientific problems is well known. He was the mathematical discoverer of the waves which twenty-five years later Hertz was able to demonstrate by experiment. His fame is a gleaming star in the firmament of Cambridge University. This eminent mathematician and physicist is described as having been in private life a very attractive Christian character. When occupied with the highest problems he had time and took care to lead his family, guests, and servants in evening devotions. He was a regular attendant at church, and a communicant each month. At Easter time he made it a point always to leave Cambridge in time to officiate at communion in the little Scottish kirk of which he was an elder. He was a liberal contributor to religious funds and gave freely of his time to the charitable efforts of the parish in which he resided. He expressed firm faith in the incarnation of God in Jesus Christ, in the atonement, and in the work of the Holy Spirit. He is said to have been kindly and companionable, but not enamored of shallow disbelief. Guthrie Tait says of Maxwell that "though perfectly free from any trace of envy or self-will, on fit occasions he showed his contempt for the pseudo-science which seeks applause of ignorance by professing to reduce the whole system of the universe to a fortuitous sequence of uncaused events." A physician paid the high tribute to James Clerk Maxwell which has been quoted in a few other cases, "a most perfect example of a Christian gentleman." Maxwell preserved to the closing hours of his life the fine attitude toward nature and God which is expressed in the students' evening hymn composed in 1853 during his undergraduate days:

> "Teach me so Thy works to read
>   That my faith new strength accruing,
> May from world to world proceed,
>   Wisdom's fruitful search pursuing,
>   Till thy breath my mind imbuing,
> I proclaim the eternal creed
>   Of the glorious theme renewing,
> God our Lord is God indeed."[27]

Turning to representatives of other departments of scientific work, we may pause a moment with René Théophile Hyacinth Laënnec, discoverer of auscultation, to note that it would be difficult indeed to find finer tributes to Christian piety and devotion than those penned concerning this discoverer by Sir Benjamin Ward Richardson. He describes Laënnec as sincerely Christian, constantly engaged in religious and social tasks. He was a practical Catholic, attached to his church relations through good or evil report. His maturer reason but confirmed his earlier religious principles. He approached the end of his days with composure, and his death was that of a Christian.[28] Of Sir David Brewster, optician and discoverer concerning the polarization of light, it is said that it was intended that he should devote himself to the work of the church, but, since he felt that he was more fit for the laboratory than the pulpit, with-

---

[27]*James Clerk Maxwell and Modern Physics,* R. T. Glazebrook, p. 91, Cassell & Co., Ltd., London.

[28]*Disciples of Aesculapius,* p. 316, E. P. Dutton & Company.

out losing interest in religion he gave his life to nature. He combined mastery of science with firm
evangelical beliefs and a sincere love of Jesus Christ.
He was author of a standard *Life of Newton* for
which he used the private papers left by the philosopher. He also wrote *More Worlds Than One, the
Creed of the Philosopher and the Hope of the Christian.* He remarked toward the close of his life, "I
have had the light for many years." The appropriate
legend on the Brewster tomb in the Abbey of Melrose
therefore is, "The Lord is My Light."

Sir James Y. Simpson, who "fought the fight of
anæsthesia," is said to have had throughout his career a simple but all-sufficient religious faith. He
advised his students to rely on Omnipotence for
steady guidance. He told a nephew that in Jesus
he had unshaken confidence, and that though he
had mixed with men of various opinions, some of
whom criticized the Christian gospel, he had never
had a doubt of it. "The Buik" he had been taught to
read as a child was continually with him. He was a
great admirer and follower of Thomas Guthrie, the
zealous preacher. His portrait appears in Hill's picture of the Free Church leaders. He declared that his
greatest discovery was that he had a Saviour. Many
sorrows in his family experience but ripened his
faith. He healed many by use of medicine, and not a
few by Christian influences. His body was offered
a place in Westminster Abbey, but his wife, who survived him but a few days, preferred that their burial
should be in their beloved Scotland.[29]

Leverrier, astronomer and one of the mathematical
discoverers of Neptune, "was a pious Catholic." He
was outspoken in his advocacy of the Christian religion, even in the Academy. When dying he re-

---

[29]*Sir James Y. Simpson,* Eve Blantyre Simpson, Charles Scribner's
Sons.

peated the words of Simeon, *"Nunc dimittis servum tuum, Dominus, in pace."* Claude Bernard, the physiologist, attained the grand prize of the French Institute for his *Researches on the Uses of the Pancreas,* and wrote many valuable works on topics related to his department. His religious history is similar to that of Romanes. It is reported that for a time he was wrapped up in physical experiments and their suggestions and was drawn far away from the spiritual side of things. He failed to realize that he was exposed to what Horace Bushnell termed "the danger that comes from what may be called a bondage under the method of science—as if nothing could be true save as it is proved by the scientific method. Whereas, the method of all the higher truths of religion is different, being the method of faith; a verification by the heart, and not by the notions of the head."[30] After a time, Bernard became convinced of his error, came back to his higher self, and "the great physiologist died a true Christian."

It was said of Adam Sedgwick that in his hands geology was the handmaid of theology. *A Discourse on the Studies at the University,* delivered by Sedgwick at Trinity College, Cambridge, in December, 1832, was based on Psalm 96. 17, 18, 19, and shows that this scientist thought nature's testimony to her Creator, Lord, and King clear and distinct. "All nature is but the manifestation of a supreme intelligence." He defended religion as revealed in the gospel. "Let prayer," he urged, "be the beginning and the end of our studies."[31] He confessed his attachment to Jesus Christ and declared that God dwells in us in the person of the Holy Spirit. Sir Archibald Geikie pays his character a beautiful tribute.[32] Of the same mode of thinking was Sir J. W. Dawson, the

[30]*Nature and the Supernatural,* p. 20, Charles Scribner's Sons.
[31]Pages 18, 26 and 81.
[32]*The Founders of Geology,* p. 434.

Canadian geologist, in his day described as "the most practiced observer with the microscope." He was one of a number of scientific leaders, Virchow, Agassiz, Fabre, F. T. Buckland, Mivart and some others, who never became convinced of the truth of Darwinism. A man of both intellectual and spiritual eminence, he was highly reputed in his generation.

In Germany, at about this time, grew up Teodor Schwann, physiologist and anatomist, whose name is inseparably connected with the cell theory. He was a lifelong Catholic and opposed rationalism with a keen consciousness of religious feeling. His Christian fidelity was accompanied by a devotion to truth which would not allow him to compromise with what he believed to be fact.[33] The biographer of Baron Joseph Lister, "father of modern antiseptic surgery," Sir R. J. Godlee, describes the hesitancy of the discoverer and his "heart-searching" on separating himself from the Society of Friends, and the religious affiliation of his family, at the time of his marriage. Later Lister became a member of the Church of England, in whose fellowship he found peace and satisfaction. Religious influences governed his life, and he remained to the end of his days in sympathy with the church of his adoption.

A group of Americans may be passed in review whose names are worthy of comparison with living scientists, and the ideas of some of whom the scientific world may in the future have to meet again. At present, however, we are concerned with their personal attitude toward religion, and not with their physical teachings. Nathaniel Bowditch, mathematician, who declined a chair at Harvard, so lived that he was able to say to his son, "If I knew I were to be gone when the sun sets in the west, I would say, 'Thy will, O God, be done.'" Of John Torrey, chemist,

---

[33]See account of his attitude toward the Louise Lateau *stigmata* in *Makers of Modern Medicine,* James J. Walsh, p. 267.

and botanical teacher, among whose pupils was Asa
Gray, it is recorded that, "a devoted Christian, he
never obtruded his Christianity, but let it appear in
every relation of life. Belonging to a denomination
that is by some considered exceedingly strict, he
was most charitable concerning the opinions of those
who believed differently."[34] With Torrey in joint
authorship of *Flora in North America* was his pupil,
Asa Gray. This author of many botanical works was
in religious character worthy of his instructor. In
the preface to his *Darwiniana,* Gray described himself as "one who is scientifically, and in his own
fashion, a Darwinian, philosophically a convinced
theist, and religiously an accepter of the 'creed commonly called the Nicene' as the exponent of the
Christian faith."[35] Gray maintained that variation
in all departments of organic life is guided by supreme intelligence and purpose, and that evolution
as a principle can be reconciled to the strictest
church creeds. Speaking of the early controversy
over Darwin's ideas, Dean Church said that Asa Gray
softened and directed the discussion, and that things
would surely have gone more crossly and unreason-
ably if his combination of fearless religion and clearness of mind and wise love of truth had not told on
the controversy.

Concerning Louis Agassiz, the Swiss-American
naturalist, David Starr Jordan states that "to Agassiz, each natural object was a thought of God, and
trifling with God's truth as expressed in nature was
the basest of sacrilege."[36] It is said that Agassiz
began life as an atheist, but that his study of nature
led him step by step to a fervent belief in a divine

[34]*Pioneers of Science in America,* Youmans, p. 335, D. Appleton
& Company.

[35]VI, D. Appleton & Company.

[36]*Leading American Men of Science,* p. 164, Henry Holt and Company.

intelligence and purpose back of its phenomena. A
friend paid him the tribute that he was at all times
"one of God Almighty's gentlemen."   C. F. Holder
commented: "No one can contemplate the character of
Agassiz without realizing its nobility, its strength,
its sweetness, and his joyous nature. He was notably
a Christian in all the term implies."[37]   In his marine
laboratory, the first of its kind, on Penikese Island,
Buzzards Bay, this fruitful teacher inspired such
students as David Starr Jordan, William K. Brooks,
Charles O. Whitman, and Charles S. Minot.   Whit-
tier's "Prayer of Agassiz" preserves the memory of
an eminent scientific Christian.

Charles Leo Lesquereux was educated and became
a botanical teacher in Switzerland, but was brought
by Agassiz to America. At twenty-five he became totally deaf, but went forward bravely with his scientific observations and writings. "He lived and died
in the communion of the Lutheran Church, and never
felt the essentials of his religious belief disturbed
by the advances of science."[38]   James D. Dana, in
"Biographical Memoirs of Arnold Guyot," described
Arnold Henry Guyot, physical geographer and author of *The Earth and Man* and of various textbooks,
as a "fervently religious man living as if ever in communication with his heavenly Parent; a Christian,
following closely in the footsteps of his Master."[39]
Henry C. Cameron, who was closely associated with
Guyot for more than a quarter century, paid a high
tribute to his attainments and worth: "I have known
no man who could generalize as he could. His knowledge of history and philosophy, his acquaintance with
theology, and his scientific attainments were wonderful.   Everything was assimilated and systema-

[37]*Ibid.*, p. 169.
[38]W. J. Youmans, M.D., *Op. cit.*, p. 463, D. Appleton & Company.
[39]Smithsonian Report, 1887, p. 720.

tized, so that all he had learned seemed always to be at perfect command. A perfect gentleman, a model Christian, a man whose equal I have never seen."[40] In 1861 Guyot was a Presbyterian delegate to the Evangelical Alliance Convention held in Geneva. He wrote from Paris of his great pleasure in attending, in that old stronghold of Protestant faith, the large and exceedingly interesting meeting. It seemed to him a thrilling experience to behold the grand spectacle of so many sympathizing Christians from all quarters of Christendom uniting in religious services with perfect freedom and unanimity.[41]

James D. Dana, geologist, is remembered for his firm belief in divine creation, in the Holy Scriptures and in the Christian life. J. M. Coulter gives him the highest compliment: "Dana's character was intensely ethical. And with him ethics was always sanctified and glorified by religious faith. . . . In his scientific investigations he always felt, like Kepler, that he was thinking God's thoughts after him. Dana was not only a theist but a Christian. Religion was the dominant principle in his life . . . While residing in New Haven as assistant to Professor Silliman, he became a member of the First Congregational Church in that city. His letters written amid the perils of shipwrecks and cannibals in the 'Exploring Expedition' reveal the sincerity of his faith in the providential care of the heavenly Father."[42]

These names bring us near to our own times. Space is lacking for similar facts and testimonies in case of men like Benjamin Silliman, to whose Christian character Wyman, the anatomist, witnesses, O. M.

---

[40]*Pioneers of Science in America, ut supra*, p. 499, D. Appleton & Company.

[41]J. D. Dana, *supra.*

[42]In *Leading American Men of Science*, D. S. Jordan, ed., p. 266, Henry Holt and Company.

Mitchel, Sanborn Tenny, Ebenezer Emmons, John as well as Joseph LeConte, Hubert Newton, William A. Rogers, Louis de Pourtales, M. F. Maury, Alexander Winchell, Methodist geologist and author *Reconciliation of Science and Religion;* Saint George Mivart, modern Catholic biologist; Sereno Watson, W. K. Brooks, John J. Brown, Mayo-Smith, and many others.

In passing it may be noted that a large number of men of science in all lands have been sons or grandsons of preachers. The father and foster-father of Linnæus were clergymen. Henry Augustus Rowland, physicist, was both a son and a grandson of ministers of the gospel, and was so far from being the hypothetical "minister's son" that Ira Remsen could testify of him that "he was as free from anything that could fairly be called sin as anyone I have ever known."[43] Among other preachers' sons may be mentioned Hermann Boerhaave, physician and botanist,[44] Edward Jenner, physician and naturalist, G. H. E. Muhlenberg, botanist, Samuel F. B. Morse, artist and inventor, Louis Agassiz, naturalist, Elias Loomis, mathematician, Sir George Gabriel Stokes, mathematician and physicist, Francis T. Buckland, zoologist, John Wesley Powell, anthropologist and explorer, Karl A. von Zittel, palæontologist, George John Romanes, zoologist and psychologist, William Bateson, surgeon and biologist, Franklin H. Giddings, sociologist, T. M. Lowry, chemist, Robert A. Millikan, physicist. William A. Riley, entomologist, Edward L. Rice, and George T. Hargitt, zoologists, and William M. Goldsmith, biologist, are Methodist sons of preachers. The father of Josiah Willard Gibbs, mathematician and physicist, was a theological pro-

---

[43]*Ibid.,* p. 426.

[44]Boerhaave for some years planned to enter the Christian ministry. For this and a high character tribute see *Disciples of Aesculapius,* Sir B. W. Richardson, pp. 96, 98 and 107.

fessor of sacred literature. Major Walter Reed, physician, surgeon, and master spirit in the conquest of yellow fever, was a child of a Methodist parsonage.

Not a few scientific characters were themselves Christian ministers. Isaac Barrow, John Ray, John Michell, Michael Faraday, Adam Sedgwick, Joseph Priestley, Stephen Hales, Edward Hitchcock, Elisha Mitchell, Thomas George Bonney, and others mentioned elsewhere in this book, being examples. Edmund Cartwright, inventor, John Playfair, mathematician and natural philosopher, and William Buckland, geologist, were Anglican preachers and sons of preachers. Robert Boyle, William Hunter, René Just Haüy, Sir David Brewster, and Geoffrey Sainte-Hilaire once contemplated clerical orders. Charles Darwin, too! He was sent to Cambridge to be educated for the Christian ministry, but Gibson reports that he was weak on classics and mathematics, and that his chief interest was in natural subjects. Copernicus was appointed canon of Frauenburg by his uncle, the bishop of Ermeland. Roger Bacon, Christoph Clavius, the mathematician, who made the Gregorian Calendar, Giuseppe Piazzi, and Pietro Angelo Sacchi, astronomers, Gregor Johann Mendel, botanist, and many other men of science were monks. Lazzaro Spallanzani was a priest. Nicholas Steno, physician and anatomist, to whom the International Congress of Geologists unveiled a tablet as the founder of their science, was a Catholic bishop. Poggendorf's list of scientists of all times previous to the middle of the seventeenth century contains many names of Catholic clerics. Some scientific leaders, Sir Humphry Davy and Sir Charles Lyell being examples, were educated in schools kept by clergymen. Anyone who will take pains to look over lists of members of scientific societies of the past century may be surprised to discover so many clerical names in these records.

Hugh Miller, the Scottish geologist, edited the *Witness,* an organ of the Free Church, and wrote much on religious as well as on natural themes. His *Footprints of the Creator* ran to many editions. Henry Drummond was a delightful puzzle. Was he more preacher than scientist, or more scientist than preacher? This, at all events, is certain: he was a Christian of whom George Adam Smith could affirm that his friends were sure that his was the most Christlike life they ever knew. His *Natural Law in the Spiritual World* and *Ascent of Man* made a sensation in their day. He was a remarkable teacher and a sincere student of the works and ways of God.

A life history of peculiar interest to those who have sensed a conflict between scientific and religious impulses is that of George James Romanes, zoologist and psychologist, author of many biological and literary works. This able and attractive man at twenty-five years of age won at Cambridge the Burney Prize for an essay on *Christian Prayer Considered in Relation to the Belief that the Almighty Governs the World by General Laws.*[45] This thesis represented a deep natural piety, but soon after Romanes drifted into reasoned skepticism concerning the existence of God. He was restored to theistic belief it is said in good part by the influence of a missionary to Japan, John Thomas Gulick. The latter was a naturalist and was so painstaking in his scientific work that he gained the respect of Romanes, who questioned him as to the grounds of his Christian faith. Impressed by the answers to his queries as well as by other influences, among these Pascal's Pensées,[46] the ardent scientist and voluminous author returned to the communion of the church and fully espoused and main-

---

[45] This essay was published in 1874, with an appendix on "The Physical Efficacy of Prayer."

[46] On this, *The Life and Letters of George John Romanes,* by Mrs. Romanes, p. 371.

tained Christianity. *Mind and Motion* records his opposition to materialism. His last work, *Thoughts on Religion,* was published by Charles Gore after the lamented death of the writer at the age of forty-six years.

Three names have been reserved for presentation together. Jean Henri Fabre, poet of science, whom Maeterlinck named "the Insect's Homer," was a son of parents so poor and dull that they had never opened a book in their lives. He earned his own education. He handled the prescribed classical studies so easily that he had spare time to investigate in the secrecy of his desk the fruit of the oleander, the flower of the snapdragon, the sting of a wasp, the wing-cover of a gardener-beetle. In time he became a teacher and later a physicist and chemist at Ajaccio and afterward at Avignon. His devotion to his "vats and his insects" attracted wide attention, and brought him Legion of Honor decoration and audience with the emperor, which was not to his taste. He sought a home in the country, where for long years he accumulated facts for the *Souvenirs Entomologiques,* which was crowned by the Institute and caused Darwin to pronounce him an incomparable observer. Fabre had the deepest veneration for Darwin's character and honesty, but could never accept the theory associated with his name. *"Les faits tels que je les observe, m'éloignent des théories de Darwin."*[47] This view of Fabre is said to have been due in part to the tendency of certain scientists to regard evolution as a substitute for God, ignoring Darwin's explicit statement that there is no incompatibility between his theory and belief in a personal Creator; as well as Wallace's belief, similar to Fabre's own, that adaptations in plants, animals, birds and insects are proofs

---

[47]*Revue des Deux Mondes,* 1910, p. 891. He said that only one term of duration (past, present, future) escapes the selection theory, namely the present, which is free from the phantasies of hypothesis.

of organizing mind. Fabre never lost his love for nature, his sense of its beauty, and his consciousness of spiritual verities. His religious character must be judged by broad standards. He had a confidence in God which came not from belief alone, but from consciousness of direct perception. "I see Him. Without Him I understand nothing; without Him all is darkness. Not only have I retained this conviction; I have *aggravated* or *ameliorated* it, whichever you please." He once exclaimed: "I regard atheism as a mania. It is the malady of the age. You could take my skin from me more easily than my faith in God."[48]

We must now think of Louis Pasteur, another scion of simple country folk, who had his own ambition. His father had been a soldier, and became a tanner. His mother was a sensible woman with high ideals which the whole family shared. At fifteen Louis was sent to Paris to work for his *baccalauréat*, but suffered from nostalgia until his father came and took him back home. Later he went to Besançon, which was nearer by, and did so well and gained so much courage that he went back to Paris and made the *Ecole Normale*, where he attracted the enthusiastic interest of Biot. To the dismay of the latter, the government soon appointed Pasteur professor of physics at Dijon, taking him from research work. As this post did not offer sufficient opportunities for his special gifts, he was soon offered the chair of professor of chemistry at Strasbourg, where he went forward with renewed energy in the investigation of acids and ferments. The list of his achievements is perhaps as well known as is the work of any modern scientist. He produced racemic from tartaric acid. He replaced the notion that chemical actions during

---

[48]*Stories of Scientific Discovery*, D. B. Hammond, University Press, Cambridge, England, p. 88.

fermentation and allied changes can be explained on
the basis of molecular physics alone, with the knowledge that they require the action of bacteria. He
insisted and proved against much opposition that
fermentation, decomposition, putrefaction are caused
by life, in the absence of which they are impossible.
He studied and conquered silk-worm diseases, saving
a great industry. He found a way to master anthrax.
The account of Pasteur's victory over rabies touched
the imagination of the world and made his name a
household word. It is a long life history—full of
toil, peril, conquest. One of the best tributes paid
him is in the saying of Hammond: "To him, service
to man was service to God."[49] Walsh quotes this expression from the lips of one who has a better right
to be heard than have the sciolists to whom he refers: "Posterity will one day laugh at the sublime
foolishness of the modern materialistic philosophers.
The more I study nature, the more I stand amazed at
the work of the Creator. I pray while I am engaged
at my work in the laboratory."[50] One of his sentences, written at the time when he was struggling
with the anthrax problem, gives the secret of his
amazing success: "I have a lasting provision of faith
and fire." He had both scientific and religious faith,
a combination which is not easy to defeat, and which
cannot be dismayed—the absence of which may account for the relatively small results of many investigators. Tyndall states that Pasteur considered that
his researches point to a physical barrier which exists between organic and inorganic nature. The arguments of Jungfleisch and others did not cause him
to change his opinion, which he believed to be based
on scientific determination.

One of the chief Christian figures of scientific his-

---

[49]*Stories of Scientific Discovery*, D. B. Hammond, University Press,
Cambridge, England, p. 193.

[50]*Makers of Modern Medicine*, J. J. Walsh, p. 318.

tory was mentioned at the beginning of this chapter in Larmor's high tribute to genius—William Thomson, Lord Kelvin. A fellow student of Thomson was David Livingstone, and it may be possible that the character and life of the famous missionary explorer were not without some bearing on the mind of a youth so precocious that at sixteen he sent a paper to the Cambridge Mathematical Journal showing that Kelland in his *Theory of Heat* had erred in attacking Fourier, the French mathematician. That Kelland was great enough, though hurt at first, to forgive the wound thus made, and become the friend of the author of it is a tribute to his own good judgment, as well as to his breadth of character. At seventeen, Kelvin entered Cambridge. Very shortly one of the college examiners remarked to another, "You and I are just about fit to mend Thomson's pens." William Thomson became professor of natural philosophy at Glasgow at twenty-two. He began his scientific labors under the difficulties which at the time embarrassed nearly all investigators. His early experiments in the University of Glasgow were performed in his private room and in an abandoned coal-cellar, but during his fifty years as a teacher in this institution he witnessed vast changes. He made valuable additions to knowledge in the departments of dynamics, sound, light, heat, magnetism, and electricity. His improved mariner's compass saved many lives. "Throw Thomson overboard," cried the imperiled navigator who desired to know the depth of the sea beneath him, and he depended on the genius of Kelvin to give him reliable soundings. He produced a galvanometer, quadrant, electrometer. He demonstrated mathematically the principle of the electric oscillator. He worked out the problem of electrical signaling over a submarine cable, as Kirchhoff later solved it for land lines. The relation of Kelvin to the laying of the Atlantic cables made his name famous in many lands, and his reputation is enhanced by new revelations of his career.

It certainly is not without significance that the loftiest minds have witnessed strong faith in a power superior to the forces of nature. Kelvin reported a conversation which he once had with Baron Justus von Liebig, whose discoveries in the field of organic chemistry are justly celebrated, when they were walking together in the country, in which he asked him if he believed that the grass and flowers about their path grew by mere chemical forces. "No," was the unhesitating reply, "no more than I could believe that a book of botany describing them could grow by mere chemical forces." Lord Kelvin himself, man of towering mind and imposing scientific achievements that he was, took the firmest position in this matter. To the Christian Association of University College, London, he stated that "the phenomena of such living things as a sprig of moss, a microbe, a living animal—looked at and considered as matters of scientific investigation—compel us to conclude that there is scientific reason for believing in the existence of a creative and directing power." Sylvanus P. Thompson, Lord Kelvin's biographer, represents him as possessing a faith which was of a very simple and child-like nature, undogmatic and unaffected by sectarian bitterness. It pained him to hear crudely atheistic views expressed by young men who had never known the deeper side of existence. "If you think strongly enough," remarked this intellectual athlete to his associates in a scientific meeting, "you will be forced by science to the belief in God which is the foundation of all religion." It is noteworthy that "Kelvin was a regular and sincere worshiper." Millikan points out that "it was Kelvin who first estimated the age of the earth at something like a hundred million years without seeing the least incompatibility between that scientific conclusion and his adherence to the church of which he was a life-long member and a constant attendant."[51]

It may be said by some who read this chapter that names of prominence in the history of science have been omitted. This is necessarily true. Too many of those in this field of service have been representative Christians to mention a large percentage of them. But it may be urged, what about the other side, that of scientists opposed to Christianity? It is not claimed that there is no other side. It is well known that there have been and are some materialists, atheists, and scoffers occupying scientific positions. What has been stated and evidenced in this chapter and book is that the list of Christian believers among scientific men compares favorably with similar records from other occupations, and that it is indeed exceedingly impressive both as to numbers and quality. Undoubtedly, the religious attitude of a number of students of nature is obscure. For example, it has been said of Humboldt's *Kosmos* that "the general effect of the book is rendered to some extent unsatisfactory by its tendency to substitute the indefinite for the infinite, and thus to ignore, while it does not deny, the existence of a power outside and beyond nature."[52] This quality in the writing of Humboldt is elsewhere shown to represent his relation to ethics, but probably is not a complete or true account of his position concerning subjects outside the realm of his life-work. In the case of certain scientists who are often quoted as having been hostile to the church and teachings of Christ, accounts vary. For example, Charles R. Gibson thought that Charles Darwin, despite his statements of doubt, appeared to be a good Christian, since he acted hon-

---

[51]*Science and Religion,* bulletin xxxii, number 38, California Institute of Technology, p. 7.

[52]Agnes Mary Clerke, historian of science, *Encyclopedia Britannica,* thirteenth edition.

estly and uprightly, according to his serious beliefs.

It should be remembered that Darwin spent part of his early life on explorations at a distance from civilization, and, of course, from gospel teaching; that he was for many years an invalid and almost a recluse, and that his long-continued and absorbing observations of natural objects and processes tended to atrophy certain of his personal aptitudes and powers, as, for example, his appreciation of music. It is not strange that he lacked certain forms of knowledge and experience, including those of religion, such as are common to many. Nevertheless, the author of the *Origin of Species* and the *Descent of Man* was no scoffer or skeptical dogmatist. In a letter which Francis Darwin prints in his life of his father, Darwin wrote J. Fordyce: "In my most extreme fluctuations I have never been an atheist in the sense of denying the existence of God. I think that generally (and more and more as I grow older), but not always, that an agnostic would be the more correct description of my state of mind."[53] Note the "generally" and "but not always." Note also the items prepared for an autobiography in 1876, six years before his death, in which he decides that he deserves to be called a theist and gives arguments for the existence of God which had occurred to him at various times. It should be remembered that the closing paragraph of the *Origin of Species* speaks of the Creator who originally breathed life into a few forms or into one. Charles F. Holder not only points out Darwin's belief in a First Cause, but claims that though in theory agnostic he was in practice an orthodox Christian of the broadest type.[54] It was his travel observations, as well as the persuasions of Admiral Sullivan, which made Darwin a contributor

[53] *Life and Letters of Charles Darwin*, Francis Darwin, p. 274, D. Appleton & Company.
[54] *Charles Darwin, His Life and Work*, p. 148.

to Christian missions. I have read a circumstantial account, based on the best testimony, that of women, that during his last days the great biologist spent much time in reading the Holy Scriptures and in devotions. If, in the serious hours of approaching dissolution, Darwin communed with his Maker and read his Word, he followed the example of other men fully his equals, and furnished one more illustration of the fact that, after all, a new mollusk, polyp, planet, or law gives little sustenance to the nature of man, and is of small importance in comparison with the knowledge of eternal life through Jesus Christ, and of the personal assurance of salvation by faith in him.

Alfred Russel Wallace was a naturalist and a spiritualist. His view of his theological position is indicated in a letter to the Reverend J. B. Henderson, "It is probable that in your sense of the word I am not a Christian." He earnestly contended that he had scientifically established the necessity of ever-present mind as the cause of physical and biological evolution. He believed that an agency analogous to that which first originated life and thus consciousness has been the source of intellectual and spiritual development.

Alexander Macmillan used vast hyperbole when he said to John Fiske that there was enough genuine Christianity in Huxley so that if divided among the people of the British Isles it would suffice to save the souls of all of them, with plenty to spare. If such a generalization were formulated on any matter of natural history, would not the proper remark be that of Romanes, made with reference to another subject: *"C'est magnifique, mais ce n'est pas la science"?* If Dewar and Finn are correct, Thomas H. Huxley had some extra- or infra-Christian characteristics. In *The Making of Species,* these authors assert that one of his intellectual caliber was able, like a clever attorney, to make out a case for any theory which he chose to maintain. One of Mr. Huxley's sayings about himself, significant though not attractive, is that he had ever been Darwin's bulldog. When one reflects on the nature, variety, and energy of a bulldog's activities, it is hardly strange, though he said it was, that Henry Fairfield Osborn concluded concerning Huxley "that he did not add a single new fact to the principle of evolution."[55]

It should be set down to the credit of Huxley that he approved Christian ethics and directed his life in accordance with most of them, that he advocated the moral and educational value of the Bible, that he even made some financial contributions to the church, and that despite his attacks on persons and doctrines obnoxious to him he was loyal to his friends and to the causes he espoused. As to the extravagant claim of certain enthusiasts made in behalf of scientists in general and of Huxley in particular, that they seek truth only, while all others are guided by expediency and self-interest, the comment of many a master in science would be that of the fair-minded William James: A good deal of humbug about that! Huxley, as well as Darwin, was distant from religious influences during part of his life, and he also suffered by reactions from the attitude of unwise Christian leaders of his times. Nevertheless, he wrote Archdeacon James M. Wilson that to strive toward a synthesis of science and faith was in an especial sense the duty of his generation.

Like Darwin and Huxley, John Tyndall insisted that he was not an atheist. He was far from anything of the kind. The case of Helmholtz is representative of a group of quiet, reserved men, occupied with abstruse problems, and not sufficiently given to revealing their deepest thoughts, even to their most intimate associates. It is said that his

---

[55]*Impressions of Great Naturalists,* autobiographical foreword, xxv.

opinion on religious questions can not be stated with
any degree of precision. Such topics were not with
him subjects of conversation. His writings breathe
a spirit of reverence. His pure and noble life was
a high testimony of his worth. A very intimate associate of this master in realms of light, sound, and
electricity, and formulator of the principle of the conservation of energy, looked upon him as one who
seemed too busy thinking divine thoughts to converse
much about his own personal opinions and experiences. On the lowest terms, Helmholtz must be
credited as being far above impiety, and as a devoted
servant of mankind.

Concerning the various Christian examples and
testimonies which have been considered, it may be
said that one quite understands the distress which
such items must cause persons who have no place
in their thinking for a Divine Being or system, and
to whom any religious expression smacks of hypocrisy. But science deals with facts and claims to face
them justly, whether they are congenial or not. And
with all due allowance for errors not only are such
data as we have been reviewing collectable, but in
almost unbelievable variety and quantity.

In studying the lives of many of the most eminent men who have made possible the present knowledge of the scientific world, in what way can their
Christian qualities and faith, shown in so many impressive instances, be denied or evaded? Is it not
also worth considering, as I have elsewhere intimated,
that their vocational success may not have been without a spiritual basis? At all events the facts adduced
in these pages are part of the biography of science and
of competent judgments expressed by some of its
foremost representatives. If anyone objects that
these exhibits cover only past history, the next chapter is open to his perusal.

CHAPTER IX

THE PRESENT SITUATION

IN connection with the rapid progress made by science during the latter portion of the nineteenth century and the first part of the twentieth century, intellectual and theological issues, many of them not necessarily involved in facts on which they were alleged to be based, were raised so swiftly that few, even of the most careful observers, were fully prepared to meet them. Although not a little confusion of thought and breaking of conventions has taken place, especially immediately following the World War, the impression which is in many minds that present-day science is mainly atheistic and hostile to Christianity is very far from the truth. It may be said that serious differences of opinion as to religious teaching are more frequently found in philosophical and theological than in scientific literature.

The recurrence of apparent conflict between science and religion is not to be attributed wholly to either of the two parties named. "I am not going to place the whole blame for the existence of this controversy upon misguided leaders of religion," says Robert A. Millikan. "The responsibility is a divided one, for science is just as often misrepresented as is religion by men of little vision, of no appreciation of its limitations, and of imperfect comprehension of the real rôle it plays in human life—by men who lose sight of all spiritual values and therefore exert an influence upon youth which is unsettling, irreligious, and sometimes immoral."[1] Of this sort was

---

[1] Bulletin, California Institute of Technology, "Science and Religion," March, 1922, pp. 5, 6.

266

the teacher in a midwestern college, who, speaking with an air of finality, is reported to have said to his class, "Evolution has now been firmly established; therefore it is no longer possible for an intelligent man to believe in a personal God." It is unfortunate that immature minds receiving such a statement are unaware that evolution requires definition and orientation before it is made the basis of far-reaching determinations. Doubtless also not a few pupils of this teacher were without sufficient training to enable them to recognize his utterance as a logical fallacy. It is possible that the man is one of those apt mimics who catch up and pass on dicta of the Julian Huxley sort—infallibilities which yield nothing to the most dogmatic ecclesiastical bulls. He was certainly not in touch with Locy's clear perception that the evolution issue is not one of theology but of creative method. Therefore the problem cannot be given an anti-theological solution.

The suitable answer to the bald assertion that it is impossible for intelligent men to believe in a God who possesses personality, and who is related to the universe of persons is, They do so believe, thousands of them, including large numbers of important scientific leaders. Were this not the case, all intelligent men would be atheists, since an impersonal God is no God at all, an illogical, preposterous, and ultimately unthinkable proposition.

In preceding chapters of this book it has been shown that scientific thought, through its loftiest representatives, has paid remarkable tributes to Christian teaching and sentiment, including the witness of adherence to the ideals and relationships of the Christian Church. As Webster once observed concerning certain records of history, "The past at least is secure." It must be noted also that thought never gets entirely away from its former attainments. It has been said by a scientist that "if you look more closely, you will see that all the old facts have been incorporated in the new theories, and that surprisingly few of the old statements have been found to be so false that they had to be discarded. Science grows like a snowball, englobing what has gone before."[2] Precisely the same statement may be made in behalf of Christian teaching. Its development carries forward as well as drops off its possessions. If science and Christianity are both true processes, as we believe, a day of closer relationship than that of the past between the two forces which minister most helpfully to human welfare is certainly coming —it may be rapidly.

The affirmations which have just been made may seem to some to be courageous and to others may appear presumptuous in face of opposing attitudes and tendencies which have been and still are manifesting themselves in certain quarters. It must be admitted that influences are at work in literature, in schoolroom, and in church which call for the serious attention both of Christian thinkers and of all well-wishers of mankind. During seasons of general criticism and restlessness inhibitions are relaxed, and men who at heart have always been materialists, atheists, and pessimists begin more assiduously and openly to pour their virus into the veins of youth and into the public mind. Occasionally such teachers are found in school faculties, even of denominational institutions. Any attempt to weed one of them out is widely advertised as constituting "persecution of science." Sensational publicists who are not at all scientists, though occasionally quoted as such, put forth teachings which are as scientifically unreliable as they are sometimes ethically dangerous. Science should not be held accountable for McCabe's rationalism or for Sprading's libertarian dogmatism.

[2] *Sermons of a Chemist*, E. E. Slosson, p. 36, Harcourt, Brace and Company.

Others are preaching animalism, all-inclusive mechanism, naturalism, or a mixture of these primitive
dogmas, not always without ability, and, of course,
not without appealing to some undoubted truths
which help make their doses palatable to untrained
minds. Certain positivists, behaviorists, physico-
humanists declaim harmful or doubtful doctrines
with a show of erudition calculated to overawe and
to check any disposition to question the least of their
conclusions. Highly technical terms and euphemistic
phrases conceal destructive principles. With this
column of militant anti-Christians fall in teachers
weak in philosophy and without theological knowledge; materialistic preachers; followers of prevailing winds, of thought fashions and fads, of the *zeit-
geist;* a brood of weaklings and apostates from worth-
while systems of solid thinking and belief, and camp-
followers who wish to be classed with such "scholars"
(?) and to receive a share of the honors and emolu-
ments heaped upon them by those whose brains are
shallow and empty.

The drift of reversionary rather than revolutionary
thinking and teaching may easily induce a sense of
depression, if not of pessimism. One might think,
as he reads reviews of atavistic modernisms, that the
whole array of scholarship is against the teachings
of the New Testament, against Christianity, even
against Jesus Christ. When one gets beneath the
poetry and eloquence which clever writers prate about
our Lord while they dissect and destroy the flower
of his unique personality—and the vital message and
power of his influence—he finds only a body of death.
This, as we have seen, is not the complete story.
However dark the picture may appear to any who
read the literature of negation, especially its so-
called theological literature, the account is not closed
by this representation. For three reasons there is a
spot of light, brighter than that of any Rembrandt,

in the very heart of the canvas. First, because "the foolishness of God is wiser than men" and his Truth ultimately prevails. Second, because "God chose the things that were folly to the world, that he might put to shame them that were wise." This folly of the world but wisdom of God the common people of old heard gladly, and to this hour the heart of humanity is undeceived by its head. Pray God it may remain so, materialist, for if ever those deepest logicians, the fathers and mothers of men and the good citizens, lose their hold on Christianity not even the endowments of old-time piety will be able to pay salaries to modern infidels, and to keep their inanities and insanities vocal. But, further, and especially to the present purpose, it appears that representatives of the wisdom which is born of observation, experimentation, and verification of facts which are embodied in the material universe as well as in the mind and heart of man are friendly to Christianity and are supporting its undertakings. To-day, as formerly, where teachings subversive to religion are presented in the name of science, they meet opposition from higher authorities in the same field. As Newton refuted the negations of Halley, Virchow the materialism of Vogt, and Kelvin the atheism of his day, men of the highest distinction in scientific circles are now attacking vacuous and false philosophies concerning facts which have spiritual meaning and value.

Nevertheless, for the time being we are in heaviness because of the folly of such persons as the one quoted in the opening of this chapter, and the radical professor whose views have been described by William Lowe Bryan, psychologist-educator. This man, an apostle of freedom (?), declared as he left the institution where he had taught for seven years that but two of the five hundred faculty members, himself and one other, stood foursquare for the truth.

Bryan reports him as insisting that "the personal and moral life of the individual must be absolutely free; I mean absolutely. I do not mean that hoary iniquity, that vile excuse for conscription and sex slavery, 'liberty but not license'—I mean that every man shall practice his own liberty, even though it seems license to another." His idea of liberty finds further and sufficient illustration in his report of a colleague who was publicly converted to Christianity. He said that this man should have been promptly dismissed from his position. "The fact," he declared, "that he was not thereupon privately fired, that he was still thought capable of teaching his science, symbolized the situation in its naked horror."[3]

It seems probable, despite some fanatical charges made, that the number of scientists who oppose Christianity in their classrooms is not large, and is proportionately less than is the case in some other departments of instruction. There are exceptional teachers of science, however, who furnish examples of the fact stated by Edwin E. Slosson, chemist, that "the doctrine of evolution is capable of very pernicious perversions both in theory and in practice, as the world has seen. It has been adduced as justification of the claim that 'might is right.' The 'survival of the fittest' has been interpreted as the 'survival of the fightest.' "[4] Henry Fairfield Osborn, zoologist, in *Evolution and Religion* expresses the conviction that evolution "should be taught in our schools simply as nature speaks to us about it and entirely separated from the opinions, materialistic or theistic, which have clustered about it. This simple direct teaching of nature is full of moral and spiritual force." He offers the ethical and spiritual principle which may be presented therewith as his answer

[3]"Youth in Revolt." Address, President William Lowe Bryan, 1926.
[4]*Sermons of a Chemist*, p. 243, Harcourt, Brace and Company.

to "very natural solicitude about the influence of evolution in our schools and colleges—a solicitude not inherent," he declares, "in the subject itself, but in the foolishness and conceit of certain of the teachers who are privileged to teach of the processes of life."[5] There is, then, a way of looking upon nature and life and a way in which science may be taught which is positively dangerous. The peril is not simply to the individual student but to the nation and to humanity. It ought to be recalled by scientists and others that Rudolph Virchow, German pathologist, at the naturalists' convention at Munich many years before the late conflagration in Europe, exclaimed with emphasis, "I only hope that the theory of evolution may not produce those horrors in our country which similar theories have actually brought our neighbors." Virchow's warning as to the influence of scientific dogmatisms as they were advocated in his time has been forgotten, but everybody knows what happened in 1914–1918. But yesterday, looking at a photograph of bodies of poor lads, huddled in trenches and awaiting hasty burial, the thought arose: You were slain, not by the weapons of foes, but by the godless science, philosophy, religion, from which as yet no land or age has been wholly free.[6]

At bottom the question of Christianity, and of any religion at all, depends on belief in Deity. Without a source and Supreme Object of faith, religion cannot be more than an abstraction or sentiment. What is known and taught to-day which affects belief in the existence and character of God and which former generations did not know or teach? The general theory of life-process, which we term evolution, is not of recent origin, and its relationship to the question

---

[5] Pages 16 and 17, Charles Scribner's Sons.

[6] A discussion of some recent applications of the doctrine of natural selection is found in *The Higher Usefulness of Science*, W. E. Ritter, pp. 7-10.

of causation was considered long since. Augustine
knew something of the principle which underlies
natural philosophy, but it did not cost him his Christian faith. He rightly warned his associates not to
take a position with reference to scientific truth,
which is unnecessary to religion and would only make
them ridiculous.[7] Thomas Aquinas had some conception of development in nature, and with Jonathan
Edwards has been claimed as a forerunner of Einstein. Whatever ideas these men had on such subjects they were able to incorporate into their Christian system. We must not make too much of the scientific knowledge of these leaders, or even of John
Wesley. It is true that the latter, in 1763, published
A Survey of the Wisdom of God in the Creation or a
Compendium of Natural Philosophy, enlarged in
1770. The thoughts of many philosophers and scientists are presented. In Vol. II, from page 180, is an
extensive condensation of Charles Bonnet's *The Contemplation of Nature,* described by Wesley as a beautiful work by one of the finest writers of the age.
Bonnet, Swiss naturalist, who also wrote on *The Faculties of the Soul* and *Philosophical Researches on the
Evidences of Christianity,* expresses belief in a First
Cause, who produced and preserves the universe. He
describes the immense system of coexistent and successive beings, which he says, "is no less one in succession than in co-ordination; since the first link is
connected with the last by the intermediate ones."
"Between the lowest and highest degree of corporal
and spiritual perfection there is an almost infinite
number of intermediate degrees." "One Sole Being
is out of this chain, and that is He that made it."
"The polypus links the vegetable to the animal. The
flying squirrel unites the birds to the quadruped.
The ape bears affinity to the quadruped and the man."

[7]H. W. Wood has discussed *Augustine and Evolution.*

"Mankind have their gradations, as well as other productions of our globe. There is a prodigious number of continued links between the most perfect man and the ape." Despite these citations, it should be noted that elsewhere Wesley said, "Adam came directly out of the hands of God without the intervention of any creature." The great evangelist, reformer, and religious statesman had no sympathy with any form of anti-theistic philosophy. The safe conclusion to draw is simply that John Wesley was hospitable to the teachings of science within its own realm, and was able to constitute within himself a unity of scientific and Christian conceptions. Cardinal Wiseman is said to have taken a similar attitude. Bishop Joseph Butler, author of *The Analogy of Religion, Natural and Revealed, to the Constitution and Course of Nature,* considered the question of a physical origin of man a century before Darwin. He is said to have asked, "Why should it be a more repulsive idea to have sprung from something less than man in brain and body, than to have been fashioned, according to the expression in Genesis, out of the dust of the ground?"

What other and greater difficulties for Christian faith are being considered than those which the Christian leaders of the more recent past knew and faced in fact or in anticipation? We have new conceptions of matter, and our "atoms" are composed of positive and negative electrons. What are these? Particles of electricity. What is electricity and what is its origin? An answer of Pupin is given in another connection, and who can disprove it? The judgment of Millikan and of other competent men is well known. The simple truth is that this knowledge—that of the electrical basis of matter—contains nothing which to the slightest degree changes the old problem which has always been met by theistic explanations. Another source of new information is found in the field

of cytology, namely, the living cell and its contents
—the parent of all tissues and structure of living
bodies. What is in the cell which Schleiden and
Schwann, who, in 1839, enunciated the cellular hypothesis, and which Virchow, who, in 1858, introduced
"Cellular Pathology," did not perceive there? These
observers believed in God, but what did they know
about chromosomes and electrons? By no means all
that is now known. But if one has learned the latest
fact which biological and physical science have been
able to establish by anything like irrefragable evidence, does this furnish refutation of the existence
of a Designer, Creator, and Preserver of the universe? Not many scientists assert that this is the
case, and when one so claims, does he do so on
the basis of science, or of his particular brand of philosophy?

It is one thing to accept the principle of evolution
as a working method in nature. It is quite another
thing to swing to a position which Darwin, Huxley,
and Tyndall regarded as being absurd and unscientific, namely, atheism. Alexander Winchell once asserted that a certain type of scientific teaching would
summon us to the funeral of God. Nor does the invention of specious phrases about "Truth" or "Nature" change the character of this transaction. It is
either a god = idolatry of nature, or it is the God of
Christianity. There is no middle ground. Extravagant bowing and scraping to physical reality, beauty,
or righteousness does not deceive. Christianity will
not turn its back on the truth, but it knows that
nothing can be the truth which turns its back on
God. The church is not in general sympathy with
attempts by legislature to dictate what shall be taught
in the schools, though it might and probably would
be forced into approval if atheism were shown to
be organizing to control the training of youth. When
anything is taught which is dangerous to society and

to religion, there should be another remedy than that of politics, namely, the pressure of enlightened public opinion. Any type of instruction which does not succeed in convincing the public that its teachings are safe, that it is not a destructive principle, threatening the foundations of society, of personal morality and of Christian faith will have to give account of itself. Education must be free from the peril of unethical and anti-religious teaching. Obscurantism of the deepest dye is preferable to moral and spiritual anarchy. Culture which is apsychical, amoral, atheistical, is a deadly plague, against which normal and healthful forces, both religious and scientific, must and do contend. Academic freedom there must be, certainly, but not license to enslave the minds of coming generations under the concept of soulless mechanism or mechano-chemism. The sound heart and logical brain of humanity are truthfully represented by Harry Webb Farrington as crying out against monstrous and mortal falsehoods concerning the universe:

> "Oh, not a cosmos, rigid, stern—
>   Devoid of tender smile and nod;
> I know there is within it all
>   A bleeding and a brooding God."[8]

If the protest just made falls upon any mind without eliciting concern, it would be well for him to consider the suggestion of Sir J. F. Stephen that the effects of atheism are not to be determined from the conduct of those who have been educated as believers in God, and in nations which maintain this belief. If we should ever see a generation which attached no meaning at all to the word "God," there would be a light on this subject which would be sufficiently lurid.

One of the dangers of all thinking is that of mis-

---

[8] From *Rough and Brown,* by Major Harry Webb Farrington. Used by permission.

application of ideas, principles, and systems of reaching truth and reality. If it be preposterous to conceive of a religious science, and to bend facts in order to create such a monstrosity, it is equally perilous to attempt to make a scientific religion. The scientist requires the religion which meets the needs of other men, and not the spurious make-shift described by William Hamilton Wood's *The Religion of Science*. The author summed up in terse sentences what seemed to him to be beginning to take form in certain circles as a religious system designed to replace Christianity. In this "religion," truth, beauty, goodness are objects of worship. When one sees the cosmic drift he becomes serious and reverent. Therefore he is religious. His "Eternal" is a quasi-personalized, eternally developing world, an eternal humanity, or both; and this object is to be rendered holy service by the development of science. He may or may not believe in God as First Cause, as an emotion, or as an immanence in nature. He does not need an organized church or institution in order to be religious. He is a Truth-seeker, and not a sectarian, and the best place to worship is out of doors. His morality is individual and social aspiration and progress. He is a balanced character, and shuns all make-believe. Rationality is his watchword, and he needs no traditional faith. Altruism is a product of evolution, but charity to the weak needs greater circumspection. Civilization is not the product of ideals, nor of reason, but of transmission of variants and constants in evolution. There is but one test of truth—conformity to nature. There are canons, a creed, and faith—all of which are natural products. The supernatural simply must not be tolerated. Nature is everything there is. Man, body, mind, society are results of purely natural forces. The problem of evil is to be solved by establishing harmony with our environment. The Bible is a human literature. God did not pre-exist, and there is no Providence. We are masters of our own fate, which ends on this planet, except as it survives in posterity and civilization. The hope of the future lies in breeding a better race.

This summary may be denied, in whole or in part, as representing the belief of any particular individual. What must be admitted, nevertheless, is that some of these expressions, and others like them, have been on the lips of a group of men who do not hesitate to say what kind of a religion, or even Christianity, as it is sometimes named, can be permitted to continue as an impelling force in human affairs. I have just run through a book about *Science as Revelation*. The theme is attractive. Many of the ideas expressed, none of which is quite the news the author seems to suppose it is, are capable of meaning for Christianity. Nevertheless, one cannot help noting the obscurity, indefiniteness or else the positive naturalism in the James Ward definition of the term, which characterizes this production. The author assumes to speak for all the sciences. Is this not the same as sweeping science out of consideration altogether? He quotes, and apparently needs to quote, few scientists. You may take his word for it. The whole tone seems to be that of one whose *ipse dixit* is science and therefore authority. He believes that man is and should be incurably religious, but hopes he will not be incurably theological. If theology is knowledge of God, this view appears to be the same as intimating that there is no God, that we cannot know God, or that God is not worth knowing. Yet the author appears to believe in God, provided he is solely God of nature, or God of the energy which pervades the universe. He seems to recognize the supernatural, though he says he does not, and holds that it is the unknown natural. This view, if correctly apprehended, who would wish to disparage? He believes in revelation, but nature through science is the only revelator. Nature is all. Man has nothing without it. With it everything is his. In knowledge of the cosmos man finds inspiration and the only possible good. God is revealed in nature, and in precise proportion as we learn the laws that form our environment and co-operate with them, heaven arrives now and here. In an early passage occurs a reference to the important teachings of Jesus Christ, leading us to query, Which are *the important* teachings of Jesus?

What do such writers really mean? Truths, half-truths, sweeping universals, evident under and over-statements, poetry, mystery! What really is this "New" Religion, whose content is partly concealed, partly revealed, like the mythical deities and faiths of Greece? It is called "scientific," not certainly in the sense that it is a development of the long-time belief of eminent scientists, which has been brought closer to perfection by recent achievements—the truth-giving process—but as representing something discovered by some sort of "modern" science. Is it not easy to see what has been done with God in such a scheme as this? Has he not been sacrificed on the altar of materialism? And is it not evident that to capitalize the word "Nature," and to bow down before this term, or that for which it stands, or before any principle in nature, as if it represented Deity, is merely an ancient error tricked out in contemporary finery, and a form of idolatry more pitiable than that of "a pagan suckled in a creed outworn"? Over against this view is the attitude expressed by Vernon L. Kellogg, zoologist: "The cause of things may be called God; the manner of things, Science."[9] Such statements are usually intended to mean, as it is evident from his other writings Kellogg does here signify, The cause of things, as we conceive it, *is* God. "Evo-

---

[9]Science bulletin, confirmed by author.

lution by no means takes God out of the universe," asserts Henry F. Osborn,[10] who also testifies to the theistic faith of John Muir, the naturalist, and of Cope. Of the former he says: "In the splendid journey which I had the privilege of taking with him to Alaska in 1896, I first became aware of his passionate love of nature in all its forms, and his reverence for it as the direct handiwork of the Creator. He retained from his early religious training under his father this belief, which is so strongly expressed in the Old Testament, that all the works of nature are directly the works of God. In this sense I have never known anyone whose nature-philosophy was more thoroughly theistic; at the same time he was a thorough-going evolutionist."[11] Of Edward Drinker Cope, American palæontologist, Osborn also affirms that "as a natural philosopher he was creative and constructive, his metaphysics ending in theism rather than in agnosticism."[12]

In *Direction of American Evolution* Edwin Grant Conklin indicates that in all law God is found, and he expresses his judgment that the theory of evolution furnishes sublimer conceptions of the world and of its Creator.[13] "I am sure," says Richard Swann Lull, palæontologist, in a contribution to *Christianity and Modern Thought,* "that belief in a divine Author and Upholder of the universe is more widespread among my colleagues than is generally supposed."[14] He quotes Henry S. Pritchett, astronomer and educator, to the effect that faith in God and in human progress is found in science.

It is evident from recent writings of representative men that no impotent, absent or indifferent deity

---

[10]*Evolution and Religion,* p. 11, Charles Scribner's Sons.

[11]*Impressions of Great Naturalists,* p. 199, Charles Scribner's Sons.

[12]*Ibid.,* p. 163.

[13]Vide p. 213.

[14]Pages 54 and 55, Yale University Press.

commands their confidence. "The belief that God wound up the world in the beginning and set it running," says Edwin E. Slosson, "and that it has been running by itself ever since, except for a little regulating now and then, is rank materialism. We believe in God the Sustainer, as well as in God the Creator. We believe in a God of the present; not merely a God who did something once, but a God who does everything now."[15] "Of God in isolation from the world," says C. Lloyd Morgan in *Emergent Evolution,* "I can form no adequate conception." This zo-ologist and psychologist also says, "In my belief in God, on whom all things depend, I am certainly not alone."[16]

George John Blewett, in *The Study of Nature and the Vision of God,* teaches that the true inspiration of life is the love of God, its true object his glory and the perfection of human life oneness with him."

In his article "The Method of Science," in Mathew's *Contributions of Science to Religion,* William E. Ritter says that "seeing God in the universe is no more difficult than seeing electrons there. We have ample testimony concerning both; concerning neither have we complete and final knowledge." He then uses John 16. 13 to show that we have a God of revelation, "Howbeit when he, the Spirit of truth, is come, he shall guide you into all the truth." The quotation suggests to his memory the pathological incident of a preacher who was conducting a prayer meeting in a church which Dr. Ritter formerly attended. When asked whether "all the truth" in the saying of Jesus might be taken as covering for example the teaching of chemistry, the preacher said, "It refers only to sacred truth." Whereon the sensible comment is made that the preacher's "hold on the realities of life might have been stronger had he realized that

---

[15]*Sermons of a Chemist,* p. 88, Harcourt, Brace and Company.
[16]Page 299, Henry Holt and Company.

truth is one, that it cannot be divided into sacred, chemical, and physical varieties in such a completely isolable way."[17]

In the day when the revelations of nature are more perfectly comprehended will it not appear to be the case, as Colfelt contended, that enlargement of our conceptions of the universe, instead of disproving its divine authorship, exalts our conceptions of God. There is probably very little danger, H. N. Russell affirms, that our idea of God may be pitched too high.[18] Who can doubt that Millikan is right in suggesting that finite minds are only beginning by searching to find adequate conceptions of the Deity.[19] What seems to be certain is that those who think deeply are coming not only to know Him whom to know aright is life eternal, but that they are finding him to be in all respects more divine and more resourceful than was the God revealed in earlier ages. Is not this to be expected? For a savage, a powerful tyrant sufficed as an object of worship. To better minds, but simple, a bread-and-butter deity, a mere provider of good and a shock-absorber and tornado-shelter answered the purpose. As the race developed, the higher attributes of God could be apprehended, and the movement toward a better theism will continue. It is a fundamental error to describe this process as merely anthropomorphic; metamorphic is nearer the truth. Man is not creating God; *He* is still making man into his own image, into higher forms of intellectual and spiritual capacity and quality. As to the recognition of these great facts, it seems evident that percipients too often see only what they are looking for. Generally also they observe little more than they are competent to find. Does not this ex-

---

[17]*Op. cit.*, p. 18, D. Appleton and Company.
[18]Lecture, "God and Man," in *Fate and Freedom*, from p. 61, Yale University Press.
[19]See final paragraph, *Evolution in Science and Religion*, R. A. Millikan.

plain why Haeckel looked at the world and saw in it
no Spirit, while Kelvin, gazing at the same vast pano-
rama, declared, "Science positively affirms a creating
and directing Power"? Neither misrepresented what
he observed. The godless man sees no God, but as
Philip Cabot says and as many accord: "No rational
man, it seems to me, who will give his mind to it and
will examine the evidence, can remain in doubt that
God is the source of life."[20] Saint Paul's clear statement is modernized in phrase and in experience:
"Now the sheer naturalist receiveth not the things of
the Spirit of God: for to such a man they are foolishness and he cannot know them, because they are spiritually examined." If anyone is inclined to scoff at
this view of method, let it be observed that exactly
the same thing is often said with respect to science,
namely, that it does not exist for him who does not
approach nature in the right spirit.

It is too evident to be denied that the proper bounds
of science or of particular scientific departments are
sometimes ignored by one who claims to represent
its teachings. When this occurs it is usually found,
as above stated, that an authority competent to do
so makes suitable protest. In this way John
Tyndall was helpful to the cause of religion when,
speaking of Carlyle, he said that to him "it was the
illegitimate science, which in its claims overstepped
its warrant—professing to explain everything and to
sweep the world clear of mystery—that was really
repugnant."[21] Tyndall assigned to interpretation of
the results of physical researches some such metes
and bounds as the author of *Limits of Evolution* emphasized in the warning, "Let men of science keep
the method of science within the limits of science; let
their readers, at all events, beware to do so. Within

---

[20] *Except Ye Be Born Again*, p. 32, The Macmillan Company.
[21] *New Fragments*, p. 388, D. Appleton and Company.

these limits," George Holmes Howison, philosopher, continues, "there is complete compatibility with religion, and forever will be."[22] "There must be no trespassing on either side," justly declares J. Arthur Thomson, "and it is a little too acquiescent," he adds, "to think of science as the only kind of knowledge, or to think of its laws as complete and finished formulæ. Just because it restricts itself to what can be established by certain methods, science is bound to be partial and abstract. In this sense science knows in part."[23] G. B. Jeffery, mathematician, is one of many who have held that the mystery and significance of the things which science describes will still face investigators after their purposes have been accomplished in the simplest possible description of the material universe. The logic of this is apparent. Room is left in the universe for truths attainable by spiritual methods. May it not be that, when divine-human principles have been more competently worked out, theology, if not again regarded as *scientia scientiarum,* will at least gain full recognition in its own realm.

Christianity acknowledges the value of every discoverable physical truth and approves the justice of scientists who have such an attitude of mind as that shown by Count Alfred Korzybski, Polish engineer, in the preface to his *Manhood of Humanity:* "This book has not been written with indifference to that great, perhaps the greatest, urge of the human heart, the craving for spiritual truth, our yearning for the higher potentialities of that which we call 'mind,' 'soul,' and 'spirit.' "[24] Louis T. More, in *The Limitations of Science,* gives credit to the well-founded knowledge that there exist, "in addition to material

[22]Page 54, The Macmillan Company.

[23]Article, "Science and Religion," *Homiletic Review,* December, 1923, Funk & Wagnalls Company.

[24]E. P. Dutton & Company.

forces, others of an essentially different kind, which may be called, for want of a better name, spiritual powers."[25] Sylvanus P. Thompson, author of *A Not Impossible Religion,* was a bridge-builder between the realm of ascertained truth and the realm of reasonable faith, teaching the divineness of duty, the sacredness of time and sense and the multiplicity of the sacraments of God. Every sincere suggestion on this theme is worthy of consideration, whether it be found in such sturdy statements as those of James Y. Simpson, in *The Spiritual Interpretation of Nature,* or even in cryptic and defective utterances of honest students. It seems paltry, of course, when men refer to "spiritual values" of knowledge from which by assumptions made they have eliminated religious or ethical qualities, but it is something that even by the use of terms which have been robbed of their rightful content they confess the poverty of merely physical conceptions of the world. Such expressions may be those of groping minds, not purposively seeking to be blind leaders.

The problems which confront thoughtfulness are very profound, but it is science itself which has taught men not to be content with the undetermined and the indefinite, but to explore all regions and depths. The masses are therefore not irrational in their restlessness and disappointment when offered the husks of agnosticism, materialism, or spiritual solipsism in place of the ripe grain of divine truth. They are encouraged when truth is looked at both in its partial manifestations and in its totality, and the way left open which leads forward and upward. Truth often has aspects which are apparently contradictory. If nature is not self-caused and self-sufficient, it must be found to contain evidences of purpose. Weismann paradoxically believed that the extremest mechanism

---

[25]Page 260, Henry Holt & Company.

is consistent with teleology. H. N. Russell, in *Fate and Freedom,* relates a strong spiritual faith to a mechanistic view of the physical universe. Lawrence J. Henderson, in *The Order of Nature,* brings the duality of the universe into a clearer synthesis when he asserts that science finds reason "to conclude that the contrast of mechanism with teleology is the very foundation of the order of nature, which must ever be regarded from two complementary points of view—as a vast assemblage of changing systems, and as a harmonious unity of changeless laws and qualities, working together in the process of evolution."[26] The denial of design in nature which Descartes began and which Comte wrought into a system finds refutation in conclusions such as these. If Paley's illustrations of design are obsolete, the principle is not destroyed, and William North Rice, geologist, in *The Return to Faith* affirmed that, "though making no approach to demonstration, the argument from design, as it may be reconstructed in adaptation to an evolutionary conception of nature, does establish a real probability for the existence of a personal God."[27] Such observations are very interesting even to those who believe with Bushnell that the life and passion of Jesus do more to evidence Deity in the universe than do all mechanical adaptations.[28]

In periods of superficial thinking, when it is asserted by some who essay authority that natural intelligence and reason account for all observable phenomena, it is interesting and valuable to read such discussions as that of the mathematician Cassius J. Keyser, in his Phi Beta Kappa address on *Science and Religion.* "My thesis is that the Rational implies

[26] Page 209, Harvard University Press.
[27] Page 98, The Abingdon Press.
[28] Vide, *Nature and the Supernatural,* Horace Bushnell, p. 509.

and reveals the Superrational," he maintains, and he
sustains the thesis by facts which establish the truth
that "as the light of reason spreads and intensifies,
it more and more reveals evidences and intimations
that over and above reason's domain, overarching and
compassing it about, there lie regions of reality unto
which the rational nature of man indeed aspires, ap-
proximates and points, as unto its ideal and over-
world." Even space and number yield a mathesis of
this realm, as wholly beyond the range of the rational as the latter is above the domain of sense and
of the subrational. The creed which ascribes to reason all that we do not share jointly with the beasts
is repudiated as false. The conclusion, logically
reached, is that since it points unmistakably to the
superrational "the light of knowledge, instead of being inimical to religion, is destined to be its purer and
fuller source."[29]

The mere term as well as the idea of the "supernatural" seems to be an object of repugnance to those
who follow the trend of thinking to which Voltaire
gave impetus. Nevertheless, one may find accordant
statements of men who have given a lifetime to the
study of nature. Charles W. Hargitt, zoologist, in his
article on "Problems of Science and Faith," expressed
this conviction : "When we come to recognize the fact
that the natural and spiritual are not separate and
unrelated realms ruled by distinctly different laws,
but, rather, different expressions of one and the same
universe, and governed by the same infinite and
eternal Energy from which all things proceed, we
shall find ourselves exclaiming with one of ancient
time, 'The heavens declare the glory of God, and the
firmament showeth his handiwork. Day unto day
uttereth speech and night unto night showeth knowledge.' These realms are his kingdom of which there

---

[29]*Op. cit.,* p. 52, Yale University Press.

shall be no end, neither shadow of turning."[30]   How far removed from such a judgment is that which contends that the spiritual must be driven out of the realm of thought!   Of course, as we have seen, it is the very business of science to enlarge the sphere of the known natural, and many supposed supernaturals have thus been explained.   The strange result is, however, not the destruction of the idea of the supernatural but the enlargement of the boundaries of the unknown and the superrational.   The constructive imagination of modern science has produced a numerous offspring of atoms, electrons, ions, quanta, colloids, vitamines, which are as much beyond ordinary comprehension as are the most recondite doctrines of religion, while the supernaturalism of the whole evolutionary process is a concept of reality which is making intellectual seizure of many careful students.   Clear thinking on this topic seems to be coming with such expressions as that of T. M. Lowry, chemist: "We must show and see God whole. Religion is supernatural, not anti-natural.   It may be beyond one's knowledge, but it is not contrary to the rules."[31]

Behaviorism and similar tendencies in psychology, in the hands of unwise advocates, threaten spiritual and moral values, but the very absolutism, intolerance, and pride which too frequently characterize these systems are evidence that they are neither firmly grounded nor sure of themselves.   A letter in my possession says, "I fear some of the biological psychologists will give me scant approval."   The reference is to a piece of work in which a psychologist clearly enunciates facts which are significant to Christian thought.   The writer is somewhat apprehensive of the injury which may be done to his reputa-

[30]*Methodist Review*, November-December, 1924, p. 844.

[31]"An Interview With Doctor T. Martin Lowry," Arthur Herbert, *Methodist Magazine*, London, England, January, 1924.

tion by the comments of a group of broad-minded
(?) colleagues. This is not all his concern, however.
Speaking of the behaviorist psychology as it is being
taught by extremists in some of our schools, and
which professes fully to explain human experience,
he says: "You know what the implications of such
psychology are, and they are pretty disastrous to religious faith. The self = 0; the hope of personal immortality goes; and God = ? ? Or God is identified
with an 'Idealized Human Society,' à la Auguste
Comte." Fortunately, there are men in all departments of science who are not intimidated by "the fear
of the pack" or carried away by impermanent popular
philosophies.

Former disparagement of emotion as experience
and as a source of knowledge went too far, and reaction has set in. Keyser speaks of "emotional knowledge" or "knowledge-in-immediate-experience," which,
he affirms, "a scientific man may have as well as
another, but he cannot win it or have it in his capacity as a scientific student. None but a lover really
knows love."[32] Sir Oliver Lodge must have approval
from sensible persons when he protests that "if a
man of science seeks to dogmatize concerning the
Emotions and the Will, and asserts that he can reduce them to atomic forces and motions he is exhib-
iting the smallness of his conceptions and gibbeting
himself as a laughing-stock to future generations."[33]
The statements of Sir G. G. Stokes and of J. Arthur
Thomson, quoted elsewhere, are based on the knowledge which intimacy with human beings reveals,
namely, that they are related not only to a "fact"
world and an "idea" world but also to a "feeling"
world in which they not only believe but in which
they "live and move and have their being." There-

[32]*Science and Religion,* Cassius J. Keyser, p. 6, Yale University
Press.

[33]*Hibbert Journal.*

fore, while men will always respect science and admire its achievements, many will not regard it as being complete and satisfactory if it ignores or belittles the meaning of human emotions. Loisy, devoted to scientific doctrine, was right in insisting that souls require other hearths than those of a science whose light gives no warmth.

Psychology has an opportunity, which competent men will use effectively, to bring science into helpful relations with the heart of humanity. William McDougall in *Body and Mind* makes a detailed examination of facts involved in the problem which these terms present and reaches from a strictly scientific point of view the conclusion implied by the concept "soul." He denies that merely mechanical principles can supply an adequate explanation of biological phenomena, individual, racial, or social. A firm basis is laid for intelligent—may one not say scientific?—Christianity.[34] Francis L. Strickland comments on affective consciousness, reactions, and emotions. In *Psychology of Religious Experience* he explains, to those who oppose basing certainty upon any form of the feeling consciousness, that feeling-states are not the individual possessions which they are often supposed to be. Their nature may be just as universal as are rational processes and states. Men are often "sharers in something common" through feelings which point to the same values. He shows that "feeling, while it always accompanies percepts, images, or ideas, is nevertheless, in the last analysis, the basis upon which we determine the value of these images or ideas, and hence it governs us in the assent we give to them. Now, this assent is usually immediate, and when reason does not subsequently forbid, we rest in it as final." He declares that the great common feelings of human

---

[34]*Op. cit.*, Vide p. 356, and the remarks on creative power and freedom in the closing chapter of McDougall's *Outline of Psychology*.

experience have a universality above that of merely personal feelings, and that "it is through this growing community of feeling that we are brought into the larger relations with the world of other selves, and ultimately with the Supreme Self." This is science ministering to the deeper life.[35]

The work of psychology and philosophy in the field of creativity and of freedom contains implications and an ultimate logic of interest and helpfulness to Christianity, which is certainly a creative religion, operating in a free and living universe. William Lowe Bryan takes a constructive psychological attitude when he says, "Our race has come up the long way out of the dust, sharing all the way in the creative work of the living God."[36] *Creative Chemistry*, by Edwin E. Slosson, by its very title suggests as does Bergson's *Creative Evolution* that divine and human intelligences are working together in universal tasks. If creative personality is a valid concept and fact, its importance in the development of Christian teaching and experience is very evident. Religious creativity is related to all phases of Christian instruction, worship, service and, above all, life.

The infelicitously named book by William M. Goldsmith, biologist, *Evolution or Christianity*, contains a number of statements of scientific teachers who see no anti-Christian bearing in evolution. H. F. Nachtrieb, zoologist, thinks that when this doctrine is properly taught "it should not conflict with the life of Jesus Christ." A. C. Moore, biologist, says that evolution "will make for more careful and exact teaching of the Bible. Evolution is one fact in a great philosophy of life, and must be made to fit into that philosophy." D. B. Casteel, zoologist, is considered by Goldsmith to say admirably that "as a scientific generalization, the doctrine of evolution bears no

---

[35] *Op. cit.*, pp. 168-170, The Abingdon Press.
[36] *Youth in Revolt*, p. 12.

necessary relation to miracles. In its broader sense an evolutionary interpretation of nature in no way denies the actuality of a controlling power, and this conception of the method of creation will, if rightly understood, lead to a truer appreciation of the extent of the omniscience and the omnipotence resident in divinity." Another interesting statement is that of John F. Bovard, zoologist, who believes that "the doctrine of evolution is not inconsistent with the miracles commonly attributed to Christ in the New Testament."[37]

A number of scientific men make a distinction between "religion" and "institutional religion." It was in defense of the former that *A Joint Statement Upon the Relations of Science and Religion,* numerously signed by scientists and religious leaders, was issued a few years since. The paper contained a pacific prelude, the signers' conception of the functions of science and of religion, and this affirmation: "It is a sublime conception of God which is furnished by science, and one wholly consonant with the highest ideals of religion, when it represents him as revealing himself through countless ages in the development of the earth as an abode for man and in the age-long inbreathing of life into its constituent matter, culminating in man with his spiritual nature and all his godlike powers." Among the names appended to this document are some of the most notable in present American science, most, if not all, of whom are those of active Christian men.

The treatment of our theme should not be concluded without both a more general and a more personal review of the present situation in some chief centers of the world's thought. Better news than formerly comes from Germany. When Georg Wobbermin wrote one of his important works, *Christian*

---

[37]The quotations of this paragraph occur on pp. 84 and 85, Haldeman-Julius Company.

Belief in God, he placed in opposition to the idea contained in the term *"l'homme machine"* the names of
such natural philosophers as Liebmann, Paulsen, and
Wundt, and of such natural scientists as Johannes
Reinke, botanist, and Oskar Hertwig, anatomist and
biologist. Wobbermin quoted Reinke, who rejects
pantheism utterly, as saying in *Die Welt als Tat* concerning origins, "Reasoning after the methods of
induction and analogy, the natural scientist will find
that reducing the nature and existence of organisms
to a creating Deity is not only the most plausible but
the only conceivable explanation—for him this follows with convincing logic from the facts."[38]

Dr. Friedrich Wunderlich has made a statement
covering more recent conditions than those which
Wobbermin considered, and prepared for the purposes
of this chapter, in the course of which he says that
Professor Girgensohn agrees with him in saying that
"natural science has too long stood under the banner
of mechanism and is only now beginning to free itself
from the rigid dogmatism by which it has been governed. The natural scientist of to-day prefers to limit
himself to manifestations lying within his own range
of science." Nevertheless, he says, "It appears to me
that more has been done over here to overcome the
standpoint of mechanism in the world outlook than
in America, although in other respects religion and
natural science are nearer to each other there than
in Germany." Wunderlich states that Albert G. P.
Fleischmann, zoologist, "does not give expression to
his attitude toward Christianity in any way, but contents himself with opposing the teachings of Darwin and his scholars."[39] Of Hans Driesch, of Leipzig,
author of *The Science and Philosophy of the Organism,* "who graduated under Ernst Haeckel, having

---

[38]*Op. cit.,* p. 95, Yale University Press.

[39]Among critics of Darwinism are Wiegand, Gustav Wolff, natural
scientists, Rudolph Otto, and K. Portig.

later on worked in Haeckel's laboratory as assistant," he remarks, "Already, during the course of his studies, he was at variance with his teacher, and to-day openly confesses to be a rival of Haeckel. His aim is to become quite free from the authority of mechanism, confining the same only to the inorganic world, and to recognize a power in the organic and psychical world—that of Teleology. The consequences ensuing therefrom for metaphysics are very evident. At any rate, a physical dogmatism is not to be found here any more." Another observation of Wunderlich is: "Psychology has also undergone a very interesting development in the last twenty years. It has also become free from the overruling idea of Mechanism (to a much greater extent than in America). The 'Marburg School' was one of the first to fight for this." The same writer adds: "Among the natural scientists taking a positive attitude toward Christianity, Dennert is the most prominent."[40]

Catholic publications have widely disseminated the views of Gustav Hauser, pathological anatomist, as they are presented in his recent Leipzig autobiography. In his youth this German scholar was an atheist, which fact he attributes to immaturity. When he entered manhood and became absorbed in natural philosophy, as the wonders of the universe disclosed themselves to him he was deeply impressed with the thought that science is infinitely far from a perception of the secrets of the world, and that the mind must seek guidance elsewhere. Hauser denounces as criminal the disturbance of public faith in God, and declares the nation to be doomed to utter ruin which loses confidence in Deity and in transcendental things.

Dr. J. Arthur Thomson, Aberdeen biologist, writes me to this effect: "I know that many men like Profes-

---

[40]Statement obtained by courtesy of Bishop John L. Nuelsen, Zurich, Switzerland.

sor E. W. Macbride, zoologist; Sir William Bragg, chemist; Professor E. T. Whittaker, zoologist; and so on, are devout, reverent, religious men." Principal H. B. Workman, London, says that Silvanus P. Thompson "was a man of the highest eminence and a thorough Christian." He states that Thomas Martin Lowry, Cambridge chemist, is a Wesleyan local preacher, and remarks, "Few men have a higher standing in the world of science." He describes Sir J. J. Thomson, physicist, as being one of the greatest leaders of England in abstract thought, and says, "Professor Thomson certainly acknowledges himself to be a Christian." Dr. J. Y. Simpson, Edinburgh, places among the men of science in his country "who are quite definitely Christian men and have let their fellows know this," Charles G. Barkla, physicist; E. T. Whittaker, above mentioned; and T. J. Jehu, geologist. He thinks that the same may be said of H. S. Allen, physicist; that Herbert Westren Turnbull, mathematician, and C. Lloyd Morgan, author of *Life, Mind, and Spirit*, who has been called the founder of comparative psychology, would certainly be found on that side. Simpson adds, "I am quite certain that there are many others." My correspondence indicates that Christianity has many adherents among living scientists in Great Britain, and on the continent of Europe. France and Italy continue, as of old, to furnish examples as distinguished as those of the northern countries.

During a conversation at the American Colony, Jerusalem, in 1927, Frank D. Adams, member of the Research Council of Canada, and for many years geologist at McGill University, said that if he were asked to name scientists of Canada who are opposed or hostile to Christianity he would be put to it to name over two or three in all. Among former McGill scientists who took a definite Christian position, Doctor Adams talked of Sir J. W. Dawson, geologist;

Sir William Osler, medicine; and H. M. Tory, physicist, now president of Alberta University. He also spoke of the Christian character of the late Eugene Haanel, of Stanley McKenzie, and of A. P. Coleman. The men mentioned are members of Church of England, Methodist, or Presbyterian bodies. Doctor Adams also stated that a long list of Christian characters among the younger scientists of Canada could be easily secured.

What may be said about scientists of the United States? In 1922 Robert A. Millikan published the following statement concerning the attitude toward religion in general of a number of prominent scientific characters of America. After discussing some of the great personalities of the past, the first physicist to isolate the electron, a member of the Congregational Church, said: "I can bring the evidence strictly up to date by asking you to name the dozen most outstanding scientists in America to-day and then showing you that the great majority of them will bear emphatic testimony, not only to the complete lack of antagonism between the fields of science and religion, but to their own fundamental religious convictions. One naturally begins with the man who occupies the most conspicuous scientific position in the United States, namely, the president of the National Academy of Sciences, who is at present both the head of the Smithsonian Institution of Washington and the president of the American Association for the Advancement of Science, Dr. Charles D. Walcott,[41] one of the foremost of American students of the evolution of life in the early geologic ages. He is personally known to me to be a man of deep religious conviction and has recently written me asking that he be described for the purposes of this address, which he has seen, as an

---

[41] Since deceased.

active church worker. The same is true of Henry
Fairfield Osborn, the director of the American Museum of Natural History of New York, and one of
the foremost exponents of evolution in the country.
Another rival for eminence in this field is Edwin G.
Conklin, of Princeton, who in recently published ar-
ticles has definitely shown himself a proponent of
the religious interpretation of life. In the same category I know, also from direct correspondence, that I
may place John C. Merriam, president of the Carnegie Institution of Washington, and America's foremost palæontologist; Michael Pupin, the very first
of our electrical experts, who has approved every
word of this address ("Science and Religion"), and
recently delivered a better one at Columbia University on this same subject; John Coulter, dean of
American botanists; A. A. and W. A. Noyes, foremost
among our chemists; James R. Angell, president of
Yale University, an eminent psychologist, with
whom I have had an exchange of letters on this
subject; James H. Breasted, our most eminent archæologist, who served with me for years on the board
of trustees of a Chicago church, upon which also T. C.
Chamberlin, dean of American geologists, was a constant attendant; Dr. C. G. Abbot, home secretary of
the National Academy of Sciences, eminent astronomer and active churchman; and so on through the
list of most of the scientists of special eminence in
this country." A letter from M. I. Pupin bears this
testimony: "I am a member of the Serbian branch of
the Orthodox Church, but I am affiliated with every
movement which has for its object the spiritual uplift of man."[42] With the above list the late Charles
W. Hargitt placed the names of William North Rice,
geologist, author of *Christian Faith in an Age of
Science, The Return to Faith,* and *Science and Re-*

[42] Letter to author.

ligion: Five So-called Conflicts; Edward L. Rice, zoologist, and Ira Remsen, chemist and educator, saying, "Time would fail me to cite scores of others, men of the highest Christian character." Recent publications contain the names of H. N. Russell, astronomer, and A. H. Compton, physicist, among Presbyterian scientists.

What finer tribute could be paid to a scientist and Christian than the following concerning William A. Locy, zoologist, who slipped away toward the close of 1924 after a regular day's work at his task: "As a member of the Presbyterian Church whose scientific attainments seemed to strengthen his Christian faith, Professor Locy was always concerned for the religious as well as the scientific welfare of his students. No pupil of his ever received a superficial view of biological truth, nor was one ever known to become unsettled in his Christian faith or in his attitude toward religion because of Professor Locy's scientific teaching. Science in the hands of such Christian teachers strengthens faith."[43] Dayton C. Miller has penned a similar statement concerning John A. Brashear, astronomer and Methodist lay preacher: "There never lived a man who did more to help his fellows and who inspired them with more noble ideals." A recent letter concerning a scientist who is exceedingly punctual and devout in Christian worship brought to mind an account by George S. Clifford of a visit to his friend, Edward Emerson Barnard, astronomer.[44] This trained observer discovered sixteen comets and the fifth satellite of Jupiter. He won the Lalande and Janssen gold medals of the French Academy and the Janssen prize of the French Astronomical Society. When visiting the Yerkes Observatory and being entertained by Professor Barnard, Clifford says that

---

[43]Locy thought that biology gives religion and ethics a broader basis. See *Biology and Its Makers,* p. 456.
[44]Given the author by Doctor Clifford.

one evening after dinner his host remarked to his
friends that it was the habit of the family to attend
prayer meeting, and that they were invited to ac-
company them that night.   The invitation was accepted by all.   Is there anything in this simple
reminiscence which should surprise the reader?   If
Faraday, after captivating a learned audience with a
brilliant treatise on magnetism, refusing to wait even
for the compliments of royalty, could hurry off to his
village church to be in time for a service there, who
is too great to be obedient to the call to worship?   I
have known men of science who were as thoughtful
of church responsibilities and as thoroughly convinced of the value of Christian practices as were any
others in the community in which they lived. At about
the date of the writing of this paragraph I recall
meeting in various Christian activities a physicist, a
geologist, a zoologist, and a historian, all of whom
are eminent enough to be recorded in the best lists
of authorities in their respective departments, and in
Who's Who.   These men are connected with church
boards and committees, and give faithful attention to
the duties imposed by such relationships.

Modern medical authorities give strong evidence
of religious belief.   An interesting question and answer by John M. Dodson is given in *Contributions of
Science to Religion*.   He asks, "Have the recent advances in the medical sciences developed anything
which should disturb religious faith?"   The reply is,
"Not at all!"[45]   Sir William Whitla, author of a
Materia Medica which has run to eleven editions, and
president of the Irish Medical Schools, for several
years served as president of the Young Men's Christian Association of Belfast.   It is not easy to over-
state the value of such Christian testimonies as that
of Howard A. Kelly, gynecologist, surgeon, authority

---

[45]Page 283, Shailer Mathews, D. Appleton & Company.

on radium, and writer on reptilia and fungi, who in the *American* for December, 1924, gave tribute to his indebtedness to the Bible and to the Christian experience which may be found by the method indicated in John 7. 17, "If any man will do his will, he shall know of the doctrine, whether it be of God, or whether I speak of myself." *A Scientific Man and the Bible* contains a later testimony of Kelly. A strong witness of Christian faith is that of Dr. Thomas Bodley Scott. In his work on *Endocrine Therapeutics* he remarks that "our human laws are often mere changing compromises, serving their purpose for a time, but," he says, "the divine law that we observe in nature is one only, never swerving, unchangeable, just and true. We are only now getting glimpses of its higher potentialities and of its divine simplicity. There seems to be one power alone that governs and moves the whole universe, matter and mind alike. In practical therapeutics it must be our aim to get knowledge of this power and to utilize it, as Christ did, in the service of mankind. We must, I think, look on his miracles as evidences of his knowledge and use of natural powers that are as yet unknown to us. As yet, our low spiritual development and our selfishness, national and individual, would render such powers dangerous weapons. 'Such knowledge is too wonderful for me; I cannot attain unto it,' says David, but higher spiritual and altruistic ideals will fit us for the glorious possession."[46]

William W. Keen, practicing, educational and army surgeon, whose views are quoted elsewhere, is a Baptist layman and lifelong trustee of one of the institutions founded by that body of Christians. The sketch of Richard C. Cabot, physician and educator, published in *Who's Who,* contains the significant notation, "Christian." In his *What Men Live By* are

---

[46] Introductory chapter, H. K. Lewis, London.

sympathetic treatments of confession, petition, praise, communion, answer to prayer. The main problem of prayer is viewed through the medium of Christ's prayer in Gethsemane, to which various references are made. Worship is described as being the only adequate expression of "the torrent of thankfulness I feel to Christ."[47] Sir Bertram C. A. Windle, M. D., of Toronto, in *The Catholic Church and Its Reactions With Science,* gives the reader views of one who sees no inconsistency in adhering to both scientific fact and Christian faith.

Frequent and more definite testimonies to the value of Christianity are being given by men of scientific standing. Just as President E. D. Burton had done shortly before his death, Edwin E. Slosson, in *Sermons of a Chemist,* names Jesus as teacher—Burton said author—of the scientific method: "The teacher does not say, 'Look at the name of the author and doubt it if you dare.' No, he says, 'Go into the laboratory and try it for yourself.' That is the scientific method and that is the method of Jesus." In support of this statement he cites the passage quoted by Kelly, John 7. 17, and adds: "John sent two of his disciples to Jesus to ask if he were the Christ; 'Then Jesus answering said unto them, Go your way, and tell John what things ye have seen and heard.' It was the pragmatic test to which he appealed, how his religion worked, the severest and the certainest test in the world. Christianity, insofar as it is truly Christian, rests upon the same solid foundations as chemistry."[48] To be completely stated, the scientific method, which is also the method of Jesus, is threefold—the text and reference book, the teacher, and observation and experiment in field or laboratory. We get our Christianity by the same process as that by which we get our science.

---

[47] *Op. cit.,* p. 311, Houghton Mifflin Company.
[48] *Op. cit.,* p. 69, Harcourt, Brace and Company.

John Merle and M. C. Coulter, botanists, in their compact little book, *Where Evolution and Religion Meet,* are very outspoken both in defense of their scientific views and of their attitude toward Christianity. They exclaim: "The reason why so many scientific men believe in Christianity is that they find it to be so thoroughly scientific. What can be called a scientific approach to religion may be outlined as follows: Religion is now known to be a universal human impulse." "Any universal impulse must have some function." "It seems obvious that the function of the religious impulse is to develop the greatest efficiency, to bring man to the highest expression of his being. The resulting efficiency all depends on the ideal selected." "The most effective ideal for the religious impulse is love stimulating service. This is the ideal of the Christian religion, and it makes scientific men choose it as the only religion with a scientific approach." "Furthermore, since it has selected our most masterful passion as the stimulus, it is the final religion." "It is clear," the authors also assure their readers, "that Christianity has a scientific basis in the nature of man, and that its results have been demonstrated as clearly as those of experimental evolution. The fact is that these two great fields, so far from being contradictory, are mutually helpful. In this way the revelation of God in nature has supplemented his revelation through Christ." A further statement on this theme is that "when one has been completely informed concerning evolution he realizes that it does not contradict the Bible in any serious way, but really teaches the same fundamental truths from a different point of view."[49] It is evidently a similar view of the relationship between natural and scriptural teachings which led my friend and former coworker in Christian service, the late Charles W.

[49]Op. cit., pp. 103-104, The Macmillan Company.

Hargitt, to exclaim: "There is no such thing as conflict of religion and science. It is the bickerings of bigotry or ignorance of partisans, both scientists and religionists, who have ends to serve other than that truth of God declared to make men free."[50]

Dayton C. Miller, author of *Laboratory Physics*, and of researches in problems connected with relativity, a member of the Congregational Church, relates historic and prophetic judgments in the opinion that "the essence of the old wisdom is religious faith, and when this is combined with the new science there results a true and sound philosophy. Saint Paul expresses the modern scientific spirit when he says, 'Prove all things; hold fast that which is good.' "[51] Louis Trenchard More, physicist and graduate educator, Episcopalian, gives Christianity this approval: "I have become far more in sympathy with the essential beliefs of the Christian religion than I have with the humanitarian and mechanistic doctrines of sociologists. I have come to a profound belief in the immutable laws of what may be called the spiritual world, and find in the life and teachings of Jesus the best and fullest expression of these laws."[52]

The author of *Evolution and Christian Faith*, Henry Higgins Lane, biologist, member Disciples of Christ, argues for a God of immanence and transcendence, of law and order, of gravitation and evolution. Becoming definite in his expressions he expresses the thought that "if the Christianity of the New Testament is good and true, as we believe it is, the discoveries of science should not contradict it, but complete its verification,"[53] and he quotes F. H. Giddings,[54] sociologist, to the effect that as a matter of

---

[50]Letter to author.   [51]Letter to author.

[52]*Idem.*

[53]See especially p. 194, Princeton University Press.

[54]Author, *Studies in the Theory of Human Society,* and other books on sociology.

fact they have been verifying it. Lane thinks Christ, as part of the Godhead, not subject to science. Incarnation is to be accepted by the believer as a unique event. Miracles occur by unknown laws. Gravitation is superseded by other laws, and it is not miraculous to us that this transpires. Christianity is God's plan in the spiritual world, as the laws of nature are his plan in the physical world. Henry Norris Russell, astronomer, gives allegiance to Christ in his spiritual transcendence and power, his amazing translocation of values, his unique character and life, his teachings concerning immortality, and in the whole range of his attitude toward God and man.[55]

Are scientists in or out of the Christian Church, and what is their general relationship to the activities of organized Christianity? In order to test this question letters were sent to a number of pastors and educators, closely allied with college communities, only one of which is the seat of a denominational institution. There was no questionnaire. The very brief inquiry was, "Are any of the scientists of (name of institution) active in the Christian life and its relationship?" The replies received were from Harvard, Yale, Pennsylvania, Oberlin, State universities of Illinois, Iowa, California, Minnesota, and Wisconsin, from Chicago, Southwestern, and Washington, D. C. From one of the State universities the general message came: "I am happy to say that a very large number of the scientific men at the university are not only Christian men but active in the life of the churches here at the campus. In fact, I do not know of any of our scientists who are hostile or negative in their teaching."

An interesting review of leading scientific authorities in Washington, D. C., furnished through the

---

[55]*Fate and Freedom,* many passages, Yale University Press.

agency of his pastor by a professor in the Smithsonian Institution, listed eighteen scientists prominent in church membership and activity. The first name was that of Charles D. Walcott, geologist, whose translation from earthly relationships was announced within a week of the receipt of this record. Walcott was the noted secretary of the Smithsonian Institution, and was an official of the Presbyterian Church. Of the seventeen others reported as merely a partial representation, one is a Catholic, and the others Presbyterians, Methodists, Congregationalists, Baptists, and Disciples of Christ. Striking comments are made with reference to official responsibilities in Christian service.

It will be noted that the question sent (q. v. *supra*) contained no request whatever for details. Nevertheless, pastors of five denominations, whose churches are located beside seven prominent universities, all save one of the so-called "secular" class, in replying, sent the names of ninety-three scientists of note, some of them among the foremost American leaders, who are definitely committed to the Christian life and to the duties of church membership. Thirteen chemists, twelve geologists, eleven biologists, nine physicists, five psychologists, as well as astronomers, mathematicians, botanists, engineers, and others make up this total. Several have said that, if it were desired, more names could easily be supplied. Comments made in individual cases are illuminating, as, for example: "An outstanding Christian," "One of the most sincerely religious men in this community," "Very active in church work," "Very active in Wesley Foundation work," "Keenly interested in religion; never misses church service," "Regular attendant, morning and evening and prayer service," "A man of prayer; takes responsibility," "One of the most positive Christian influences in the city," "A regular attendant, one of the most devout and active workers," "In evangelistic services the most outstanding factor." Two or three are marked "Not very active," or "Fairly regular." Besides these lists and personalities, two other letters, one from a college president and one from a pastor, state that in the institutions where they are a hundred scientific professors and assistants are identified with the membership and life of the local churches.

The following excerpt from a letter received from a well known physicist represents a conscientiousness with respect to public expression of religious interest which I am convinced is not at all an infrequent characteristic of men of his class: "I go rather regularly to the services (of divine worship) because I obtain spiritual satisfaction from them, and also, if you will pardon the egotism, because I think my example as a known man of science is a wholesome one at a time when the intellectual and spiritual interests of the world are at an appallingly low level."

It will be asked, What about the younger men? General statements are made about whole departments, without reference to age. "The chemistry department of the university is the center of the most dynamic kind of Christianity." "What is true of the heads of the different departments is true of their assistants." An item in one list says, "One of the keen young physical scientists (Ph.D. man) is my Sunday-school superintendent, a very faithful and loyal Christian in every way." "Two assistant professors have voluntarily united with the church on profession of faith." Another adds to a list of Christian leaders, "and a whole string of assistants." It is generally the case that the younger men in any profession are more preoccupied with their secular tasks and less serious-minded and philosophical than their elders. It is probable that this is no whit more true in the field of science than elsewhere. A dean of one of the State institutions not mentioned above sent me this word: "As far as the University is concerned, I believe there is a very high percentage of men who are truly religious and exert a wholesome influence on a large number of students." One of my correspondents closes a careful letter, representing facts connected with one of the oldest, richest, and most scholarly of American institutions, by saying, "I have answered at some length, because I think this question a vital one, and now repeat out of my experience that the most effective Christian leaders in university life are connected with the scientific departments; and if there is any such thing as an intellectual snobbery with regard to religion, it comes from other departments. There is something wholesome in the reverence for truth of the scientific mind. It seems to be producing in this day a genuine Christian leadership."

No attempt has been made to list in this book the denominational fellowship of each individual mentioned. I have taken no pains to collect such data, but have included enough items of this nature, which came to my notice, to serve as evidence that all great branches of the Christian religion include in their membership men whose life's work is in scientific fields.

In view of several tests made, including the above mentioned one, and of much other correspondence, it is easy to believe that, if required, a thousand names of competent scientists could be assembled immediately which would represent, as would many more, as pronounced adherence to the truths and undertakings of Christianity as would any similar group taken from other classes of American life. This could be done without including those who are disposed, as a few of my own correspondents have shown themselves, to dictate to the various Christian bodies just what kind of religion they may be permitted to have. One says that Christian faith will not be impaired by science "if such faith is not based on any system of

objective facts." Is the objection to the system or to
the facts? One disparages "petty technicalities of theology," as who, in view of the adjective, should not?
One thinks religion must surrender "supernaturals."
But what is supernatural? And, by the same token,
what is not supernatural, unless it be the conceit of
materialism? The latter is pretty colossal, and almost superhuman in some instances. Sentimental
religion finds an occasional scientific opponent—a
person who might let go pretty emotionally at a
ball game. All such minutiæ or greater objections are
beside the mark. The testimony of science, including
that of Judaism, on the part of an altogether sufficient multitude of witnesses, confirms the necessity,
the reality, and the value of religion, and the Christian faith rejoices in the adherence of many scientific personalities, including some that are most eminent in character and service. No one need think that
he must choose between religion and science as long
as such men as Michael Pupin can say, "Science does
not prevent a man from being a Christian, but makes
him a better Christian. My religion does not contradict a single element of the religion which my mother
and the people of my native village held when I was a
boy. Science has simply brought to me a higher,
broader view of the Creator. Science will make better Christians of all men and women who try to
understand its simple and beautiful laws, because
they are laws of God."[56]

[56]Interview in *American Magazine,* September, 1927. Confirmation,
a letter to the author.

CHAPTER X

SCIENCE AND IMMORTALITY

In his last moments Nathaniel Southgate Shaler
remarked, "All things do prophesy the life to come."[1]
This utterance was the summing up and the conclusion of one whose devotion to natural studies is well
known. It was more than this. Mark Twain expressed the idea that in his *Autobiography* he was
speaking from the grave. He seemed to think that
thus only can a man be perfectly frank. The saying
of Shaler, which is quoted here, represents the
thought of one who never trifled with life or with
facts, and who in his dying hour expressed his views
freely, not as a literary effort, but as a witness to
his friends of his ultimate philosophy and his con-
quering faith.

But is it true that "all things do prophesy the life
to come"? Not in detail, certainly. One who holds
such a view, so far as he conceives it to be based on
scientific grounds, must do so as the result of generalizations which grow out of natural instincts and
intuitions, or which come to him as interpretations
and inferences from the totality of facts, and from
the laws and implications of his experience as a human being. This is not quite the same as saying with
Pasteur that in each of us are two men—the scientist, who seeks knowledge of nature through observation, trial, and reasoning; and the man who feels, and
believes; who grieves over his dead children and cannot prove that he will see them again, but believes he
will do so, and lives in this hope. The two realms are

---

[1] *The Autobiography of Nathaniel Southgate Shaler,* p. 411,
Houghton Mifflin Company.

distinct, and woe to him who permits them to trespass on each other.

The last sentence awakens a painful, if well-nigh forgotten memory. A quarter of a century ago, shortly after it first appeared, the perusal of Leonard Huxley's two-volume life of his father revealed the latter's correspondence with Charles Kingsley at the time when Thomas H. Huxley had lost his first son, Noel.[2] Kingsley had written him a long and earnest letter of consolation. The full reply is given, and it shows touching evidence that the writer had not only allowed the two domains in his being to trespass on each other, but had permitted the aggression of an exaggerated loyalty to the method of physical determination to rob his heart, and that of his companion as well, of the reassuring belief which their feelings must have craved. Since no one more insisted on frankness and naked truth on the part of his own voice and pen than did Huxley, it is not unfair to go further and express the opinion that, under the circumstances, this letter but too plainly reveals the dehumanizing effects of a mistaken philosophy—for such it is, and not science—which may rob one, not well trained in philosophical studies, of the most natural solace in the hour of sorrow. Mr. Huxley was polite to Kingsley, even paying him, and also Maurice, the back-handed compliment of intimating that their logic, as both intelligent men and Christian believers, he was not able to comprehend. He professed to be replying as frankly and fully as he had been addressed. But—and here is the bitterness of it—one can hardly read that letter, with the text of which the writer has again familiarized himself, without unhappy impressions. The author of it seems to have sought relief from sorrow in dialectics, finding in what verged on a polemical discussion a discharge for his feelings

[2] *Life and Letters of Thomas H. Huxley*, Leonard Huxley, vol. i, pp. 233-238. D. Appleton & Company.

which most men experience in tears, hope, and prayer. He showed that his mind was closed—see the reference to Hamilton's essay and Mansel's reply —to any philosophy of life and of its experiences, which is not based on such evidence as that of the law of the inverse squares. It is evident that he was not only not disposed to exercise what William James declared is the right, if not the duty, of the intelligent man, namely, the will to believe, but that his attitude was the very reverse. But, as if feeling that his position was not satisfactory or altogether scientific, he added that he did not dare think and act otherwise.

Huxley then insisted in effect, and six years later specifically, taking the term from a reference of Saint Paul to pagan worship, that he was an agnostic. How mistaken!—as we all easily are about ourselves. To many, who in this calmer day, and without any desire to be unjust, consider his writings as a whole, as well as this striking example, he seems to have proved himself a philosophical Gnostic. He appeared to trust, with few exceptions, no man's judgment save his own, and he was sometimes severely contemptuous of the opinions and sensibilities of others, and of the help which he might have received from their knowledge and experience. Is not this one of the results likely to follow when, within the profound depths of our being which Pasteur described, and whose component parts should be harmonious and mutually helpful, the man of intuition and feeling is overcome by the man of materialistic self-limitations and judgments? Nevertheless, Mr. Huxley, in the document cited, said, among other items, that he neither affirmed nor denied immortality, and that he had no *a priori* objections to the doctrine. In the same paragraph he showed that he anticipated the error of Henry Drummond, though with reverse conclusions, that natural law, so called, must be universally valid. In nature, his sole authority, he found no proof of immortality. Therefore there could be no assurance concerning it. However, it is characteristic of this interesting but chameleonic man that it could be said of him by Canon Ottley that he spoke to him with reverence and humility about the ultimate mysteries of life, and of the limitations of their complete scientific elucidation.

Aristotle was given to thoughtful consideration of the profoundest themes. He taught that whatever it may be within man that thinks, feels, and desires, is divine and celestial, and therefore imperishable.

In various portions of this book appear statements of early scientists bearing upon this theme. An expression which will appeal to lovers of the quaint in thought and language may be found in Sir Thomas Browne's *Religio Medici:* "I boast nothing, but plainly say, we all labor against our own cure; for death is the cure of all diseases. There is no Catholicon or universal remedy I know but this, which though nauseous to queasy stomachs, yet to prepared appetites is nectar, and a pleasant potion of immortality."[3]

The imperishable interest which attaches itself to questions as to futurity and to the effect upon life of our thinking on this subject is well stated by Pascal: "The immortality of the soul is a thing which concerns us so mightily, which touches us so deeply, that it is necessary to have lost all feeling in order to be indifferent about it. All our actions and thoughts must take different paths according as there will be or will not be eternal goods to be hoped for, so that it is impossible to do anything with intelligence and judgment if it is not regulated by the view of that point which ought to be our final object."[4]   The proof

---

[3] *The Works of Sir Thomas Browne*, p. 102.

[4] *Pensées de Pascal*, 1670, "Upon the Indifference of Atheists." Another translation, not essentially different, in *Thoughts on Religion and Evidences of Christianity of Pascal*, Faugère and Pearce, p. 6.

of this assertion of Pascal is easy to discover, both by
reference to history and by observance of contemporaries. The behavior of humanity, even after all exceptions are noted and allowed for, plainly and ade-
quately discloses the fact that *vita vitæ mortalis est
spes vitæ immortalis.*[5] When one attempts to account,
not only for thoroughly rational conduct, but for the
most illustrious deeds of service and sacrifice which
have made glorious the records of time, is it not
difficult to escape acknowledgment that a great proportion of them have been inspired by belief in the
persistence of life, and by the resulting enhanced conception of its present and ultimate values?

The faith in a future life of Robert Boyle, physicist
and chemist, is indicated by the unique record that
his only reason for fearing death was because after
it he would know everything, and would no longer
have the delight of making discoveries. At a much
later date Francis T. Buckland thought of a future
estate as a time when the gates of omniscience will
be thrown open and when the mind will be given
greater scope of knowledge with greater reward for
those occupied on earth in investigating the works of
the Creator. The career of Buckland, whose thirst
for knowledge is described as an obsession, has suggested that perhaps death forces a rest until the re-
freshed spirit, with new energy, may resume its pursuits under new and improved circumstances.[6]
Franklin held that life is a state of embryo, a preparation for life. A man is not completely born until he
has passed through death. Does not this, in a manner, recall what Plato in his *Phædo* represents Socrates as saying at the last to his disconsolate disciples,
"You may bury me if you can catch me"?

---

[5]Inscription monument John Foxe, St. Giles, Cripplegate, London.
See memorial by William Winters, Transactions of the Royal Society,
1877, p. 36.

[6]See *Diary, Log Book of a Fisherman and Zoölogist,* and reference
in *Beacon Lights of Science,* T. F. Van Wagenen, p. 349.

Sir Humphry Davy, whose intuitive faith very appropriately accompanied an indisputably poetic nature, expressed his thought of the future in this way: "There may be beings, thinking beings, surrounding us, which we do not perceive, which we can never imagine. We know very little; but, in my opinion, we know enough to hope for immortality, the individual immortality, of the better part of man."[7]

A clear statement of belief in the permanence of human life closes the *Treatise on Astronomy* of Olinthus Gilbert Gregory, mathematician and philosopher, dedicated in 1800 to Hutton. "We must consider our present state," says the author of this imposing work, "as only the dawn of our existence, a state of preparation for something far more exalted and grand than anything the eye hath beheld, or the most lofty imagination hath conceived. We may, however, even now, form extensive and noble conceptions of the immensity of the universe and of the unbounded power and wisdom of the Almighty Creator, and we may look forward to that happy period when we shall drink full draughts from the fountain-head of knowledge, rejoicing above all things that our hope rests not upon ingenious speculations, but that God hath brought life and immortality to light through the gospel."

Thomas George Bonney, petrologist, in his life of Sir Charles Lyell, gives a picture of what might be called a religion of common sense. "Lyell's views on religious questions accorded," he says, "as might be expected, with the general bent of his mind. He was a member of the Church of England, appreciated its services—but he failed to understand why nonconformity should entail penalties, whether legal or social. His mind was essentially undogmatic; feel-

---

[7] *Memoirs of the Life of Sir Humphry Davy*, John Davy, p. 452. See, *Consolations in Travel*, or *The Last Days of a Philosopher*, especially dialogue the fourth, "The Proteus, or Immortality."

ing that certainty was impossible in questions where
the ordinary means of verification could not be employed, he abstained from speculation and shrank
from formulating his ideas, even when he was convinced of their general truth. He was content, however, to believe where he could not prove, and to trust,
not faintly, the larger hope. So he worked on in
calm confidence that the honest searcher after truth
would never go far astray, and that the God of nature and of revelation was one. He sought in this
life to follow the way of righteousness, justice, and
goodness, and he died in the hope of immortality."[8]

Hugh Miller, geologist of *The Old Red Sandstone*
and of *Footprints of the Creator,* is represented as
asking and answering a question which has occurred
to other observers of nature, and to which some have
similarly replied: "In looking on the lower animals,
whom instinct never deceives, can we hold that man,
immeasurably higher in his place, and infinitely
higher in his hopes and aspirations, should be the
befooled expectant of a happy future which he is
never to see? Assuredly no. He who keeps faith
with his humbler creatures—who gives to even the
bee and the dormouse the winter for which they prepare—will to a certainty not break faith with man."[9]
It should be noted *in passu,* that representative scientists have thought that desire and fitness for
another and higher life, however accounted for, deserve to be considered in connection with the problem
of immortality. Even if adaptation in nature and
the teachings of the Christian revelation be denied,
the longing of man's mind, the needs of his developing
spirit, and the possibilities of his incomplete but
ambitious experience have been recognized as being

---

[8]*Charles Lyell and Modern Geology,* p. 212, Cassell & Company, Ltd.

[9]*The Testimony of the Rocks, or Geology in Its Bearings on the Two
Theologies, Natural and Revealed,* p. 139, Gould and Lincoln.

indubitable and significant facts which are related to other phenomena bearing upon this subject.

Certain physical analogues have appeared to various lovers of nature as having import for those whose faith lays hold on futurity. The figure of the three states of caterpillar, larva, and butterfly, which, as Davy noted, have, since the time of the Greek poets, been applied to typify the human being—its terrestrial form, apparent death, and ultimate celestial destination—is beautifully embodied by Alice Freeman Palmer, lifelong educator, in her lines of apostrophe to a butterfly:

"I hold you at last in my hand,
    Exquisite child of the air.
Can I ever understand
    How you grew to be so fair?

"You came to my linden-tree
    To taste its delicious sweet,
I sitting here in the shadow and shine
    Playing around its feet.

"Now I hold you fast in my hand,
    You marvelous butterfly,
Till you help me to understand
    The eternal mystery.

"From that creeping thing in the dust
    To this shining bliss in the blue!
God give me courage to trust
    I can break my chrysalis too!"[10]

Sir James Y. Simpson caused to be carved on his tomb at Warriston, Scotland, the figure of a butterfly, underneath which appear the words, "Nevertheless I live!"

While it is true that there are those to whom the analogies of nature as applied to human life and

[10]Printed by permission of and arrangement with Houghton Mifflin Company, Boston.

destiny seem altogether fanciful, if not misleading, it is, as we have seen (Chapter IV), a scientific fact, and therefore not to be ignored, that the use of the general principle of analogy has strongly appealed to many minds, including some which have had the best culture and have attained proficiency in various forms of physical research.   Lecky goes so far as to claim that the chief influence of physical sciences in philosophy has been, not that of immediate logical proof discrediting old beliefs, but, rather, of new analogy.   This reminds one that Saint George Jackson Mivart claimed that it is characteristic of a sagacious scientist that he wisely seeks out analogies and resemblances.   H. N. Russell's elaboration of modern theories of light in their relation to the doctrine of conservation affords the latest significant scientific analogy bearing on the thought of continuity and permanence.   The illustration is one of great beauty.[11]

It should not appear at all surprising that such scientists as Haeckel have opposed the whole conception of immortality.   John Fiske makes this comment on his sayings: "When Haeckel tells us that the doctrine of evolution forbids us to believe in a future life, it is not because he has rationally deduced such a conclusion from the doctrine, but because he takes his opinions on such matters ready-made from Ludwig Büchner, who is simply an echo of the eighteenth-century atheist, La Mettrie.   We shall see that the doctrine of evolution has implications very different from what Haeckel supposes."[12]   The disciples of Haeckel have followed him as he followed Büchner. Darwin, however, who certainly has prominence in evolutionary history, uttered expressions which confirm Fiske's view rather than that of Haeckel. What did Darwin mean by saying, "Few persons feel any

---

[11]*Fate and Freedom,* Henry Norris Russell, pp. 141-157, Yale University Press.

[12]*Through Nature to God,* p. 144, Houghton Mifflin Company.

anxiety from the impossibility of determining at what precise period in the development of the individual, from the first trace of a minute germinal vesicle, man becomes an immortal being, and there is no greater cause for anxiety because the period cannot possibly be determined in the gradually ascending organic scale"?[13] "It is an intolerable thought," he wrote, "that man and all other sentient beings are doomed to complete annihilation after such long-continued slow progress."[14] Was he thinking only of a future for the race when he said of man, who has arrived at the very summit of the organic scale, that "the fact of his having thus risen, instead of having been aboriginally placed there, may give him hope for a still higher destiny in the distant future"?[15] Whatever meaning may be attached to these sayings, traditions of the attitude of Darwin indicate that he was not opposed to the conception of human life as permanent, and that he was not without thoughts of his own survival. One of the most ardent of the early followers and exponents of Darwin in America, above mentioned, had very positive views on the subject of the persistence of human life. John Fiske explained the basis of his judgment by saying: "For my own part I believe in the immortality of the soul, not in the sense that I accept the demonstrable truths of science, but as a supreme act of faith in the reasonableness of God's work."[16] Fiske also expressed the conviction that modern scientific discoveries and hypotheses support and at least do not destroy the faith in immortality, which, he declared, "is likely to be shared by all who look upon the genesis of the highest spiritual qualities in man as the goal of nature's creative work. This view has survived the Copernican revo-

---

[13]*Descent of Man,* Charles Darwin, p. 700.
[14]*Animals and Plants,* iii, p. 431.
[15]*Descent of Man,* p. 707.
[16]*The Destiny of Man,* p. 116, Houghton Mifflin Company.

lution in science and it has survived the Darwinian revolution. The future is lighted for us with the radiant colors of hope."[17]

A unique expression on this theme closed Alexander Winchell's *Sketches of Creation*. After giving utterance to the conception of geology with reference to the future of nature, eloquent and expressive questions are so framed as to convey their own answer: "But what is the spirit of man, whose thoughts thus wander through eternity? What is the intelligence of man which climbs the battlements of the place of Omnipotence—which seizes hold on infinity—which, though chained in the flesh, spurns its fetters and feels evermore that it is the offspring of God—the brother of angels—the heir of perpetuity—and will soon shake its shambles down amongst the rubbish of decaying worlds, and dwell superior to the mutations of matter and the revolutions of the ages? What, in comparison with the crumbling of mountains and the decay of worlds, is the being possessed of such a consciousness and such a destiny? Who shall tremble at the wreck of matter, when, in perpetual youth, he shall outlive suns, and systems, and firmaments, and through the ceaseless cycles of material history shall see creation rise upon creation—the ever-recurring mornings of eternal life."[18]

By far the greatest number of scientists ignore or sweep aside the efforts of the Psychical Research Society to pierce the veil of mystery which surrounds this subject, and to minister to the widespread desire for definite knowledge of another world.[19] The fact of this labor, and the existence of its literature, are entitled to mention here, however, because of the scien-

---

[17] *Ibid.*, p. 118.

[18] Pages 430-431, Harper & Brothers.

[19] Henry Norris Russell, however, thinks that competent, careful investigators may wisely seek whatever knowledge may be gained by experimentation. *Fate and Freedom*, p. 133, Yale University Press.

tific leaders who have been connected with the movement, among them Sir Oliver Lodge, Sir William Crookes, and Lord Rayleigh. Camille Flammarion, French astronomer, of a similar relationship, asserts that death is merely evolution and not by any means the last hour. *Mors janua vitæ.* The body as the organic garment of the spirit passes, but the spirit remains. James H. Hyslop, psychologist of this school, indicated the seriousness of these investigators by expressing the conviction that democratic ideals will survive or perish with the belief in immortality. As to results, Sir Oliver Joseph Lodge flatly says: "We shall certainly continue to exist; we shall certainly survive. Why do I say that? I say it on definite scientific grounds. I know that certain friends of mine still exist, because I have talked with them."[20] Many who have lost those whom they loved would give a fortune to attain like positiveness on this subject. Is it not unique, in view of former experiences, that in the case of psychical research, the strongest affirmations are those of certain scientists, while some of the most sweeping denials are by representatives of the church? Dean Inge, for example, caustically comments as follows: "A few highly educated men, who have long been playing with occultism and gratifying their intellectual curiosity by exploring the dark places of perverted mysticism, have been swept off their feet by it, and their authority, as men of science, has dispelled the hesitation of many more to accept what they dearly wish to believe. The longing of the bereaved has created for itself a spurious and dreary satisfaction."[21]

Is science to-day opposed to the Christian view of

---

[20] Author of many scientific works and of *Reason and Belief, Survival of Man, Continuity.* The above quotation is confirmed by a letter from Sir Oliver Lodge to the author of this book.

[21] *Outspoken Essays,* William R. Inge, p. 267, Longmans, Green & Company, Ltd.

the divine purpose and destiny of human beings? In
expressing the view that this is more than doubtful
the writer has not failed to give consideration to the
facts he could discover, such as, for example, the
statistics and conclusions of James H. Leuba, in
The Belief in God and Immortality. Questionnaires
were sent to lists of American scientists, sociologists,
historians, and psychologists, who were asked their
attitude toward God and personal immortality. It
was thought to be impracticable to include philosophers. Why not, at least, in a group of their own?
And are not medical men, aside from those recognized
in scientific societies and books, as well as some other
classes of investigators and practitioners, to be regarded as a part of the scientific forces whose judgment is as worth while as that of any class of students? Whoever is interested in the details of such
an examination will find them spread over many
pages and expressed by tables and charts. The questions were not unfairly put, although the answers
expected and hoped for were not wholly unindicated.
In the discussion of individual replies the author
quite too evidently read his own subjectivity into at
least a portion of his interpretations. In the scientific group, so called, one thousand out of fifty-five
hundred names in *American Men of Science* were
addressed, and were divided into greater and lesser
lights on the basis of starred names. Nearly a fourth
did not reply, for reasons which the author correctly
assumed, or quite possibly for other reasons. Of
those who answered the queries, it appears that in
this group, composed of physical and biological scientists, definite believers in God amounted to 41.8
per cent of those who replied, and believers in immortality a trifle over 50 per cent. In both cases a considerable percentage of agnostics and doubters was
joined with the number held to be disbelievers. The
total results in the case of historians and sociolo-

gists were not strikingly different, but the psychologists—were they at all influenced by the known sophistication of the inquirer?—showed a much lower level of belief than that of the other classes, which was also the case in later Leuba exhibits.

What does all this mean? Not much of anything, some have said. A few comments may well be made, however, before the question of value should be considered. In the first place, whatever may be thought of the questionnaire method in general, it seems that it is not unfair to suggest that there is no possible use of it which would be more likely to yield unsatisfactory results than in case of anything so recondite and intimate as personal faith. Even a questionnaire on love might be more scientific, as well as both humorous and pathetic in its results. It is quite possible also that men so closely occupied with other and insistent affairs as are the classes canvassed may not have given the most careful and balanced thought to their answers to inquiries so general and vague. This may or may not account for some of the expressed agnosticism (I do not know!) and perhaps for a portion of the confessed doubt, included with reported disbelief. "Honest doubt" is often asserted—and is there not truth in this?—to be far from opposition to faith. May not one of the reasons why many of the scientists addressed did not reply to the questions, aside from such causes as absence, sickness, death, preoccupation, or indifference, have been lack of sympathy with or of confidence in the method employed in determining values in a field of such admitted importance and scientific difficulty? It is not necessary to stress the point that the answers received to this questionnaire, and the conclusions drawn from them, covered only between six and seven hundred out of fifty-five hundred names in a list of scientists which of necessity cannot be complete. Nor need too much be made of the fact that

the replies given did not have to be signed. Anonymous letters are, of course, not the best authority in
the world, and anonymous, and therefore mainly
irresponsible statements of faith, may easily be rather
hastily written, not to say altogether misleading.

These tests, as well as some which have more recently been made and published by English and
American periodicals, suggest the query, Are God and
immortality to be determined by vote? The humor of
the very suggestion of balloting on such issues is indicated by a story, preserved by Rayleigh, of a debate
and division on the existence of Deity, which took
place in an Aberdeen society. Someone reporting it
remarked, "I am glad to say He got a working majority." The views of scientists, philosophers,
preachers, mechanics, and others may be determined
far more accurately by other methods. If any are to
exercise franchise on such subjects, remembering that
our sublime Teacher said, "The pure in heart shall
see God," I would propose that a vote be taken of the
intelligent wives and mothers of men, many of whom
seem to know God by direct approach, and to attain
a conviction of immortality as Frazer says primitive
minds possess it, not by speculation and conjecture
but by a practical certainty as real as that of their
conscious existence. If there is a personal God, does
it not seem possible that he may be known as we know
our best friends, not by their faces, language or acts,
but by affinity? If one may "enter into life eternal,"
irrespective of death, may not the consciousness of
the existence which is nonending arrive and accredit
itself without aid of reasoning, or even in the scorn
of consequences to other forms of knowledge? These
questions should not, however, be taken as indicating
that the pathway to religious assurance is closed to
all save mystics.

While the survey of the faith of scientific men to
which reference has been made was partial and

dubious in its method, it is no unwelcome information that so large a number of those addressed expressed definite faith in two central affirmations of religion—God and immortality. These great conceptions would not necessarily be false if but one scientist held to them. He might be right and all the others wrong—a scientific *Athanasius contra mundum!* Nor would religion fall, if it were established that not one person trained in natural subjects regarded it as possessing any scientific evidence whatever. Religion rests upon a basis which neither physical nor intellectual philosophy can overturn. Nevertheless, it means very much to the progress of religious undertakings and influence that so many American scientists, as well as those of other lands, are shareholders in its faith and in sympathy with its ideals. If the same proportion held for the balance of the fifty-five hundred and more listed men of science in America as for those counted (and our own judgment would be that the proportion would substantially increase), it follows that well toward three thousand American scientists were at the time believers in at least two of the foremost religious principles. This number is surely of sufficient magnitude so that taken together with various individual testimonies, ancient and modern, including those of men in whom we trust, not only to controvert any notion that science has disproved immortality, but also to establish the fact that the arguments for the future life are congenial to the higher thought and feeling of competent students of nature. In view of the periods through which we have been passing, the new discoveries, the new or reborn sciences which have upset thinking, the prosperity and materialism of the age, the struggles of classes and nations, the diversities of Christian and of all religious philosophies, it appears somewhat remarkable that so large a number and proportion of men whose main and absorbing studies are in other fields should have a positive religious faith. Is not this, in itself, something in the nature of evidence of the reality and vitality of such faith, and of the objects in which it rests?

A clear thinker, who holds a high place among American scientists, feels, as I do, that the discussion of the Leuba ballot in the preceding pages is "very restrained." He says: "He was appealing to men who are accustomed by their training to seek and especially to give forth only demonstrated conclusions, and he asks men so trained to state their faith. That any considerable per cent of them should have mastered the peculiar temptation of the all but universal method of their vocation sufficiently to announce for the public a faith, is a very strong argument in favor of the faith that is able to overcome and master the very attitudes their vocation develops."[22]

In recent years the old argument for immortality, based on the beliefs of ancient and aboriginal peoples, has been subjected to scientific criticism. Sir James George Frazer, anthropologist, thinks that no savage tribes are now known who are certainly without the faith of survival after death. Nevertheless, he holds that this primitive mind contains no idea of endlessness—a conception too abstract, he believes, for simple and untutored people. Nor do religious or ethical motives inspire the belief of a savage in the permanence of human life. The non-civilized notion of continuance after death is seen to be essentially different from the belief in immortality with which we are familiar, and which was a comparatively late arrival in the history of man. Despite these observations, however, it is generally admitted that the practically unanimous refusal of man to regard death as

[22]Contributed, Arthur Lee Foley.

the end of his being and activities, while not of itself guaranteeing his immortality, is impressive and suggestive.[23] May it not be that what Hugh Miller described as the distinguishing instinct of humanity, namely, the sense of superiority over the destructive principles of nature, is a perceptive and essential element in the constitution of man?

Mention should be made of the scientific doctrine of the conservation of energy, which relativity does not disprove and which has often been regarded as confirmatory evidence of the continuance of human personality after death. If matter and force are indestructible, however they may be transformed, is it conceivable that mind, and the fair flowers of ability, genius, and character are of no permanent worth in the cosmic plan? It is felt by many, including some able men of science, that the answer is in the negative and that the suggestion, argument, and evidence of the indestructibility of matter and the conservation of energy tend to convey to the mind the thought that man cannot perish. I well recall the impressive lectures of Eugene Haanel, physicist, to this effect. Even to those to whom it suffices to believe that Jesus Christ, in himself and in his resurrection, has brought life and immortality to light, and that because he lives we shall live also, it seems more or less agreeable to the sense of the fitness of things, and to add something to the certainty of any faith which needs adventitious supports, to place Lavoisier's and Helmholtz's great laws of conservation by the side of the Christian law of immortality, as giving some natural sustenance to the thought of the indestructible existence of those who possess the life of the Spirit. Arthur L. Foley, physicist, so thinks. "To admit that matter and energy are immortal," he says, "and to deny immortality of the mind, which molds and di-

[23]Vide, *The Belief in Immortality*, vol. i, p. 468.

rects both matter and energy, is absurd."[24] Frederick
Soddy, chemist and physicist, has a paragraph on
this issue in *Science and Life,* holding that the doctrine of the immortality of the spirit has a scientific
basis in the law of unalterable reality in the physical
world.[25]

Edwin Brant Frost, of Yerkes Observatory, places
the several laws of conservation on the same scientific basis. "The idea of immortality of spirit," he
thinks, "is not far different from fundamental beliefs of physicists. The name is different, and conservation of energy is the principle. This affirms
that the sum total of energy in the universe is constant, changeable from one form to another, but essentially immortal. Now, this principle, to our thinking, cannot be rigidly demonstrated, any more than
can the immortality of spirit."[26] Sir Oliver Lodge
approves Höffding's principle of conservation of
value and thinks this is the teaching of evolutionary
process and progress. Immortality becomes the persistence of that which is real and essential.[27]

Inasmuch as most of the arguments for immortality
are metaphysical, theological, or both, they do not
come within the scope of this discussion except as
expressed or indorsed by men of science. Nearly all
writing about the future life is subject to the same
statement. Nevertheless, it is scientific doctrine
which underlies a considerable portion of this
literature. The impression one gets from reading
certain books which, even though not written by
experimental scientists, assume to represent modern
evolutionary conceptions of immortality, is that an

---

[24]Contributed.

[25]Vide, p. 152 *et seq.* The book is somewhat marred by a sophisticated attitude toward Christian teachers and teaching.

[26]*The Heavens Are Telling,* pamphlet American Institute of Sacred
Literature, pp. 24, 25.

[27]*The Immortality of the Soul,* pp. 44-47.

attempt is being made to emasculate this faith of its
former qualities and to disparage its necessity and
desirability. The crude notions of the older materialism against which Virchow so vehemently protested have been replaced by subtler theories. In
place of a survival in monads and maggots, continuance in the life of posterity and in the grateful
remembrance of our fellow men is suggested. It is
said that to persist through the triumph of good
causes should be a perfectly satisfactory outcome of
life, ignoring Kant's contention that man is an end
in himself, and not a mere means to an end. Mystical
absorption in the totality of being is another teaching, the meaning of which, however it may be cloaked,
is the death of the person. Certain writers are teaching an eternal life which consists of fellowship with
God in love and service. We may enter upon this
existence now, without any concern as to the future.
It is asserted that the thought and fact of personal
immortality are not necessary to morality or to satisfaction of mind; it is sufficient for practical life to
observe that ethical ideals are generated by society,
and that self-respect and human welfare are dependent on obedience to moral demands.

Are such conceptions as these adequate and final
representations of scientific judgment? Concerning
some of them John Fiske long ago protested, saying,
"If the world's long-cherished beliefs are to fall, in
God's name let them fall, but save us from the intellectual hypocrisy that goes about pretending that we
are none the poorer."[28] Sir J. F. Stephen, in replying
to some of Frederic Harrison's notions, commented
on the cruelty of trying to console a mourner by referring to the old letters, books and services of the
lost one as if in these and not in the man himself
were the real values. He thought a certain concep-

---

[28]*Through Nature to God,* p. 17, Houghton Mifflin Company.

tion of immortality as void and unsatisfactory as undertaker's plumes.[29]

There is a literature of negation on the subject of futurity. Raymond Pearl's *Biology of Death* presents no misnomer. Herbert Dingle closes his *Modern Astrophysics* with a remark not very evidently based on what has preceded: "It is not easy to shed the prejudices of generations, but if we can rise (*sic?*) to the condition that boundlessness is not infinite extension and immortality is not eternal existence we shall be in sight of the ground toward which the astrophysics of the future is likely to march."[30] Should one say march, or fall? The picture conveyed to my mind by such language is that of a flying machine which goes up only to come down in a nose-dive, or flat, Darius Green fashion.

Comments on Dingle's dictum have been made by three eminent authorities in astrophysics. Heber D. Curtis thinks that he bases his declaration and prophecy on his belief in a relativity conception of the universe, where space, light rays, and even time, so to speak, come back around to their starting point again, if one goes far enough. "One may follow," he says, "the devotees of the theory of relativity and postulate that this universe is an enormous quasi-sphere, that within this is all matter, space, energy, even all the time of the universe and that without this quasi-sphere *there is. not even nothing. Credat Judæus Apella!* I suppose this road equally possible (with the conception of a universe infinite in space and time factors, shown by Charlier to be mathematically and dynamically possible) but I do not believe it."[31] An astronomer of high distinction says that he does not know what Dingle means by the above remark, which he recalls: "It would look as if

[29]Vide, Preface to *Liberty, Equality and Fraternity.*
[30]The Macmillan Company.
[31]Contributed.

he were considering the immortality of a star, rather than that of a soul. I would not take an *obiter dictum* of this sort too seriously. Dingle is a competent man, but I really do *not* know what this phrase of his means." The other authority consulted comments: "Dingle has been criticized for a tendency to try to generalize from insufficient data in order to make phrases. I do not take seriously remarks by him of the sort you quote." We are asked, then, by Herbert Dingle, if he is referring to human immortality, to give up our prejudices for his—to surrender, if that is what he means, the conception of unending existence for a limited future, not confirmed by scientific fact but based on speculation.

It has been noted that it is in the newer and less well settled sciences that most disbelief in religion appears. Osborn says that "English biology soon entered the long period of confusion and lack of balance that have characterized it to the present day." One of the foremost American biologists, in a very interesting letter, gives this bit of autobiography: "I am feeling my way out of the morass into which much of the scientific work of the past fifty years has been leading biologists." A little further on he adds, "I think that I am beginning to find a path of escape from the 'Slough of Despond.' "

The tendency of the latest dogma and method is to overrun its bounds, and to attempt every form of fixation or transmutation. Such a movement carries eager minds fast and far. Time reduces enthusiasms to more modest limits, only to see them replaced by newcomers with another universal organon or panacea. There are signs of a breaking away from recent radicalism, and of an increase of courage, for instance, on the part of some excellent psychologists with respect to the pitfalls of extreme behaviorism. The deepest thinkers are seeking to conserve the higher and enduring values of human personality. This

effort is in part due to contemporary evidences of the
ethical perils of disbelief in futurity. Some years
since, however, William McDougall remarked, concerning the doctrine of immortality, that "apart from
any hope of rewards or fear of punishment after
death, the belief must have, it seems to me, a moral-
izing influence upon our thought and conduct that
we can ill afford to dispense with." Speaking of this
and of other positive religious tenets, this psychologist gravely doubted "whether whole nations could
rise to the level of austere morality, or even maintain
a decent working standard of conduct, after losing
those beliefs."[32]

The latter portion of *New Light on Immortality,* by
the physicist E. E. Fournier d'Albe, was written, he
says, despite warnings of scientific friends that he
would be found guilty of heterodoxy. The author
holds that immortalists are divided between orthodox
Christians and thinkers. He modestly writes for the
latter class. The work as a whole is an attempt at a
physical theory of immortality, but Part III discusses
phenomena unacceptable to present "official" science.
In this division of the book alleged metaphysical phenomena are considered sympathetically, but without
dogmatism, and with the distinct provision that the
working hypothesis and outlook presented does not
stand or fall with the reality or the reverse of these
incidents.

In brief, d'Albe's view is that modern philosophies
have been limited by the evil view of duality of mind
and matter, for which an idealistic monism must be
substituted. A new feature of this view is the reduc-
tion of laws of nature to laws of life, dead matter
being completely eliminated by the present conception of a universe to be interpreted in terms of Life.
Studying forms of life whose mentality is accessible,

---

[32]Preface, *Body and Mind,* The Macmillan Company.

it is found that they are life units assembled or organized of all inferior grades, having their own order and gradation from the least necessary to the most vital and essential. At the extreme limit, biological data present directive elements spread through the cells of the body, whose aggregate is the soul, and if organized alone a soul-body. For the directive elements the name assigned is "psychomeres." Possible identification of these particles of soul-body with Darwin's "gemmules" or Weismann's "biophores" is suggested. The physical nature of the soul-body is gaseous, and may have analogy with unknown forces which cause the cohesion of physical bodies, and which may be electrostatic or magnetic. Such a body, possessing individual memories, would inhabit the air and is located provisionally in the atmosphere of the earth.

The author asserts that no qualitative or quantitative absurdities can be charged against his theory, and that it is consistent with recognized phenomena of life and death and with the permanence of the conditions of earth-life. He also declares that survival after bodily death has become *thinkable* and almost calculable, entering into the realm of physics and physiology and thus allied with science. The soul is measurable and weighable, but the hypothesis is not materialistic, since all matter is living. Psychomeres survive when all else changes. Death is a process of nature—a kind of moult. Fear of death is removed. The heart finds peace. It need not sorrow for its loved ones, who are released from fettering clay and are passed into a higher joyous estate. Sinners will be revealed in their true ugliness and shunned until they conform to the standards of virtue. From each planet arise living souls mingling in ever higher destinies.[33]

[33]*New Light on Immortality*, Edmund E. Fournier d'Albe, Longmans, Green & Company, Ltd.

An address before the American Astronomical Society, in Philadelphia, 1927, by Heber D. Curtis, of Allegheny Observatory, Pittsburgh, contained the statement that the inevitable view concerning the human spirit is that of continuity. "There seems at present," he said, "to be a gap between the outer universe and that of the atom. Personally, I am ready to admit another gap between the world of matter and that of spirit, with energy, matter, space, and time continuing, with nothing lost. Are we ourselves the only manifestation that comes to an end, stops, ceases, is annihilated at threescore years and ten? What we crudely call 'spirit' of man makes new compounds, plays with the laws of chemical action, guides the forces of the atom, changes the face of the earth, gives life to new forms; a creative spirit which reasonably cannot cease to be. This thing, soul, mind, spirit, cannot well be an exception. In some way, as yet impossible to define, it too must possess continuity. The concept is old, but the conclusion is inevitable."[34]

In a letter of interpretation Curtis acknowledged frankly that "one can rarely postulate absolute certainty in a precise sense on an argument based on what the mathematician and physicist calls continuity, the philosopher probability, and the theologian analogy. We can trust implicitly the argument from the principle of continuity only when we are certain of absolutely every factor entering in. No one would be so bold as to say that we now know all the factors: to that extent such an argument fails as precise proof. However, the principle of continuity and permanence everywhere else in the universe is so unbroken that such a deduction has much in its favor, and is probably as reasonable as the deduction from man's intuition which we term faith. Both sorts of deduc-

[34]Verified by correspondence.

tion have made and will continue to make many errors, but doubtless both are tending to a single conclusion. Scientific truth, in the absolute and final sense, *cannot be wrong,* and I think the day will come when it and our similarly absolute and final religious belief will be one and the same."[35]

Frederick Soddy added to his argument previously stated a clear conception of the value of human being and of the everlastingness of this being, when he declared that the mechanical and even the animal or' vital aspects of nature "have been thrust into the background by a developed personality that consistently acts and tries to act, and therefore in the language of science, already explained, *is* a distinct being, resident in the body as a man may live in a house, and, if real, then by the canons of human thought, immortal."[36] This view is unquestionably capable of various interpretations, according to the content given to the term "developed personality." It is believed by other scientists who have thought deeply on this subject that personality attains the immortal state not by mere individualization, but by spiritual processes and attainment.

Sir William Osler made to the doctrine of immortality what may be described as a pragmatical contribution. "The scientific student," thought this medical educator, "should be ready to acknowledge the value of a belief in a hereafter as an asset in human life. In the presence of so many mysteries which have been unveiled, in the presence of so many yet unsolved, he cannot be dogmatic and deny the possibility of a future state. He will recognize that amid the turbid ebb and flow of human misery a belief in the resurrection of the dead and in the life of the world to come is the rock of safety to which

[35]Contributed.
[36]*Science and Life,* p. 169, E. P. Dutton & Company.

many of the noblest of his fellows have clung; he will
gracefully accept the incalculable comfort of such a
belief to those sorrowing for precious friends hid in
death's dateless night; he will acknowledge with
gratitude and reverence the service to humanity of
the great souls who have departed this life in a
sure and certain hope."[37]   Doctor Osler makes his
own confession of faith as to the future that of
Cicero, who preferred to be wrong with Plato rather
than to be right with those who deny immortality.[38]

One of the most interesting discussions of the future of mankind which has come from the pen of a
natural scientist is that contained in *Man and the
Attainment of Immortality*,[39] by James Y. Simpson,
of Edinburgh.   Writing on the basis of a full outline
of evolutionary science, the biological soundness of
which is strongly attested by J. Arthur Thomson,[40]
Simpson finds man attaining freedom, and, at length,
relationship with God through Jesus Christ—a life in
God which is eternal by its very nature.   The Pla-
tonic idea of universal immortality is replaced by
the concept of immortability, the high possibility of
the achievement of endless existence, actually realized
by Christian methods and discipline.   In the chapter,
"The Scriptural Doctrine of Immortality," is a careful presentation of Hebrew teaching as found in the
Old Testament, and an analysis of the views of Jesus
and of the writers of New Testament literature.
Universalism is described as an "amiable outlook,"
which "robs life of its tremendous seriousness and
meaning, reducing it to the level of a marionette-show,
and belittling man's fateful capacity to choose life
or death."   Immortality in the Old Testament sense is
described as morally conditioned.   The expression "im-

---

[37]*Science and Immortality*, pp. 39-40, Houghton Mifflin Company.
[38]*Ibid.*, p. 43.
[39]Hodder & Stoughton, Ltd.
[40]In a letter to the author of this book.

mortality of the soul," in fact, is not a biblical phrase, nor even a biblical conception.

Jesus Christ is said by Simpson to set before men the conditions of life or of death in the ultimate senses of these words, warning them of the difficulty of attaining life. "Our Lord, according to Saint Luke, spoke of a resurrection of the righteous only; it is they who have attained." In Saint Paul's writings, eternal life is shown to be the natural result of vital relationship with God, or with God through Jesus Christ. The author says, "Ultimate destiny is a matter of spiritual condition." "God's purposes," he thinks, "are not and cannot be achieved in the individual life in face of the persistent refusal of the individual." "Love is the one thing in the world that cannot be forced and does not force." "The conditional view [of immortality] stands in line, as we have seen, with the general method of evolution, which has been selective throughout."

The successor of Drummond quotes J. H. Leckie as saying that freedom, the power to choose the right, belongs to the very idea of the soul and cannot be taken away, and adds, "Exactly; but how is freedom merely the power to choose the *right?*" He believes that "the selfish or self-filled life is a life bereft of spiritual ties or relationships, which when its physical metabolism comes to an end must by reason of its separateness and apartness, its actual spiritual unrelatedness, perish." "The proof" of conscious and deathless relationship with God "is our Lord and Saviour Jesus Christ." "As a matter of simple fact, he brought life and immortality to light." The basis of the resurrection faith was not so much the empty tomb as the conviction of the disciples that they had been seeing, hearing, and speaking with the same historic Personality whom they had followed during these three years and thought they had lost forever. "I *am* the resurrection and 'the life,' he says, and in the case of every Christ-filled individual the resurrection is taking place *now*. The spiritual body is being prepared and provided *now* and death is only an incident." Resurrection is the result of being united with Christ, which "represents a spiritually and morally tempered condition of prepotency whose survival of death is natural."

The volume whose conclusions I have just outlined must be read thoroughly to get the continuity and force of the author's carefully wrought reasoning. The testimony given to the power as well as to the character and personality of Jesus Christ is exceptionally frank and sincere, in accordance with the high attitude which the theme deserves.

The position taken by Simpson reminds one of the treatment of the subject by L. P. Jacks, educational philosopher, in *A Living Universe:* "I do think that our human personalities are capable of acquiring value which a just universe would not suffer to be extinguished. I look upon immortality, then, rather as a prize to be won than as a birthright given for nothing." "In the New Testament," he declares, "we are immortal insofar as we become the sons and heirs of the immortal God." "The position of sons is one that we have to win, and our immortality follows from that."[41] This is a doctrine of spiritual, vital emergence which a teacher of natural science and an educator alike base on both rational and scriptural foundations.

William W. Keen, surgeon and medical educator, in *I Believe in God and in Evolution,* asserts that "Bodywise, man *is* an animal, but thanks be to God, his *destiny* is not the same as that of the beasts that perish. To develop great men, such as Aristotle, Plato, Shakespeare, Milton, Washington, Lincoln, and then by death to quench them in utter oblivion

---

[41] Page 105, George H. Doran Company, and Hodder & Stoughton, Ltd.

would be unworthy of Omnipotence. To my mind it
is simply an impossible conclusion. Man's soul *must*
be immortal."[42] Doctor Keen also speaks of "the
engrafting by the Creator upon his [man's] bodily
life of a moral and spiritual life, a soul with a desire
to worship, a faculty of adoration and of communion
with his heavenly Father. This wondrous love of God
for man and the final, lofty destiny of the human
race, this is to me the most impressive, the most
inspiring thought of all the ages."[43]

In a later discussion, *Everlasting Life,* the same
author expresses such convictions as these: "I am
impressed with the reality of the presence of God in
our lives." "Faith is as much a normal function of
the human mind as is logic." "We shall meet again
the dear ones who have preceded us, and in time
those who shall follow us, and spend this 'Everlasting
Life' with them. This assurance of Immortality, and
of those precious reunions is an ever-present joy to
my soul."[44]

The definite relationship of Jesus Christ to the
problem of human survival and of future existence
has never been without recognition from scientists.
Balfour Stewart and Peter Guthrie Tait, physicists,
in their book on *The Unseen Universe,* said of immortality: "We have no physical proof in favor of it unless we allow that Christ rose from the dead. But
it will be admitted that if Christ rose from the dead
a future state becomes more than possible; it becomes probable."[45] They express the opinion that
the same intelligent power which produced the universe could have accomplished the resurrection of
Christ without any break of continuity so far as the
whole universe is concerned. The book closes with

[42]Pages 102-103. J. B. Lippincott Company.
[43]*Idem.*
[44]Pages 50, 55, 61, Lippincott.
[45]Pages 258 and 273, Macmillan & Company, Ltd., London.

the great word: "Τῷ νικῶντι δώσω αὐτῷ ἐκ τοῦ ξύλου τῆς ζωῆς."[46]

Henry H. Lane, zoologist, in *Evolution and Christian Faith,* expresses the judgment that "the natural man, the product of the law of evolution, becomes transformed through the gospel of Christ into spiritual accord with the Father, becomes the spiritual child of God by adoption, and thus attains the hope of immortality."[47] It should be noted that this active scientist and member of the Disciples of Christ makes positive statements as to the mutually consistent relations of science and Christianity, one of which may be found elsewhere in this book.

The Return to Faith, by William North Rice, expresses one of the outstanding resources of troubled minds, seeking assurance as to that which lies beyond: "I go to the empty sepulcher on Easter morning," says this lifelong toiler in terrestrial fields, "and our human life grows great with the power of an endless life."[48]

And still comes Death! And the query, What then? Evidently, scientists are possessed of the same human sensibilities as are their fellow men. When Sir J. D. Hooker's much-loved six-year-old daughter was taken away, he grieved as does every afflicted mortal, and when Falconer passed on Hooker wrote Darwin: "The inconceivability of our being born for nothing better than such a petty existence as ours is gives me hope of meeting in a better world. What does it all mean?" So men—so scientists question. They wonder; they reason; they differ. Fortunately, for themselves, for their families, and for the rest of mankind, many of them have attained a confidence in religious verities which leads them to plead, as did

---

[46] Macmillan & Company, Ltd., London.
[47] Pages 198-199, Princeton University Press.
[48] Page 81, The Abingdon Press.

Ampère, when his wife was translated, "O Lord, God of mercy, unite me in heaven with those whom you have permitted me to love on earth."

The second volume of Fabre's *Souvenirs Entomologiques* was dedicated to his son Jules, from the sorrow of whose loss the author was still suffering when the inscription was made. It is said that the distressed spirit of this incomparable observer of nature found courage to master his grief and power to take up again the work of life in his insuperable faith in the Beyond. Fabre prepared his own epitaph, indicating his attitude toward futurity in the beautiful words:

"Quos periisse putamus
Praemissi sunt.
Minime finis, sed limen
Vitæ excelsioris."[49]

There are large numbers of scientists who have indicated the fact that they no more doubt the truths of religion than they doubt those of chemistry, biology, or mathematics; even though, as it is hardly necessary to say, they have no idea of trying to prove immortality just as a proposition of Euclid is proved, or as a chemical formula is determined. Many are devoted to the fellowship and views of Jesus Christ, and believe in his life, and in "the power of his resurrection." They live in the light of God's presence and communion, and share in the spirit of Shaler's life-long prayer: "O Power, who has given me being, give me the strength to live as becomes thy creature. May I stand amid the changes that whirl around me, untouched and unbroken, and when it shall please thee to end my days, may I not have lived in vain."[50] Men of this class sometimes have pleasurable anticipations of immortality, and, realizing the solemnity

[49] *The Life of Jean Henri Fabre,* Augustin Fabre, p. 397, Dodd, Mead & Company.

[50] *Autobiography, ut supra,* p. 411, Houghton Mifflin Company.

of the great event before them, when they have done
their part as worshipers in the temple of truth and as
servants of the intelligible earthly kingdom of the
Most High, may even seek such meet preparation for
the higher life as led Adam Sedgwick to exclaim with
his last breath, "Sanctify me by thy Holy Spirit." If
opportunity is given they may gather their friends
and families together as did the discoverer of oxygen,
and bid them not to mourn unduly, but to look forward with assurance to a future reunion. In his
latest moments Joseph Priestley gave to his grand-
children a simple and beautiful expression of his
Christian confidence: "I am going to sleep, like you,
but we shall awake together, and, I trust, to everlasting happiness."[51]

[51]Vide, Cuvier's biography of Priestley.

SUMMARY

I⊤ is my own conviction that the foregoing pages
contain a small but important part of voluminous
evidence which might be gathered in support of
various verifiable conclusions concerning Christianity in science.

They are deceived or deceptive who assert that
science *per se,* working in its own sphere, and apart
from erroneous metaphysics, is opposed to religion, or
that Christianity when properly comprehended and
represented is anti-scientific. Both in essence and in
personnel these chief branches of knowledge are intimately and for the greater part congenially related.

Science and Christianity have prospered together.
Neither has made great progress when unassociated
with the other. It is unlikely that either is unnecessary to its copartner.

Christianity is foster mother of modern science
through its service to educational foundation. Howard Crosby, in answer to the question, "Who founded
Heidelberg, Leipsic, Tübingen, Jena, Halle, Berlin,
Oxford, Cambridge?" replied that they were men of
the Bible, and that when the rest of mankind were
caring for mere physical necessities believers in the
Scriptures were uplifting the torch of science. Josiah
Gilbert Holland similarly inquired: "Who or what
has raised science to its present commanding position? What influence is it that has trained the
investigator and made it possible for the scientific
man to exist and the people to comprehend him?
Who built Harvard College? What motives form the
very foundation stones of Yale? To whom and to
what are the great institutions of learning scattered
all over this country indebted for their existence?"
He replies that the founders of these institutions
"were Christian men who worked simply in the inter-

342

est of their Master."[1] *A History of Education,* by
F. V. N. Painter, so well covered the historic debt
of education to Christianity that its record is of permanent worth. The motto of Harvard, *"Christo et
Ecclesiæ,"* typifies the motive of the founders of nearly
all great institutions of learning. Such books as
Pioneers of Science in America but partially disclose
the fact that large numbers of the early teachers of
science in this country were preachers of the gospel.

Science has placed Christianity greatly in debt by
reason of its devotion to truth, and because of its practical achievements, its service to humanity, and its
contributions to the fellowship and program of Christ.
The outstanding Christian leaders of scientific history are at once an honor to the productive influence
of Christianity, and a strong support of its ideals
and institutions. As we have seen, the following
statement attributed to Archbishop Ryan was correct:
"Among the most learned men living are church men,
Catholics and Protestants, who love science because
they love and serve the God of science. They see him
in the luminous worlds above them and admire the
great Designer and Governor of the universe in every
portion of his creation."[2] Is not the roll of Christian
men of science so long and imposing as to raise some
question concerning the mature wisdom of any scientist who is anti-Christian?

There does not seem to be any ethical or spiritual
teaching of Christianity which has not been accepted
by many men of science. The whole body of Christian
doctrine could be extracted from extant works of scientists of record. It is absurd, therefore, to regard
Christianity as unintelligent, irrational, or unscientific. There are Christian teachers and treatises
whose claims to intellectual respect are small, but

[1] *Every-Day Topics,* pp. 141-142, Charles Scribner's Sons.
[2] "I myself on several occasions heard the Archbishop express the
thought you quote." Letter of Dr. Joseph Corrigan, rector St.
Charles Seminary, Overbrook, Pa

the same is equally true of other teachers and books. The personal experience of the humblest Christian may be and often is as sane, logical, and verifiable as is that of the biological laboratory. This fact is attested by thousands of able scientists, many of whom have had experience of their own which confirms Christian Scriptures and principles. If the religious thinking and testimony of scientific investigators of past and present are to be regarded as incompetent or insincere, what must be thought, considering the volume and definiteness of this material, of their wisdom and reliability in other realms of knowledge and teaching? Or are we to suppose that sound judgment is with the latest or with the irreligious scientist alone? It seems to me that the zoologist Vernon Lyman Kellogg is justified in both the following record and conclusion: "There are few churches in any city of this land in which Sunday morning does not see scientific men seated side by side with laymen under more or less inspired ministrations, and they do not sit there as hypocrites— at least in any greater proportion than their non-scientific brethren."[3] In one of the public libraries someone wrote in pencil before the word "proportion" in this paragraph, the comment, "and probably less."

Christianity and science, while differing in the objects to which their attention is directed, make similar approaches to truth, namely, by instruction, study, reflection, observation, and experimentation. Individual scientists and religious thinkers alike differ in the application of their methods and in the results obtained. Their professions, creeds, and schools vary in a similar manner. Moreover, they have the same peril from specialism, whose danger is narrowness and whose folly is self-satisfied narrowness. The church man should study other systems than his own, and should seek general information on the most

[3] "Science and the Soul," *Yale Review*, January, 1923, p. 306.

vital subjects. The specialist in science should follow the same course. However excellent proficiency
in mathematics may be, a little history is necessary to
complete intelligence. Philosophy is most interesting, but one should know enough chemistry to keep
from taking poison. Astronomy is delectable, but
if one knew nothing but stars, he would stumble over
trifles on the ground, and would see more stars than
there are. The biologist has need of psychology and
ethics. Science, thought Oliver Wendell Holmes,
should be "sacredized." All men need religion, which
must be gained from experience, and not merely
from instruction. The student who does not seek
wisdom of those who toil at other tasks than his own,
at best becomes a learned ignoramus, a "bookful
blockhead, ignorantly read."

Both scientists and Christians accept much on
authority. How many physicists prove the existence
of chromosomes or hormones? How many biologists
demonstrate quanta? Few mathematicians have
great personal knowledge of bacteria, nor are many
geologists practical psychologists. Most of our present belief about electrons is known, in the scientific
sense, to very few persons. All students must rely
to a great extent on the views, experiences, and
achievements of specialists in science and philosophy.
If Christian scholarship asks the same consideration
for its own ascertained facts which is extended to
scientific investigators, there seems to be no inconsistency in this attitude. Teachers of Christianity
have truth to impart, and they can also point to accomplishments in developed character, in healings
and improvements of individual and social minds and
bodies which have the respect and admiration of
thoughtful and fair-minded scientists.

It is the right and duty of science and religion to
explore all realms open to their own methods and
opportunity without restraint, and to establish their

peculiar systems of truth and their institutions of culture in accordance with what they discover to be of value. In pursuit of their ends they may also properly adopt hypotheses and working plans, not fully proven, and which may have to be cast aside ultimately. Theories of this nature ought not to be forced upon those who are unprepared to accept them or who prefer other or even contradictory principles. Dr. A. N. Whitehead's illustrations in *Science and the Modern World,* pp. 255, *et seq.,* indicate the partial truthfulness and untruthfulness of many propositions, and the wisdom of caution as to final affirmative or negative conclusions based on them. Nevertheless, organizations have a legal right to establish tests of membership in conformity with their own opinions and to require such adherence to these formulæ as they deem desirable. Non-membership in such societies may be just as bigoted as is connection with them, and disloyalty to their vows, voluntarily assumed and not recalled, may be made as immoral as is infidelity to known truth. In passing it may be remarked that sectarianism in religion is not without some parallel in the castes of science to which Gilbert N. Lewis and others testify.[4]

It hardly seems necessary to say that scientists ought not to be expected to surrender any assured truth at the behest of theology, but may properly appeal to increasing wisdom and to time to vindicate the conformity of scientific fact with universal principles, and even with the divine evangel. Just as wise is the attitude of the religious believer who, when some new discovery of physical or intellectual phenomena or law calls in question or even seems to contradict spiritual principles or data, holds to his knowledge and experience in the conviction that in the end they will be vindicated. Perhaps, in view of the history and progress of scholarship, Faraday

[4] *The Anatomy of Science,* p. 170.

was as profoundly scientific as at any other time
when he replied, as he was wont to do, to those who
asserted that religious convictions were incompatible
with developing physical knowledge, "Nevertheless, I
am a Christian!"

Scientific and Christian teachers do well to think
and speak of each other as generously as possible, and
to co-operate in common tasks with increasing appreciation of mutual relationships and with ever greater
devotion to that which is worth while.[5] Scientists
who are Christians, despite their preoccupation with
immediate duties, frequently take occasion to express
their religious convictions, thus lending the strength
of their professional eminence to Christian evangel-
ism and service. This cannot be done too often or
definitely. It would be well if every Christian man
of science would at some time pen for his friends and
for posterity his statement of adherence to Christ.
Verba Volant: scripta manent. Does not our Lord
and Saviour have a right to such expressions from all
who know him? Are there not some who should consider thoughtfully the remark of Phillips Brooks,
"You will not be a better man by pretending that you
are not a Christian, nor a better Christian by pretending to have no dogmatic faith"?[6] Dogma of
some nature is inescapable, except to an empty or
unorganized mind. Dogmatism in the sense of ignorant, intolerant, and invincible opinion is as un-
Christian as it is unscientific; but facts, laws,
experiences, persons may be known, believed, trusted,
with our very lives. The high command comes to all
who possess valid Christian knowledge and experience, "Let your light so shine before men, that they
may see your good works, and glorify your Father
which is in heaven."

---

[5] That the issues of civilization depend upon such a rapprochement is
emphasized by Whitehead, *op. cit.*, p. 253.

[6] *Lectures on Preaching,* p. 70, E. P. Dutton & Company.

Finally, is it not clear that there should be no place for arrogance on the part of any who are sincere students of either nature or life? One of the last sayings of Laplace is true of the wisest of men, "What we know," he said, "is but little (*peu de chose*) ; that which we know not is immense." In all humility, shall we not use our "gifts differing" in the service of our fellow men, and in the spirit of the Golden Rule? Shall we not apply ourselves to the causes of truth, goodness, and beauty? Shall we not aim at the highest in thought and in aspiration? Christianity, at its best, is so minded, and confidently expects the same of science, which may properly be looked upon both as a revelation from and as a revealer of the Central Personality of the universe. In a true conception of it, nature is a mirror. But the value of the images which it presents depends largely upon the percipient. Unfortunately, some who approach it, even though possessed of much learning, not only "look through a glass darkly," but see or will to see nothing but a reflection of their own intellectual constitutions and systems of thought. But there are those who, when they behold the beauty and mystery, the order and government, the purposes and adaptations, the infinite variety and uses of natural objects, and become acquainted with the manifestations of beneficent intelligence and energy therein contained, forget themselves in perception of the marvels of nature and observe in and through them a greater Figure than any physical object which they reflect. These are the Sages and Seers of science. Their vision, reason, insight combine to bring them into the knowledge, and to lead them to seek the experience of the ageless existence and wisdom which are indicated in the sublime revelation, "This is life eternal, that they should know thee the only true God, and him whom thou didst send, even Jesus Christ."

APPENDIX

SUPPLEMENTARY QUOTATIONS FROM WRITINGS OF SCIENTISTS

MANY statements of scientific observers are recorded in this volume, but for various uses it seems best to add a few more. They are taken from the writings of some older and some newer representatives of science—men who as a rule are accustomed to speak sparingly on themes outside of their professional work. If any ask, "Why quote the men of other times?" the answer is that, with reference to scientific topics, the practice is not at all unusual, and tends to confirm the idea that truth, when in any part realized, is a constant, depending for its value, not upon its modernity, but on its consonance with fact. Moreover, it is often discovered that the colossi of the past were, in many of their observations and judgments, as close to reality as are the giants of the present. Even when it can be shown that the ancients erred, their utterances may be regarded as indicating stages in the development of knowledge, or as partial revelations of truth, now more perfectly apprehended.[1]

It will be understood that thoughts of eminent men have no binding authority upon others. A democratic spirit was shown by Galileo when he contended that "in questions of science the authority of a thousand is not worth the humble reasoning of a simple individual."[2] This attitude seems the more necessary when one considers what wide differences

---

[1] See Millikan's discussion, "New Truth and Old," in *Evolution in Science and Religion,* ii, pp. 31-63, in which the thesis is that truth is a living growth in which real values are permanent.

[2] *Biographies of Scientific Men,* Arago, p. 236.

of judgment appear in the writings of able students. Thought, at least on the surface, is divisive. Thinkers are like Greeks, of whom it is said that where two are present there are three opinions. As to a professor, either of science or of some other subject, it is said that the correct definition is that he is a person "of a different opinion." But is it necessary or wise that all ideas and reflections of different persons be identical? What a dreary world it would be if the landscape, either physical or intellectual, presented no variety of views, or if only a few classes of objects existed in the universe! Diversity is the law of nature and the mind of God. But there is unity in this diversity—the unity of law, plan, and progress. In order to find this inner unity and to enjoy its perfections it is necessary to study varieties of forms and qualities from which one may make his own generalizations.

The material below is arranged in chronological rather than in topical order, and as to its value and use the reader must, of course, be his own judge. The sayings presented are at least to be regarded as utterances of men who possessed ability to think things out for themselves, and who, if sincere, must certainly have done this. What they say gives support to the proposition that many of the best minds of history have acquired and held those general religious concepts which are virtually common to the main branches of Christianity. The individuality and genuineness of these views are not to be denied because they are at times expressed in familiar phrases or by use of scriptural quotations. Often, when the mind has labored most intently and intensely, it resolves its convictions into formulæ already known. This must be peculiarly true in the case of religion, which is not some wholly new thing. One of the facts concerning this intimate and vital reality is that its experience, and therefore, in part, especially in the apprehension of Deity and the sense of dependence upon a higher power, its knowledge is as old as humanity. Doctrinal systems change, however slowly. Organizations and institutions are affected by the progress of science and must be amended. New minds must be newly taught and exercised. The world, man, and God, however we may think about them, and whatever late revelations they may make to us, have not changed in the least in their true nature or in their possible and actual relationships to each other.

GIORDANO BRUNO was a philosopher rather than, in the true sense of the term, a scientist. Nevertheless, as he has been so often claimed as one of the "martyrs of science," the following passage from his confession to the Inquisition may be of interest.

"I hold the universe to be infinite as the result of the infinite divine potency, because it has seemed to me unworthy of the divine goodness and power to have produced merely one finite world, when it was able to bring into existence an infinity of worlds. . . . Within this universe I place a universal Providence, whereby everything lives, grows, acts and abides in its perfection. . . . God, essence, presence, potency, is in and above everything, not as a portion of it, and not as its spirit, but inexpressibly."[3]

From the writings of SIR FRANCIS BACON come these expressions: "There never was found in any age of the world either religion or law that did so highly exalt the public good as the Bible." "The scope or purpose of the Spirit of God is not to express matters of nature in the Scriptures, otherwise than in passage, and for application to man's capacity, and to matters

---

[3]For another rendering see *Giordano Bruno—His Life, Thought and Martyrdom*, William Boulting, p. 268. From Berti's documents vii-xvii, Bruno's philosophy, partially summed up above, is found in *De Minimo, De Monade and De Immenso*.

moral or divine."[4] "I had rather believe all the
fables in the Legends, the Talmud, and the Alcoran,
than that this universal frame is without a mind.
Therefore God never wrought miracles to convince
atheism, because his ordinary works convince it. It
is true that a little philosophy inclineth man's mind
to atheism; but depth in philosophy bringeth men's
minds about to religion."[5] Bacon also said: "None
deny there is a God, but those for whom it maketh
(to whose interest it would be) that there were no
God."[6] "They that deny a God destroy man's nobility, for certainly man is of kin to the beasts by
his body; and if he be not of kin to God by his spirit,
he is a base and ignoble creature."[7]

In a remarkable letter penned to Father Benedetto
Castelli, mathematician, in 1613, by GALILEO GALILEI
occur these passages: "Holy Scripture and nature are
both emanations from the Divine Word: the former
dictated by the Holy Spirit; the latter the executrix
of God's commands. Holy Scripture has to be accom-
modated to the common understanding in many
things which differ in reality from the terms used in
speaking of others: . . . I believe that the intention of Holy Writ was to persuade men of the truths
necessary to salvation; such as neither science nor
other means could render credible, but only the voice
of the Holy Spirit. But I do not think it necessary
to believe that the same God who gave us our senses,
our speech, our intellect, would have us put aside the
use of these, to teach us instead such things as with
their help we could find out for ourselves, particularly
in the case of those sciences of which there is not the
smallest mention in the Scripture."

---

[4]*The First Book of the Proficience and Advancement of Learning,*
near end. See whole paragraph.

[5]Opening words of essay, "Of Atheism."

[6]*Ibid.*

[7]*Idem.,* last paragraph.

The will of WILLIAM HARVEY contains the following words: "I do most humbly render my soul to Him that gave it and to my blessed Lord and Saviour, Christ Jesus, and my body to the earth, to be buried at the discretion of my executor hereinafter named."[8]

ISAAC BARROW, mathematician, optician, and teacher of Newton, in his *Works,* Vol. II, p. 121, exclaims: "Let us consider that the nativity of our Lord is a grand instance, a pregnant evidence, a rich earnest of Almighty God's great affection and benignity toward mankind. The power of God doth brightly shine in the creation, the wisdom of God may clearly be discerned in the government of things; but the incarnation of God is that work, is that dispensation of grace, wherein the divine goodness doth most conspicuously display itself."

Coming upon the writings of SIR THOMAS BROWNE, physician and moralist, SIR ARCHIBALD GEIKIE, Scottish geologist, approved them as satisfactory to himself.[9] He found that Sir Thomas Browne had well expressed his own conviction in his quaint words, "Surely there are in every man's life certain rubs, doubling, and wrenches, which pass awhile under the effects of chance, but at the last, well examined, prove the mere hand of God." Professor Geikie added that he summed up his faith in the profound remark that "Nature is the art of God."[10] Sir Archibald, one of the presidents of the Geological and Royal Societies, ended his own life-work with an expression of gratitude to God for health, mind, memory, and rest.

From the *Thoughts on Religion* of BLAISE PASCAL these typical expressions are taken: "Those who seek

---

[8]A convenient place to find the entire document is *William Harvey,* D'Arcy Power, pp. 176-183.

[9]Browne's *Religio Medici* was *comes viae vitaeque* of Sir William Osler for fifty-two years.

[10]*Ut supra,* Part 1, Sec. 16.

for God out of Christ, and rest in the evidences which nature furnishes, either find no solution of their inquiries or settle down in a knowledge and service of God apart from a Mediator: thence they fall into either atheism or deism—two things which the Christian religion almost equally abhors. Without Jesus Christ the world could not subsist; for it would infallibly either be destroyed, or become like hell."[11] "Mohammed established his religion by killing others; Jesus Christ, by making his followers lay down their own lives."[12]

ROBERT BOYLE, chemist and physicist, opening *A Free Enquiry into the Vulgarly Received Notion of Nature,* says: "If, in attempting to discover divers *general* mistakes, I be not so happy as to escape falling into some *particular* ones myself, and, if among these, I have been so unhappy as to make any that is injurious to religion, as I did not at all intend it, so, as soon as ever I shall discover it I shall freely disown it myself and pray that it may never mislead others. What my performance has been I have already acknowledged that I may be unfit to judge; but, for my intentions I may make bold to say they were to keep the glory of the Divine Author of things from being usurped or intrenched upon by his creatures, and to make his works more thoroughly and solidly understood by the philosophical studies of them."

In *The Final Causes of Natural Things,* Boyle reasons that "if it be irrational to ascribe the excellent fabric of the universe, such as it now is, and the actions that have manifest tendencies to determine useful ends to so blind a cause as *chance,* it will be rather more than less irrational to ascribe to chance the first formation of the universe, of which the present state of

---

[11]*Op. cit.,* preface to second part, p. 117, Longmans, Green & Co., Ltd.

[12]"On Jesus Christ," p. 324.

things is but the natural consequence or effect. For it may be plausibly said that in the present state of things the several parts of the universe are by the contrivance of the whole determined and thereby qualified to attain their ends. But it cannot be rationally pretended that at the first framing of the world there was a sufficiency in the stupid materials of it, without any particular guidance of a most wise superintendent, to frame bodies so excellently contained and fitted to their respective ends."[13]

In his "Second Vindication" of *The Reasonableness of Christianity* JOHN LOCKE makes the personal statement of faith: "I believe Jesus to be the Messiah, the King and Saviour sent by God, and, as a subject of his kingdom, I take the rule of my faith and life from his will, declared and left upon record in the inspired writings of the apostles and evangelists in the New Testament. To lead me into their true meaning I know no infallible guide but the same Holy Spirit from whom these writings at first came."[14]

JOHN RAY (in early life WRAY), botanist and zoologist, thought "that the eternal Son of God, equal with his Father, should so highly advance our nature as to unite it to the Divine in one Person so that he might be qualified by the sacrifice of himself to expiate our sins, to make an atonement for us, and to reconcile us to God—the greatness of this love, together with the freeness and unmeritedness of it, there being not any, even the least, motion on our part to invite him to it, is so matchless and stupendous that it challenges the highest degree of reciprocal affection and gratitude."[15]

Letters of SIR ISAAC NEWTON, preserved in Trinity College, Cambridge, furnish such examples of the

---

[13]Pages 233-234.
[14]Page 282.
[15]*Worthies of Science,* John Stoughton, p. 190.

logic of a great intellect as the following: "These things being rightly described, does it not appear from the phenomena that there is a Being incorporeal, living, intelligent, omnipresent, who in infinite space (as it were in his sensory) sees the things themselves, intimately, and thoroughly perceives them, and comprehends them wholly by their immediate presence to himself? And of which things the images only, carried through the organs of sense into our little sensoriums, are there seen and beheld by that which in us perceives and thinks; and though every true step made in this philosophy brings us not immediately to the knowledge of the First Cause, yet it brings us nearer to it, and on that account is to be highly valued."

RENÉ ANTOINE FERCHAULT DE RÉAUMUR, French naturalist and physicist, argued in this manner for mystical studies: "Ought we to be ashamed of ranking among our occupations observations and researches, of which the object is an acquaintance with the works on which the Supreme Being has displayed a boundless wisdom, and varied to such a degree? Natural history is the history of his works, nor is there any demonstration of his existence more intelligible to all men than that which it furnishes."[16]

France seems unable to forget BENJAMIN FRANKLIN, statesman and scientist, and America should frequently recall his wisdom. Among his recorded utterances are these: "A Bible and a newspaper in every house, a good school in every district—all studied and appreciated as they merit—are the principal support of virtue, morality, and civil liberty."

"I have never doubted the existence of the Deity; that he made the world and governs it by his Providence; that the most acceptable service to God is doing good to man; that our souls are immortal;

---

[16]*Mémoires pour servir à l'histoire des insectes.* See *Lives of Eminent Zoologists,* W. Macgillivray, p. 190.

and that all crime will be punished and virtue rewarded, either here or hereafter." See Fisher's *Biography*. In a letter to a friend, Franklin put his views into a formal statement: "Here is my creed. I believe in one God, the Creator of the universe. That he governs it by his providence. That he ought to be worshipped. That the most acceptable service we render to him is doing good to his other children. That the soul of man is immortal and will be treated with justice in another life respecting its conduct in this."

ERASMUS DARWIN has been sometimes called godless, but Krause declares that in each of his works plain statements may be found which show that he fully believed in God as the Creator (Schöpfer) of the universe. He concludes a chapter of *Zoonomia* with the words of the psalmist: "The heavens declare the glory of God, and the firmament showeth his handiwork."[17] Erasmus Darwin published an ode on the folly of atheism with the motto, "I am fearfully and wonderfully made." The poem opened:

> "Atome, die zum Schwindeltanz
> Sich regellos gesellt—
> Die bauten atheist'scher Thor,
> Das Wunderwerk der Welt?"

> "Dull atheist, could a giddy dance
> Of atoms lawless hurled,
> Construct so wonderful, so wise,
> So harmonized a world?"[18]

It is interesting to read a life experience and testimony left by PIERRE SIMON DE LAPLACE, mathema-

---

[17]*Life of Erasmus Darwin*, Ernst Krause, Leipzig ed., p. 25.

[18]*Ibid.*, p. 190, Translation.

tician and astronomer: "I have lived long enough to know what I did not at one time believe—that no society can be upheld in happiness and honor without the sentiment of religion."

In *Philosophie Zoologique* are found the world views of JEAN BAPTISTE PIERRE ANTOINE DE MONET LAMARCK, Chevalier, French zoologist, founder of invertebrate palæontology: "Assuredly nothing can exist but by the will of this Supreme Author, but can we venture to assign rules to him in the execution of his will? May not his infinite power have chosen to create an order of things which should evolve in succession all that we know, as well as all that we do not know? Whether we regard species as created or evolved, the boundlessness of his power remains unchanged, and incapable of any diminution whatsoever. Let us, then, confine ourselves simply to observing the facts around us, and if we find any clue to the path taken by nature, let us say fearlessly that it has pleased her Almighty Author that she should take this path." "I suppose, and I am glad to admit it," Lamarck also says, "a first cause, in a word, a Supreme Power which has given existence to nature and which has made it in all respects what it is."[19]

The Last Days of a Philosopher contains a statement of SIR HUMPHRY DAVY, chemist, which represents his religious experience: "Its influence (that of religion) outlives all earthly enjoyments, and becomes stronger as the organs decay and the frame dissolves. It appears as that evening star in the horizon of life which we are sure is to become, in another season, a morning star, and it throws its radiance through the gloom and shadow of death."[20]

BARON DE CUVIER, French naturalist and founder

---

[19] Pages 74–75, tom. 1. See also Lamarck's less known *Système Analytique.*

[20] *The Collected Works of Sir Humphry Davy,* John Davy, ed., vol. ix, p. 347.

of comparative anatomy, is reported in Lee's *Memoirs* as saying, "We conceive nature to be simply a production of the Almighty, regulated by a wisdom, the laws of which can only be discovered by observation."[21] Another remark by the same master is, "Beauty, richness, abundance have been the ways of the Creator, no less than simplicity."[22]

At the tenth centenary of the introduction of Christianity into Denmark, an address on "The Influence of Christianity on Science" was delivered by HANS CHRISTIAN OERSTED. The electro-magnetist said: "I may be permitted to illustrate how much Christianity has helped science and intellectual development, and how, on the other hand, it has been helped by these. Enemies of Christianity and of science have often endeavored to obscure this great truth. Generation after generation, however, has been persuaded that truth can never be at war with itself, and that our best and most zealous efforts should be given to setting forth their entire accordance, in order that the less firm friends of Christianity may not be disturbed by the distracting asseverations of pseudo-scientists."

In his journal for 1827 JOHN JAMES AUDUBON wrote: "I presume the love of mothers (of the lower orders) for their young is much the same as the love of woman for her offspring. There is but one kind of love; God is love, and all his creatures derive theirs from his; only it is modified by the different degrees of intelligence in different beings and creatures."[23] To Rufus W. Griswold, Audubon exclaimed, "Ah! how often when I have been abroad on the mountains has my heart risen in grateful praise to God that it was not my destiny to waste and pine among those noisome congregations of the city!"

[21]*Memoirs of Baron Cuvier*, p. 83.

[22]*Idem.*

[23]*Life and Adventures of John James Audubon.* Robert Buchanan, p. 115.

When no longer able to bear the privations of the wilderness, in his home beside the Hudson in 1846, five years before his death, this expression was penned, "Surrounded by all the members of my dear family, enjoying the affection of numerous friends, who have never abandoned me, and possessing a sufficient share of all that contributes to make life agreeable, I lift my grateful eyes toward the Supreme Being, and feel that I am happy."

WILLIAM WHEWELL was Master of Trinity, Cambridge, historian and philosopher of science. Among his books was the Bridgewater Treatise, *Astronomy and General Physics considered with reference to Natural Theology.* He closed his *History of the Inductive Sciences* with these words: "We have been lingering long amid the harmonies of law and symmetry, constancy and development. One passage which we have again and again caught by snatches, though sometimes interrupted and lost, at last swells in our ears full, clear and decided; and the religious 'Hymn in honor of the Creator,' to which Galen so gladly lent his voice, and in which the best physiologists of succeeding times have ever joined, is filled into a richer and deeper harmony by the greatest philosophers of these later days, and will roll on hereafter, the 'perpetual song of the temple of science.' "[24]

An enthusiastic nature lover was JOHN WILSON, "Christopher North." Who can successfully deny his tribute to two of the loftiest representatives of scientific genius?—"Such men as Newton and Linnæus are incidental, but august teachers of religion."

SIR DAVID BREWSTER, called by Airy "the father of modern experimental optics," is the author of this clear statement: "We scruple not to say that the Copernican system is not more demonstrably true than

[24]Vol. ii, p. 495.

the system of theological truth contained in the
Bible."[25]   Coming from Brewster's deathbed SIR
JAMES YOUNG SIMPSON, first to employ anæsthetics in
obstetric practice, exclaimed, "The like of this I never
saw: There is Sir David resting like a little child on
Jesus, and speaking as if in a few hours he will get
all his problems solved by him."[26]

The Life and Letters of Michael Faraday present
many of the thoughts of this exalted mind.   "The
Christian religion," he says, "is a revelation, and that
revelation is in the Word of God. According to the
promise of God, that Word is sent into all the world.
Every call and every promise is made freely to every
man to whom that Word cometh."[27]   In one of his
sermons FARADAY expressed this judgment, "Therefore our philosophy, while it shows us these things,
should lead us to think of Him who wrought them,
for it is said by authority even far above that which
these works present that the invisible things of Him,
from the creation of the world, are clearly seen, being understood by the things that are made."

SIR JOHN FREDERICK WILLIAM HERSCHEL, in his
*Preliminary Discourse on the Study of Natural
Philosophy*, protests that "nothing can be more unfounded than the objection which has been taken
in limine against the study of natural philosophy, and,
indeed, against all science—that it fosters in its cul-
tivators an undue and overweening self-conceit,
leaves them to doubt the immortality of the soul, and
to scoff at revealed religion. Its natural effect, we
may confidently assert, on every well-constituted
mind, is and must be the direct contrary."[28]   In the
same treatise Herschel speaks of assistance "by the
Providence of God," and of discoveries in nature

[25]*Worthies of Science,* Stoughton, p. 295.
[26]*Ibid.,* p. 298.
[27]Henry Bence Jones, p. 432, Longmans, Green & Co., Ltd.
[28]Page 7.

which have raised those who made them above their fellow-mortals, "and brought them nearer to their Creator."[29]

The Cambridge geologist ADAM SEDGWICK, in *A Discourse on the Studies at the University*, paid this tribute to the life and work of Christ: "Jesus Christ not only showed in himself an example of perfect purity and holiness, but opened for us a way to future happiness by the voluntary sacrifice of himself."[30]

LOUIS JOHN RUDOLPH AGASSIZ in *Contributions*, quoted in part elsewhere, averred, "Though I know those who hold it to be very unscientific to believe that thinking is not something inherent in matter, and that there is an essential difference between inorganic and living and thinking beings, I shall not be prevented, by any such pretensions of a false philosophy, from expressing my conviction that as long as it cannot be shown that matter or physical forces do actually reason, I shall consider any manifestation of thought as an evidence of the existence of a thinking being as the author of such thought, and shall look upon an intelligent and intelligible connection between the facts of nature as direct proof of the existence of a thinking God."[31] Speaking of the combination in time and space of so many thought-bearing phenomena, he says, "All these facts in their natural connection proclaim aloud the One God, whom man may know, adore, and love, and natural history must in good time become the analysis of the thoughts of the Creator of the universe as manifested in the animal and vegetable kingdoms."[32]

In a letter to the secretary of the Victoria Insti-

---

[29]*Ibid.*, p. 17.

[30]Appendix, p. 134.

[31]*Contributions to the Natural History of the United States of America*, "Essay on Classification," vol. i, pp. 10, 11.

[32]*Ibid.*, p. 135.

tute, quoted in *The Life of James Clerk Maxwell*, the latter expressed this judgment: "I think men of science as well as other men need to learn from Christ, and I think Christians whose minds are scientific are bound to study science, that their view of the glory of God may be as extensive as their being is capable of.[33] The same work contains, p. 394, a letter to Bishop Ellicott in which is found another matured opinion of this leader among physicists: "I think that each individual man should do all he can to impress his mind with the extent, the order, and the unity of the universe, and should carry these ideas with him as he reads such passages as the first chapter of the Epistle to the Colossians, just as enlarged conceptions of the extent and unity of the world of life may be of service to us in reading Psalm 8, Hebrews 2. 6, etc."

ROBERT HUNT, author of *The Poetry of Science* and *The Spirit of Nature,* in the first-named work, p. 411, affirmed that "the task of wielding the wand of science, of standing, a scientific evocator, within the charmed circle of its powers, is one which leads the mind through nature up to nature's God."

The *New Fragments* of JOHN TYNDALL, p. 496, contains these queries: "When I look at the heavens and the earth, at my own body, at my strength and imbecility of mind, even at these ponderings, and ask myself, Is there no being or thing in the universe that knows more about these matters than I do? what is my answer? Does antagonism to theology stand with none of us in the place of a religion?"[34]

THOMAS H. HUXLEY, in *Science and Education,* p. 397, presented one of his occasional encomiums on the moral value of the Scriptures: "I have always been strongly in favor of secular education, in the sense of education without theology; but I must con-

---

[33]Page 404, Campbell & Garnett, Macmillan & Company, Ltd., London.
[34]Appleton.

fess that I have been seriously perplexed to know by
what practical measures the religious feeling, which
is the essential basis of conduct, is to be kept up in
the present utterly chaotic state of opinion on these
matters, without the use of the Bible."[35]

In his *Thoughts on Religion*, GEORGE J. ROMANES,
biologist, says: "It is on all sides worth considering
(blatant ignorance or base vulgarity alone excepted)
that the revolution effected by Christianity in human
life is immeasurable and unparalleled by any other
movement in history. But not only is Christianity
thus so immeasurably in advance of all other religions. It is no less so of every other system of
thought that has ever been promulgated in regard to
all that is moral and spiritual. Whether it be true
or false, it is certain that neither philosophy, science,
nor poetry has ever produced results in thought, conduct, or beauty in any degree to be compared with it.
Only to a man wholly destitute of spiritual perception
can it be that Christianity should fail to appear the
greatest exhibition of the beautiful, the sublime, and
of all else that appeals to our spiritual nature, which
has ever been known upon our earth. The most remarkable thing about Christianity is its adaptation
to all sorts and conditions of men."[36]

In an address of GUTHRIE TAIT, physicist, to the
British Association for the Advancement of Science,
occurs a significant paragraph: "There is a numerous
group, not in the slightest degree entitled to rank as
physicists, who assert that not merely life but even
volition and consciousness are mere physical manifestations. These opposite errors, into neither of
which it is possible for a genuine scientific man to
fall, so long at least as he retains his reason, are easily
seen to be very closely allied. They are both to be

[35]D. Appleton & Company.
[36]Pages 159-161, Longmans, Green & Co., Ltd.

attributed to that credulity which is characteristic alike of ignorance and incapacity. Unfortunately, there is no cure; the case is hopeless, for great ignorance almost necessarily presumes incapacity, whether it shows itself in the comparatively harmless folly of the spiritualist or in the pernicious nonsense of the materialist."

The mathematician, SIR GEORGE GABRIEL STOKES, *On Light,* pp. 342 and 343, expresses a conception of the place of Jesus Christ in our thinking. He is represented as the bridge between nature and God: "If we shut our eyes to the grandeur of nature, and do not attempt through the things that are made to acquire higher conceptions of the eternal power and Godhead of the Maker, our conceptions of the divine being are apt to become too anthropomorphic. If, on the other hand, we confine our attention to the study of nature in all its immensity, our conceptions of its Author are in danger of merging into a sort of pantheistic abstraction, in which the idea of personality is lost. Are we, then, left to lose ourselves in an ocean of immensity, and driven to the conclusion that God is unknowable? Nay, as Christians we believe that the character of God has been revealed to us as it never had been before through that Divine Being who took our nature upon him and dwelt among us full of grace and truth. The greatness of the universe displays to us something of the greatness of its Author; but when we study the character of the Son, who is the image of the invisible God, we learn as never had been learned before the lesson that God is love."[37]

In *The Nineteenth Century and After,* LIII, Jan.-June, 1903, pp. 1068–70, James Knowles quotes WILLIAM THOMSON, LORD KELVIN (see approving reference to this passage, *"Le Radium et la Radioactivité,"*

[37]Macmillan & Company, Ltd., London.

etc., Paul Besson, Paris, 1904) : "I cannot admit that, with regard to the origin of life, science neither affirms nor denies Creative Power. Science positively affirms Creative Power. It is not in dead matter that we live and move and have our being, but in the creating and directing Power which science compels us to accept as an article of belief. We cannot escape from that conclusion when we study the physics and dynamics of living and dead matter all around. Modern biologists are coming, I believe, once more to a firm acceptance of something beyond mere gravitational, chemical, and physical forces; and that unknown thing is a vital principle. We have an unknown object put before us in science. In thinking of that object we are all agnostics. We know God only in his works, but we are absolutely forced by science to believe with perfect confidence in a Directive Power—in an influence other than physical, or dynamical, or electrical forces. Cicero (by some supposed to have been editor of Lucretius) denied that men and plants and animals could come into existence by a fortuitous concourse of atoms. There is nothing between absolute scientific belief in a Creative Power, and the acceptance of the theory of a fortuitous concourse of atoms. Just think of a number of atoms falling together of their own accord and making a crystal, a sprig of moss, a microbe, a living animal. Cicero's expression 'fortuitous concourse of atoms' is certainly not wholly inappropriate for the growth of a crystal. But modern scientific men are in agreement with him in condemning it as utterly absurd in respect to the coming into existence, or the growth, or the continuation of the molecular combinations presented in the bodies of living things. Here scientific thought is compelled to accept the idea of Creative Power."[38]

---

[38]Leonard Scott, London.

Sir Edwin Ray Lankester, zoologist, in *The Kingdom of Man,* noted that "there is often an antagonistic relation between exponents of science and exponents of religion, when the latter illegitimately misrepresent or deny the conclusions of scientific research or try to prevent its being carried on, or, again, when the former presume, by magnifying the extremely limited conclusions of science, to deal in a destructive spirit with the very existence of those beliefs and hopes which are called religion."[39] Another Lankester statement is, "Men of science seek, in all reverence, to discover the Almighty, the Everlasting. They claim sympathy and friendship with those who, like themselves, have turned away from the more material struggles of human life, and have set their hearts and minds on the knowledge of the Eternal."[40]

The author of *Discovery, or the Spirit and Service of Science,* Sir Richard Arman Gregory, makes this statement: "Though religion exists without science, there is no science without religion; and the study of the laws of nature creates a respect for them and reverence for their Maker of a far profounder kind than the ordinary mind can conceive."[41]

William Benjamin Smith, physicist, in a letter to me, says, "In general, I may say that my thinking directs me unmistakably to a purely spiritual-symbolical interpretation both of the universe around us and of the process of history, especially as exemplified in proto-Christianity."

Michael Idvorsky Pupin, physicist and inventor, thinks that "the best men in England are very anxious to establish harmony between scientific and religious thought. This harmony has always existed and, in my humble opinion, will always exist, but we

[39]Page 63, Henry Holt & Company.
[40]*Ibid.,* p. 158.   [41]Page 52.

have not yet expressed that harmony in a few and simple terms, so that the laic in science as well as in religion may well understand it."[42]

In *The New Reformation, or From Physical to Spiritual Realities,* Doctor Pupin has penned this passage: "Our Christian faith sees in the life and the teachings of Christ the highest spiritual reality which our belief in God, the fountainhead of all spiritual realities, planted in the soul of man. This reality, we believe, endowed our souls with the spiritual forces which guide us in the spiritual co-ordination of each individual life and of the life of humanity. Love, according to Christ, is the most powerful of all these co-ordinating forces. Its co-ordinating action in the spiritual world is very similar to the co-ordinating action of the gravitational force in the physical world. Christ discovered it and revealed it to us in his two commandments: 'Thou shalt love the Lord thy God with all thy heart, and with all thy soul, and with all thy mind.' 'Thou shalt love thy neighbor as thyself.' These commandments are the fundamental laws in Christ's spiritual dynamics."[43]

Two quotations from the writings of EDWIN GRANT CONKLIN, biologist, author of *The Direction of Human Evolution,* are well related to our theme: "When we remember that Beethoven's mother was a consumptive and his father a confirmed drunkard, that Michael Faraday, perhaps the greatest scientific discoverer of any age, was born over a stable, that his father was a poor, sick blacksmith, and that the only early education he had was obtained in selling newspapers on the streets of London and later in working as apprentice to a bookbinder; that Lincoln's father was a ne'er-do-well, and his early surroundings and education most unpromising; that George W. Child was a name-

---

[42] Letter to author.
[43] Epilogue, pp. 271 and 272, Charles Scribner's Sons.

less foundling, and so on through the long list of names in which democracy glories—when we remember these world-famous men and when we reflect that eugenicists and birth-controllers would have deprived the world of these superlative geniuses if they could have had their way, we may well inquire whether it is not fortunate that we are in the hands of an all-wise Providence rather than that of an unwise propaganda." "Development of the Personality," address before the American Medico-Psychological Association, New York, June, 1917.

In March, 1925, the Princeton Alumni Weekly carried a vesper address of Edwin G. Conklin on "Biology and Religion," in the course of which he said, speaking from his well-known standpoint as a biologist: "Evolution deals only with process, and does not touch the question of ultimate causation. What lies back of evolution no one knows. The atheist sees only mechanism and accident, without design or purpose. The theist sees back of the whole process divine power and plan. The Christian sees a heavenly Father. Science cannot deal with this mystery; it is a matter of faith alone; but it is plain that Christian faith gives the largest value to human life and the greatest stimulus and comfort."

J. ARTHUR THOMSON, Regius professor of natural history, Aberdeen, in a magazine article penned a discussion of "Science and Religion" in the course of which occurs the following: "Science seeks, by observing, experimenting, and reflecting, to reach empirical formulation. Religion seeks after a Vision of God. The title of a book, *God or Natural Selection,* is in itself a confusion of thought. It may be that the theory of natural selection presents certain difficulties to certain expressions of religious conviction, but to make an antithesis of them is a false dichotomy. The same radical fallacy underlies the present war-cry in some parts of America—'The Bible or Darwinism.' There may be difficulties in holding together in thought and feeling what the Bible teaches and what Darwinism teaches, even when both have been rightly understood, but an antithesis is radically impossible between a religious revelation and a scientific generalization. The two are not in the same language, and we must not attempt to speak two languages at once. If it is not pedantic, we might say that science aims at a cosmo*graphy,* while religion will be satisfied with nothing short of a cosmo*logy.*"[44]

SIR OLIVER LODGE, physicist, in *Evolution and Creation,* voices his view of incarnation: "We need raise no question of physiology, nor can we examine the incarnation in the light of science. Just as life entered at a certain stage, and mind at another stage, and the consciousness of freedom or the divine spark or soul at yet another, so now the divine spark was kindled into flame. Some of the attributes of Deity were then made manifest in human form, and a Revelation of the nature of Godhead was permitted to humanity, for its help and encouragement in its too difficult task. Henceforth man could be conscious of a Being anxious to help, when help was asked for, willing to strive and suffer, loving and hoping for love freely rendered in return. No longer need man be overwhelmed by the workings of an inscrutable Power which he could not understand: he could begin to realize that at the center of all this majestic universe lay the heart of a Father."[45]

From the pen of JOHN SCOTT HALDANE, physiologist, comes the following: "The fundamental conceptions of physical science represent only working hypotheses, corresponding, under great limitations, to partial aspects of our experience. Extraordinarily useful as these working hypotheses are, in the ab-

---

[44]*Homiletic Review,* December, 1923, Funk and Wagnalls Company. See also the book with same title, Scribners.
[45]Pages 143-4, George H. Doran Company.

sence of more detailed knowledge they do not represent reality. This appears at once when we consider
our experience as a whole. It is only when we neglect
this consideration that we seem driven into a materialistic creed. The fundamental conceptions of biology, since they take into account more than those
of the physical sciences, bring us nearer to reality,
but fail to take into account the facts of conscious
life or personality. When we take into account all
that appears in conscious life, in our conscious fellowship with one another, with those who have gone
before or will come after, and with nature, God is
revealed as the ultimate and only reality. God and
God's love and omnipotence are within and around
us behind what appears as space, time, the material
world, organic life, and individual personality. The
material world as such is an imperfect appearance,
and the only real world is the spiritual world, the
only real values spiritual values. In this knowledge
we find inward reconciliation and can go forward
without fear."[46]

The following statement represents a contribution
from WILLIAM EMERSON RITTER, biologist: "The
whole higher life, or spiritual life, I prefer to
say, of mankind stands on three quite distinct bases
or feet. It is like a tripod in this respect. Now, a
tripod is peculiar from the point of view of stability
in that it possesses the most stable of foundations
from one standpoint, but from another it is peculiarly
unstable. If any one of the three legs is knocked out,
the whole thing tumbles over. The three human
bases to which I refer are: Religion, Science, Art; or
Art, Science, Religion; or Science, Religion, Art—it
makes no difference which of the feet you begin with,
or which way you go around."[47]

---

[46]*Hibbert Journal,* April, 1923, p. 435, article, "Natural Science and
Religion."

[47]Letter to author.

ROBERT A. MILLIKAN, physicist, first to measure the
electron, in a bulletin of the California Institute of
Technology, *Science and Religion,* gives it as his judgment that "there have been just two great influences
in the history of the world which have made goodness
the outstanding characteristic in the conception of
God. The first influence was Jesus of Nazareth; the
second influence has been the growth of modern science, and particularly the growth of the theory of
evolution. All of us see much in life which tends
to make us pessimists. The good does not always
prevail. Righteousness does not always triumph.
What is the meaning of existence? Is it worth while?
Are we going anywhere? Jesus and modern science
have both answered that question in the affirmative—
Jesus took it as his mission in life to preach the
news of the goodness of God. Similarly science in
the formulation of the theory of evolution has seen
the world developing through countless ages higher
and higher qualities, moving on to better and better
things. It pictures God, however you may conceive
him, as essentially good, as providing a reason for
existence and a motive for making the most of existence, in that we may be a part of the great plan of
world progress."

In *Sermons of a Chemist,* by EDWIN E. SLOSSON,
director of Science Service, Washington, occurs this
passage: "If it had not been for the missionary efforts
of such men as Paul, Gregory, Augustine, Christianity would have been lost in the wreck of Rome, as
was Latin learning and literature. We cannot know,
any more than did the Romans, what people will be
our successors in the age to come. We can only do
the best we can by sharing with other peoples the
best we know, by teaching them what we have found
out about the laws of nature and about the laws of
God. Our religion was the best thing we inherited
from ancient Rome. It is the best thing we have to

give to others. We can be certain to Christianize our successors if we Christianize the world.[48]

WILLIAM NORTH RICE, geologist, in *Science and Religion,* pp. 15 and 53, says: "The scientific conception of the unity of nature makes every form of polytheism impossible. The student of science may be a monotheist, a pantheist, or an atheist. He cannot be a polytheist. Of the world's historical religions only one can survive. The alternative for our age is Christianity or nothing." This author also states: "The scientific questions of our age touch not the central truth of Christianity—that 'God was in Christ, reconciling the world unto himself.' The inarticulate cry of universal humanity finds its interpretation and its answer in Him through whom we see the Father. And to Him—'the same yesterday, to-day and forever'— the laboring and heavy-laden bring their burdens of doubt and question, as of sorrow and sin, and find rest unto their souls."

From the pen of CHARLES W. HARGITT, zoologist, *Methodist Review,* November-December, 1924, came the following beautiful sentences: "If I mistake not, the radiant foregleams of luminous tides, all too long obscured by pagan mists and benighted traditions, are glinting the moral skies. They may be seen glancing from the self-same stars which so shone in that olden time as to evoke shouts of joy from the sons of God; they leap in convincing splendors from his handiwork in the firmament above, and are mirrored from the depths below; they smile in the lilies of the field whose growing splendors eclipsed those of the luxury-loving Solomon. The purpling clusters ripening in Bethany's vineyards, which elicited the parable of religious husbandry for all time, were not more pregnant with blessing than the royal fruition of consecrated industry which feeds the modern world!

---

[48]Page 283, Harcourt, Brace & Company.

Now, as then, the humble sowers whose broadcast
seed is so scattered that even the fowls found some
share, and stony grounds of barren soils and intellects are allowed to reveal their poverty, become both
parable and promise, till in the full and meridian
glow, where eyes are open to see, there stands revealed that Kingdom of growth and perfection, whose
fittest parable has ever been 'First the blade, then
the ear, then the full corn in the ear,' the evolution
patent in His words and life.''[49]

Where Evolution and Religion Meet, by JOHN M.
and MERLE C. COULTER, botanists, p. 98, contains this
representation of the outcome of former controver-
sies: "Gradually the situation changed, and the hostile camps became allies in a great cause. Religion
discovered that science is honestly searching for the
truth, and science discovered that the Christian religion has a scientific basis. It seems strange now
that the two groups, each searching for the truth in
its own way, should ever have come in conflict. Truths
are not contradictory; if claimed truths are contradictory, then the truth is not clear. When it is said
that the situation has changed, it is not implied that
all of the representatives of religion and science have
declared an armistice, for in certain localities and
with certain temperaments the old notion of the incompatibility of science and religion persists. But
these are mere 'holdovers' from a former general situation. The whole tendency to-day is toward the co-
operation of religion and science.''[50]

In January, 1923, ARTHUR L. FOLEY, physicist, investigator in the realm of sound, sent an answer to a
questionnaire circulated among those engaged in
scientific pursuits. A copy of this response, which is
in my possession, contains categorical affirmations
of religious belief, church membership and support,

[49]Page 850, The Methodist Book Concern.
[50]The Macmillan Company.

and of purpose to continue in Christian affiliations and activities. A splendid tribute is given to the work of Jesus Christ, and coupled with it is a suitable rebuke to those striving to subvert Christian teaching and achievement: "Christ came into the world and in two or three years of his life expounded a system of religion entirely at variance with the day in which he lived—a system of ethics that civilization has been approaching but which is still centuries ahead of us; a system which no one—perhaps not even yourself, with the added light of two thousand years, could better in the slightest detail; a system which has been the life guide for thousands of millions of the best people that the world has produced; a system for whose furtherance millions in money are being subscribed. If a mere man could do this, what is the relative status of the man or woman who can find nothing to offer, and who has a hard time to get a few dollars for the support of a paper whose business it is to tear down?"

"What this world needs," Doctor Foley also said, "is constructive, not destructive effort. If civilization is saved from the chaos in which it finds itself to-day, it will be saved by religious men and women, not by so-called 'truth seekers,' who know nothing and are going nowhere."

In another writing this scientist has paid his respects to various forms of ignorance and error. "The absurdity of some of the claims of realists, or naturalists, or atheists force themselves upon me," he says. "They make sport of the idea that the Creator has always existed and call it absurd, yet they assume that matter has always existed. If the former idea is absurd, certainly the last one is even more so. They make sport of the idea that life was ever created. They say that the physical and chemical forces alone have been sufficient to create life; in other words, that the tremendously complicated animal machine is simply the result of the haphazard action of chemical and physical forces. Yet they cannot produce life by using all the intelligence that they possess in directing these same chemical and physical forces which they think have produced life without direction. As a matter of fact, I will go still further and say that they cannot take life, which they claim is a mere play of physical and chemical forces, and keep that life going. How much confidence should one have in the opinion of a man who thus admits that chemical and physical forces under intelligent direction cannot do what these same forces can do or 'have done' without any direction at all?"[51]

An excellent passage with which to close this list of quotations comes to me in a letter from J. E. KIRKWOOD, botanist: "At present too much is beyond our ken for either the religionist or the scientist to be dogmatic. Faith is an attribute of the finer spiritual natures, involving, as James puts it, the *will* to believe. I have often asked myself why I believe, and the same question was asked me by another within the last two weeks. To which I replied that what I knew of the history of mankind, what I have observed of the influence of Christian faith in the lives of others, and my own experience lead me to have confidence in the Christian life and to live by it where I cannot see the end."[52]

---

[51]Contributed by A. L. Foley.
[52]Contributed by J. E. Kirkwood.

INDEX

INDEX

It has not been thought necessary to place in this list the Greeks, the greater number of inventors and teachers, or names of very many scientists and public and literary men who are mentioned in the text more or less incidentally.

A

Abbot, Charles Greeley, 297
Adams, Frank D., 7, 295, 296
Adams, John Couch, 62, 63
Adler, Cyrus, 146
Agassiz, Louis Jean Rodolphe; *Contributions: Essay on Classification*, 144, 149, 249, 250, 251, 253, 362
Agramonte, Aristide, 194
Allen, H. S., 295
Ampère, André Marie; *Historical Proofs of the Divineness of Christianity*, 41, 42, 74, 85, 224, 238, 239, 240, 340
Angell, James Rowland, 297
Aquinas, Thomas, 49, 273
Arago, Dominique François; *Biographies of Scientific Men*, 41, 138, 147, 349
Arkwright, Richard, Sir, 198
Audubon, John James, 148, 359
Augustine, 273, 372

B

Bacon, Francis, Sir; *Novum Organum* and essay, Of Atheism, 33, 74, 77, 225, 228, 351, 352
Bacon, Roger; *Compendium of Theology; Opus Majus*, 31, 209, 224, 225, 254
Baetjer, Frederick Henry, 196
Ball, Robert Stawell, Sir; *Great Astronomers, The Story of the Heavens*, 189
Banting, F. G., 45
Barkla, Charles G., 295
Barnard, Edward Emerson, 298
Barrow, Isaac; Works include theological volumes, sermons, etc., 145, 224, 231, 254, 353
Bateson, William, 253
Becher, Johann Joachim, 103
Becquerel, Antoine Henri, 44, 191

Bell, Alexander Graham, 63
Bergonie, Emile, 196
Bergson, Henri; *Creative Evolution*, 291
Bernard, Claude, 37, 224, 248
Bertillon, Alphonse, 48
Best, C. H., 45
Bettex, Frederick; *Science and Christianity*, 96
Bigney, Andrew Johnson; *A Century of Progress in Scientific Thought*, 7, 107
Biot, Jean Baptiste, 146, 233, 236, 239, 257
Black, Joseph, 34
Blewett, George John; *The Study of Nature and the Vision of God*, 281
Blumenbach, Johann Friedrich, 48
Bode, Johann Elert, 40
Boerhaave, Hermann, 33, 253
Bohr, Niels, 50
Bolzano, Bernhard; *Athanasia, or Proofs of the Immortality of the Soul*, 90
Bonnet, Charles; *The Contemplation of Nature, The Faculties of the Soul and Philosophical Researches on the Evidences of Christianity*, 273
Bonney, Thomas George; *Holy Places of Jerusalem*, 105, 254, 314
Bovard, John F., 292
Bowditch, Nathaniel, 249
Boyle, Robert; *Reconcilableness of Reason and Religion, The Final Causes of Natural Things*, and *The Studies of Natural Philosophy Favorable to Religion*, 84, 103, 224, 227, 228, 254, 313, 354
Bradley, James, 33
Bragg, William, Sir, 92, 103, 295

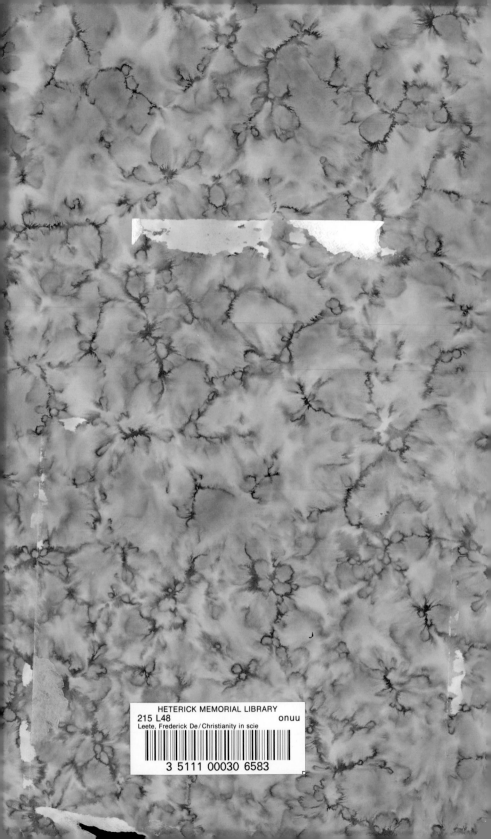